900 KNOW-HOW

How To Succeed With
Your Own 900 Number Business

Second Edition
Completely Revised and Expanded

Written by:
Robert Mastin

Other Telecom Titles by Aegis Publishing Group:

Money-Making 900 Numbers:
How Entrepreneurs Use the Telephone to Sell Information
by Carol Morse Ginsburg and Robert Mastin
ISBN: 0-9632790-1-7
$19.95
Profiles of nearly 400 actual 900-number programs -- the success stories as well as the failures.

Telecom Made Easy:
Money-Saving, Profit-Building Solutions for
Home Businesses, Telecommuters and Small Organizations
by June Langhoff
ISBN: 0-9632790-2-5
$19.95
Shows how to put all the latest telephone products and services to their best use -- in plain English.

What they are saying about this book:

"If you have decided that you are nothing but road kill on the information highway, take a look at *900 Know-How* by Robert Mastin. For those in the information-providing business, the 900 number could be an attractive source of revenue."
--The Wall Street Journal

".... a comprehensive guide to creating your own lucrative pit stop on the information highway."
--Information Week

".... a superb job of gathering and conveying the information....crammed full of information which is concise and accurate....I highly recommend it for anyone contemplating going into the 900 number business...."
--Ed Durham, Editor
Home Income Reporter

".... Solid advice to anyone wanting to start-up the business....a good starting place for 'infopreneurs' who want to get in the game....presented in a factual, concise manner that can be easily understood and digested...."
--Bruce Jones, Book Reviewer
Mailer's Review

"Nothing will guarantee success in this business, but reading this book will go a long way toward maximizing the chance for success."
--W. Brooks McCarty
a founder of the National Association
for Interactive Services (N.A.I.S.)

"It was only a matter of time until somebody wrote a frank, no-hype book on launching a 900 pay-per-call business. The author is experienced 900 number entrepreneur Robert Mastin and the title is '900 KNOW-HOW'...."
--Joyce Lain Kennedy
syndicated careers columnist

".... a resource-filled paperback covering (service) bureau basics and much more."
--Inc. magazine

".... 900 KNOW-HOW explores this explosive industry in-depth, including how to start and operate a 900 business, what pitfalls to avoid, the costs involved, and what kinds of 900 programs have been successful...."   --Business Bookshelf

Business Opportunities Journal

"Medium-to-small businesses could profit from the acquisition of a 900 number, and this title is a good place to begin. It's a detailed examination of the 900 pay-per-call option which offers detailed advice on how to succeed with a 900 number -- and what to avoid...."   --The Bookwatch

The Midwest Book Review

".... Really offers the readers non-biased information....This has to be one of the best, well written and informative books on the subject.... 900 KNOW-HOW is a must...."   --John Moreland

The Dream Merchant

"Everything one needs to know to start a 900-number phone service is surveyed ....Starting a 900 number service is relatively easy, but its success depends on the additional factors of marketing research, customer service, and costs which are also dealt with in this introductory guide."   --*The Small Press Book Review*

"Here's an exploration of one of America's growth industries. The author covers how to start and operate such a business, pitfalls, costs and marketing....a good primer on starting a business based on the 900 telephone numbers...."

--Jeff Rowe, Business Book Editor

Orange County Register

"The book provides honest information about what it takes to be successful in this business, and clearly debunks some of the hype and blatant misinformation surrounding the 900 industry...."

--*MAIL PROFITS* Magazine

".... a good primer if you have ever dreamed of making your fortune with a 900 number.... This book will help focus your thoughts and give you the resources to study how to build a successful 900 number service...."   --Kathy Mathews

Stepping Stones

".... you'll get a nuts-and-bolts guide to starting and operating a 900 service....start-up and monthly operating costs....ways to effectively market a 900 service....details on types of services that are successful...."   --Barbara Kaplowitz, Editor
What's Working in DM and Fulfillment

"This is the bible of an industry that shot from $0 to nearly $1 billion in annual sales in only four years...."
      --*SUCCESS* Magazine

"....explores the pay-per-call industry in depth....and what makes a successful 900 program...."   --*FOLIO* Magazine

"... *900 KNOW-HOW* is a comprehensive guide that helps the start-up information provider..."   --*The Newsletter on Newsletters*

".... the author shoots straight from the hip in his clearly understandable approach to the business, showing you what can and cannot be done, how and how not to do it... an extraordinary accomplishment... read it before you act..."
      --*Entrepreneur's Digest*

"If you're interested in launching a 900 pay-per-call information or entertainment service, you will find this book helpful."
      --Galen Stilson, Publisher
The DIRECT RESPONSE Specialist

"This is a valuable book to have on your bookshelf."
      --*Mail Order Entrepreneur*

"... provides in-depth coverage of the 900-number industry..."
      --*Sales and Marketing Strategies & News*

"... the first comprehensive how-to book about launching a 900 pay-per-call business... explores the ever growing pay-per-call industry, including pitfalls to avoid, effective marketing, the most successful programs to start, and much more."
      --*Income Opportunities* magazine

"... A readable, informative introduction and guide to this new business idea..."   --*COSMEP* newsletter

900 KNOW-HOW

How To Succeed With Your Own 900 Number Business

Second Edition
Completely Revised and Expanded

Written by:
Robert Mastin

Aegis Publishing Group
796 Aquidneck Avenue
Newport, Rhode Island 02842
401-849-4200

Library of Congress Catalog Card Number: 93-74809

International Standard Book Number: 0-9632790-6-8

Printed in the United States of America.
First Edition, first printing, 1992
First Edition, second printing, 1993
Second Edition, completely revised, 1994
10 9 8 7 6 5 4

This publication is designed to provide accurate and authoritative information in regard to the subject matter covered. It is sold with the understanding that neither the author nor the publisher are engaged in rendering legal, accounting or other professional service. If legal advice or other expert assistance is required, the services of a competent professional person should be sought.

Publisher's Cataloging In Publication Data
Mastin, Robert L.
900 KNOW-HOW: How To Succeed With Your Own 900 Number Business / by Robert Mastin. -- second edition, completely revised and expanded
Includes Index
1. Audiotex services industry.
HE8817.M3 1994   384.64   93-74809
ISBN 0-9632790-6-8

Acknowledgements

This book was a collaborative effort with the help of many people. Although it would be impossible to mention everyone who contributed materials, advice or assistance to this work, I would like to express my appreciation to all the participants in The 900 Roundtable, which, owing to their thoughtful contributions, is one of the most valuable sections in this book. Special thanks to Carol Morse Ginsburg, Bob Bentz, Bill Gundling, Bill Burrington, Larry Podell and Mike Urbanski for their considerable help and expertise, which was always cheerfully given despite some very busy schedules.

Thanks to Bruce Spitzer for his capable editing help, and to Kimlee Revock and Liz Sheldon for typing the manuscript. And none of this would have ever happened without the advice of my publishing consultants and gurus, Dan Poynter and John Kremer.

And finally, a special thanks to my lovely wife, Liz, whose patience and encouragement have sustained me, and to whom this book is dedicated.

Contents

Foreword

When Bob Mastin asked if I'd be willing to write a foreword to this, his latest book, I jumped at the chance. When I read his previous edition, I found it to be the first writings on the 900 industry that wasn't simply a slanted sales pitch. Here was an unbiased look at 900 as well as a valuable guide to how to make money in the field.

Anyone who knows me or *Audiotex News,* the newsletter I publish and edit, now into its sixth year, is clearly aware of my belief in this industry as one with great substance and enormous possibilities. Although I'm acquainted with its dark side, the incredible potential as 900 matures allows me to recognize the positives. And now and again I catch glimpses of a pay-per-call application that pushes the envelope of technology -- moving to deliver the next best innovation.

If you've been searching for a book that gives you a substantial view of 900 while showing you practical ways to make money in it, Bob Mastin's work within these covers is your best entry into the arena. The pay-per-call industry is an exciting, volatile business with twisted turns and sharp corners. Mastin has been able to illuminate the darkness -- no small task!

Rapid technological changes and the individual creativity of each entrepreneurial spirit make the future profile of the industry difficult to predict. I do not doubt that at this very moment, someone reading my words has the concept for what will be a winning 900 number. Future uses for 900 exceed the imagination, possibly because we old-timers have our headsets filled with adult, weather, horoscopes, jokes and soaps. So it is you, the newly arrived reader, who will discover what the public will buy and how much they will pay for it.

Major corporations will continue to use 900 services wherever feasible. In this era of cost-cutting, 900 pay-per-call offers a simple way to conduct business with the added advantage of having the caller share the cost.

At a recent conference I attended, television executives reported that there was no way they could conduct an 800 campaign for a prize or game contest because they could not handle the calls. The 95 cents per 900 call made the difference -not so much in offsetting the costs, but in controlling the call volume.

Fax and phone give entrepreneurs the opportunity to provide a printed page of data delivered immediately for a small price, with both billing and collection taken care of through the 900 media.

There are opportunities to provide 900 programs through AT&T's 900-555 and 900-225 (dedicated business exchanges). With certain criteria to meet, businesses can unblock their phones for these services.

The promise of the information age is boundless. 900 pay-per-call is like Pandora's box -- once opened, the contents can't be put back. Entrepreneurial interest will push business and individuals to offer new and creative programming that in turn will drive public use to higher and higher levels. Soon, when we ask for a show of hands for how many people have used 900, it will be the majority in the room.

It's ironic that some of the most creative uses of 900 have been by governments. So while on the one hand they have gone about almost dissolving the business, with the other they have embraced it. This increased use of 900 by municipalities and companies like Microsoft and Better Business Bureaus will also lead to making 900 a household fixture.

If anyone needs further proof of 900's potential, they can look at how the TelCos put up with the industry's early problems -- high chargebacks, low value programs and scams. But still, the bad reputation of the early days is hard to lose. For some callers, years of positive reinforcement must occur before we can tempt them to pick up the phone.

But this will happen and 900 usage will become standard. I believe the entertainment category still will dominate the industry, in terms of call volume, repeat business and holding times, to a lesser extent than we now see it, but still a very major component.

The limitless potential of the 900 pay-per-call industry is humbling. Just think -- now we can only deliver information, but what if we could accomplish product fulfillment? And what about screen phones? As they become widely used, how will they affect 900? What will be the impact on pay-per-call when almost every home will have a fax machine?

I don't know yet. What I do know is that only those of us who stay the course to learn and understand the action will be the winners!

Want to be in on the action? Then learn the basics and everything you need to know to create the thriving, lucrative 900 business of the future. This book contains the information you need to succeed.

Carol Morse Ginsburg
Editor/Publisher, *Audiotex News*

Chapter 1
Background

The Information Age has arrived. President Clinton's information superhighway isn't some distant vision of the future -- it is here today in the form of telephone networks, cable TV systems, satellite links, cellular networks and fiber optic cable transmission systems. What President Clinton is talking about is adding extra lanes, interchanges, mileage and other improvements to the existing highway, making it more accessible to, and useful for, everyone. And capable of transporting the more exotic, supercharged vehicles of the future.

900 number information services are but one lane on the information superhighway, though admittedly one of the middle lanes. The fast lane is currently claimed by on-line computer services such as CompuServe and Prodigy, accessible only to those with fast cars and the ability to drive them. The slow lane consists of POTS (Plain Old Telephone Service) lines.

According to Link Resources, a market research firm, only 30 percent of the 96.3 million U.S. households have a PC. And most of these are used for games and entertainment, not for sophisticated communications and data retrieval using the fast lane of the information superhighway. That leaves 67 million households without

PCs of any kind, and no access to the fast lane. People with PCs and the skills to put them to good use aren't the only ones who need specialized information. We can all benefit from access to information that helps make our lives more convenient, productive and enjoyable: stock and commodity prices, airline flight information, technical or professional assistance, movie reviews, sports scores, ski conditions, car pricing information and so on.

Interactive voice processing has merged with 900 information services to open up a new lane on the information superhighway for people who do not have access to PCs. The telephone keypad becomes the equivalent of the computer keyboard, and any telephone owner has access to the same wide array of database information available to on-line computer service subscribers. A lot more people have telephones than have computers, and virtually all of them know how to operate their telephones with relative competence. Imaginative entrepreneurs are responding to the challenge by providing an ever expanding array of information services, accessible to anyone with a telephone.

Will computers eventually replace the basic telephone? After all, many people are hanging their hats on computer-telephone integration (CTI), a new buzz term you'll hear more and more about. Well, nobody really knows exactly where we're headed, and trying to predict the future is somewhat risky given the rapid pace of technological advancement in computers and telecommunications. Whatever happens, it won't happen overnight. A reasonably powerful computer, with the necessary peripherals and software, still costs around $2,000, while the lowly telephone can be purchased for $20 or less. Most of us cannot afford to indulge in buying the latest and greatest gadgets when they first hit the marketplace. We still wait for the paperback book version to save a few bucks, because price is important and we don't have unlimited resources. My guess is that the basic telephone will be around for many more years to come.

The Business Opportunity

What's all the fuss about? Why are some people touting 900 numbers as the best entrepreneurial opportunity since the pet rock or the hula hoop? Why the proliferation of infomercials and hyped-up seminars that promise easy riches and everlasting happiness?

Because most of these claims, however inflated, are based on truth. You can start a 900 business from home with a fairly small initial investment. You can get started pretty quickly. You can reach a national market that has 24-hour access to your service. And perhaps best of all, a huge, reputable *Fortune 500* company does all your billings and collections for you, sending you one check each month.

These are some pretty compelling reasons to get excited about the potential of 900 numbers, and would whet the appetite of any would-be entrepreneur. Nonetheless, being an easy business to get into doesn't necessarily equate with easy success. Far from it. To succeed in 900 is just as difficult as in any other industry, if not more difficult than most. Direct response selling, which is what 900 numbers are all about, is not the kind of marketing endeavor that should be undertaken by the meek of heart or slight of budget. It takes some real money and talent to make those direct sales. We'll talk a lot more about this later.

The fact remains, why should 900 be any different from any other type of business? We all know -- or at least we should know -- that there is no such thing as a guaranteed get-rich-quick-and-easy scheme. If there were, we'd all be rich, and you would be soaking up the sun in Martinique, not reading this book. I, for one, would certainly not be spending a lot of time writing this book.

The days of being able to make money easily in 900 are long gone. Yes, there was a time when you could throw just about any 900 program against the wall, and it stuck. The novelty has since worn off. Callers want something of value for their money. Many people still equate 900 with dial-a-porn, and won't even consider calling any kind of 900 program. Now, as never before, it will take a lot of time, effort, and most importantly, knowledge, to be successful in the 900 industry.

Larry Podell, a 900 consultant and publisher of the *Audiotex Directory & Buyer's Guide* (see Resource Guide), estimates that only 5 to 10 percent of all new 900 programs succeed after 6 to 12 months - primarily because it is so easy to get into this business, which attracts an overabundance of get-rich-quick dreamers who jump in without really knowing what they're getting into.

You will fall into the same trap, and possibly lose your shirt, if you try to jump onto the bandwagon without first being equipped with as much knowledge and information as you can get your hands on. This book is a good start, but don't stop here. Go to the Resource Guide and get as many of those publications as you can afford. Information and knowledge are absolute prerequisites for success. Launching a 900 program is just like starting any other kind of business, and success will be quite elusive unless you do your homework and start out with a firm foundation of knowledge regarding all facets of the industry.

This book is intended for individuals or businesses who wish to get started in the 900 pay-per-call information or entertainment industry. You will learn, step-by-step, how to launch a 900 information program. You will learn how to become an "Information Provider" (IP), or perhaps even more descriptive, an "Infopreneur." You will get ideas for possible 900 applications, how to market your service, how to choose a service bureau, how to project revenues, and how to measure and improve your advertising effectiveness. You will find a comprehensive Resource Guide at the end of this book, with useful nuts-and-bolts information to help you get started.

History

What is the 900 industry? First of all, calling it an industry is a bit of a stretch, but I'll keep doing it anyway in the interest of brevity, instead of calling it "The 900 pay-per-call information delivery service" or by some other equally unwieldy title.

A 900 number is simply an alternative method of paying for information over the telephone. It is nothing more or less than a convenient information delivery medium, with a very efficient way of exchanging payment for information delivered. Whether the charge is by the minute or a flat rate for the call, the caller is charged for the telephone call on his or her monthly phone bill. Basically, the reverse of an 800 number. The person offering the information or entertainment, the Information Provider, has the latitude of charging whatever the market will bear, within some fairly generous limits imposed by the long distance telephone carrier. You will also see the terms "pay-per-call," "976," and "caller-paid" used interchangeably along with simply, "900." They all mean essentially the same thing: the caller is charged for the telephone call, at a rate in excess of normal toll charges, in exchange for the information or entertainment services provided.

The 900 industry was launched in 1980 by AT&T, then calling it "DIAL-IT 900 Service," with the premier of DIAL-IT National Sports in September, followed shortly thereafter in October by ABC-TV's use of the service during the Reagan-Carter presidential debates to poll viewer opinion. On the final night of the debates, 500,000 people paid 50 cents each to register their opinions.

Maybe you remember the *Saturday Night Live* episode when viewers were asked to call a 900 number to vote whether or not Eddie Murphy should boil Larry the Lobster. A whopping 500,000 callers participated, voting to save poor Larry, but Eddie boiled him anyway.

The industry really didn't take off, however, until 1987 when AT&T began offering premium billing services. This allowed IPs to generate profits from calls instead of simply covering the program costs. During the same year, Telesphere initiated the first interactive 900 service. By 1989, the three major long distance carriers (AT&T, MCI and Sprint) were offering interactive 900 services, and industry revenues were growing very quickly. By 1990 revenues reached 1 billion dollars, with more than 10,000 pay-per-call programs available.

Table 1-1 shows 900 revenue growth from 1987, projected through 1996. As you can see, revenues peaked in 1990, then slid to a bottom of $770 million in 1992, roughly corresponding to the recessionary economy. 1993 marks the beginning of a slower, more sustainable growth rate for the industry.

900 INDUSTRY GROWTH		
Year	Total Revenue (M. Dollars)	Total Number of 900 Lines
1987	$35	368
1988	152	1555
1989	324	2800
1990	1026	10300
1991	859	13000
1992	770	12000
1993	851	10000
1994	916	10800
1995	984	11900
1996	1125	13200
Source: LINK Resources Corporation		

Table 1-1

Although the growth of the 900 industry was nothing short of explosive in its formative years, it has experienced some definite growing pains along the way. Because the quick profit potential is so attractive, many less-than-reputable players jumped onto the bandwagon early with dial-a-porn type programs or straight rip-off programs. Predictably, with virtually no rules or regulations in place, there were many abuses, and the 900 industry earned itself a bad reputation which it is still trying to shake off.

As you may already know, dial-a-porn programs haven't been the worst examples of sleaze in this industry. Indeed, most of them delivered exactly what was promised, which was why they were so wildly successful. The real abuses have been with dishonest variations of the sweepstakes, credit card and job search lines. While a few of these programs may be legitimate, the vast majority have been unequivocal rip-offs of the worst kind, preying upon unfortunate people who can least afford to part with their hard-earned money.

There was little regulation in this emerging industry, and a lot of unscrupulous people took advantage of this fact. Many people still equate 900 with sleaze. This is now changing, and the industry is working hard to clean itself up. The National Association for Interactive Services (NAIS) and the Information Industry Association (IIA) are two industry trade organizations that have established stringent codes of practice for their members. State and Federal laws are being debated and passed. More and more reputable companies are using the power of 900, resulting in hundreds of legitimate, useful, and valuable 900 information services.

It will take time for the 900 industry to clean up its image. The press and media have been really blasting the industry, and only lately have any positive articles appeared. The June 1991 issue of *U.S. News & World Report* featured a well-balanced article that emphasized some of the positive trends in the industry. But much more typical are articles like the one in the August 1991 issue of *Reader's Digest*, which really slammed the industry.

It is going to take awhile for the media to fully recognize the positive trends in the 900 industry, and it's beginning to happen already. As favorable publicity begins transforming the negative perception many people still have, won't this actually enhance the overall opportunity for legitimate 900 businesses? Of course it will. If there is good profit potential now, at the bottom of the credibility curve, imagine how much better business will be after the 900 industry shakes off its negative reputation. And there is no question about it -- the 900 industry will soon become as well-respected and indispensable as any other established industry.

There are plenty of opportunities in valuable, helpful information or entertainment applications. Like any maturing industry, the questionable fast-buck days are just about over. You can no longer count on the novelty of 900 to make just about any 900 program successful. In order to successfully compete now and into the future, you must offer sound value for the money you charge. This holds true for any product or service, and the 900 industry is no exception.

The Future of 900

What accounts for the explosive growth of the 900 industry? Is it a fad that will fade away after the novelty wears off? Will people continue to pick up the telephone, knowing that they are paying for the information? Will the industry still be around a few years from now?

First of all, we are already in the habit of using the telephone for getting information quickly. We call the airline for flight information, we call our stock broker for the latest price of Disney stock, we call the IRS help line for tax questions, or we call the weather service for local forecasts. We pull out the *Yellow Pages* and let our fingers do the walking. The telephone is the quickest and easiest way to get specific information exactly when we need it.

Why in the world would we pay for information when it can be had for free? Using the above examples, the airline may put us on hold for several minutes, we may trade phone calls with our broker a few times before speaking to him, we might get inept tax advice from the IRS (not unusual!), or we may want more specialized weather information.

Not being able to get exactly the information you want when you need it can be very inconvenient in this hectic electronic age. Will we pay for accurate, timely information? Absolutely! As long as the cost of the information seems to be reasonable when balanced against the extra convenience of getting what we need when we want it.

You want to pack a small suitcase for a brief trip to a city 500 miles away. You pick up the phone and call the friend you'll be visiting for the latest weather forecast, so you'll know what kind of clothes to pack. You just paid for that information because it was a long distance call. But it was worth it to you because now you don't have to lug around your overcoat. If a 900 weather line offered the same information, you could have avoided bothering your friend at 10:15 pm in the middle of his favorite TV program.

One of the factors behind the success of the 900 industry is our penchant for instant gratification or instant results. In this busy electronic information age we have come to expect instantaneous information or results. Operation Desert Storm was brought into our living rooms live and in color, and we couldn't get enough of it. Instead of composing a thoughtful letter to a friend or relative, we pick up the telephone and call. We use the fax machine to send a document that doesn't really need to be there instantly, but it's easier than mailing it. We call our doctor and try to describe our minor ailment and hope he gives us a diagnosis over the phone, because there's simply no time to get down to his office for an examination. We all lead busy, hectic lives. We enthusiastically embrace anything that saves us time and effort -- witness the proliferation of prepared and ready-made foods we couldn't possibly live without.

Of course, this never really helps, because we just try to cram more activities into the time saved elsewhere, but that's just human nature and beyond the scope of this book.

In this book you will learn that many large, respectable companies are launching pay-per-call services in ever increasing numbers. Media companies are using 900 as a logical extension of their existing services, often enhancing their profitability. As of this writing, the Regional Bell Operating Companies (RBOCs) cannot offer enhanced information services in direct competition with entrepreneurial IPs, but these restrictions may soon disappear.

What does all this mean for you, the start-up IP? Obviously, this evolving business climate has created some real challenges for anyone who may eventually have to compete with such huge, well-financed companies. On the other hand, the increasing willingness of such companies to enter this field may offer some unique opportunities for the imaginative entrepreneur.

Why not come up with a well-conceived, workable 900 concept and then team-up with such a company? Form a joint venture partnership with a financially sound company that has the funds to properly promote and launch a new 900 program. Design an entertainment program that can be licensed to a broad range of promotional or media partners.

The point is that you needn't necessarily limit your thinking to going it alone with all phases of program development and execution. Other alternatives are available. The real imagination is in the development, and the big dollars are in the execution. Instead of competing head-to-head with a huge corporation, join it in a win-win relationship that is financially beneficial to both parties.

Big companies are rarely imbued with a plethora of entrepreneurial imagination, but they have the big bucks. Entrepreneurs rarely have unlimited financial resources, but they often have great money-making ideas. Put the two together and it just might be a winning combination!

Definitions

Before reading any further, you need to understand several commonly used terms in the 900 industry. This is by no means a comprehensive glossary, which can be found at the end of this book.

Audiotext (also Audiotex). This term broadly describes various telecommunications equipment and services that enable users to send or receive information by interacting with a voice processing system via a telephone connection, using audio input. Voice mail, interactive 800 or 900 programs, and telephone banking transactions are examples of applications that fall under this generic category.

Information Provider (IP). A business or individual who delivers information or entertainment services to end users (callers) with the use of communications equipment and computer facilities.

The call handling equipment is often not owned by the IP, and a separate service bureau is hired for this purpose.

Interactive. An audiotext capability that allows the caller to select options from a menu of programmed choices in order to control the flow of information. As the term implies, the caller truly interacts with the computer, following the program instructions and selecting the information he or she wishes to receive.

Interexchange Carrier (IXC). This term technically applies to carriers that provide telephone service between LATAs (see below). Long distance companies such as AT&T, Sprint, and MCI are also known as interexchange carriers.

Local Access Transport Area (LATA). This is a geographic service area that generally conforms to standard metropolitan and statistical areas (SMSAs), and some 200 were created with the breakup of AT&T. The local telephone companies provide service within each LATA (Intra-LATA), while a long distance carrier (IXC) must be used for service between LATAs (Inter-LATA).

Local Exchange Carrier (LEC). This is the local telephone company that provides service within each LATA. Also included in this category are independent LECs such as General Telephone (GTE). The LEC handles all billing and collections within its LATA, often including long distance charges (Inter-LATA), which are collected and forwarded to the appropriate interexchange carriers.

Pay-Per-Call. We have already talked about this with regard to 900. The callers pays a pre-determined charge for accessing information services. This is not, however, the only type of pay-per-call service available. For local, intra-LATA applications, a seven digit number is available with a 976 or 540 prefix. This service is usually quite a bit less expensive than long distance 900 services, and should be seriously considered for any local or regional pay-per-call applications that will not have the potential for expanding nationwide.

Pay-per-call services may also be offered over 800 or regular toll lines using credit card or other third party billing mechanisms. When the caller pays a premium above the regular transport charges for the information content of the program, regardless of how payment is made, it is considered a pay-per-call service (the FCC's definition of pay-per-call, however, includes only 900 numbers - see Appendix G).

Regional Bell Operating Company (RBOC). These are the seven holding companies that were created by the breakup of AT&T (also known as Baby Bells):

1. NYNEX
2. Bell Atlantic
3. AMERITECH
4. Bell South
5. Southwestern Bell Corp.
6. U.S. West
7. Pacific Telesis

These companies own many of the various LECs. For example, NYNEX owns both New England Telephone and New York Telephone. However, there are numerous independent LECs that are not owned by any RBOC. For example, Southern New England Telecommunications Corp. (SNET) is an independent LEC serving most of Connecticut's residential customers, and has nothing to do with NYNEX.

Service Bureau. A company that provides voice processing / call handling / audiotext equipment and services and connection to telephone network facilities. For a fee, these companies allow an information provider (IP) to offer a pay-per-call program using the service bureau's equipment and facilities.

The Joke Exchange

My first 900 program, launched back in 1991, was The Joke Exchange. Basically, the premise of the program was for callers to get the latest jokes so they would be the life of the party, or leave their best joke for a shot at winning a $500 prize for the funniest joke of the month. The purpose of the contest, besides getting more people to call, was to help ensure participation by callers in leaving jokes, so there would be a constant supply of fresh new jokes in the program.

My intent was to make it a true joke exchange, with callers both hearing and leaving the very latest jokes.

Why did I choose such a program? At the time it seemed like a pretty good idea, although it wasn't the first joke line. Foremost, I wanted to launch some kind of 900 program in order to learn about the business. I was just beginning to research the first edition of this book, and there is no better way to learn about something than by jumping right in and doing it. First hand experience. Unfortunately, one of the reasons for picking a joke line was because such a program was relatively easy to get off the ground -- a pretty lousy reason for choosing any kind of program!

The second reason, however, was a little more defensible. I have always had a hard time remembering jokes, and I have never been known as the life of the party. On the contrary, my attempts at humor were often met with yawns or even audible groans. Here was an opportunity to improve my social standing among my friends by being more amusing, while having some fun at the same time. And maybe I could make some money too!

It was a lot of fun setting up the program. The first step was selecting West Interactive in Omaha as my service bureau, because it had experience with similar programs, a solid reputation and the enormous call handling capacity that I knew would be quite essential for the huge call volume that would be generated by my program (virtually all start-up IPs are afflicted with terminal optimism!). Then I dug up about 30 good jokes to start with, and West Interactive forwarded them to AT&T, our long distance carrier, for review and approval. AT&T gave the thumbs down to several jokes on the basis of being borderline salacious or ethnically demeaning. The ethnically unacceptable jokes were easily fixed: just substitute lawyers or blonds for the ethnic minority in question (it's perfectly acceptable, indeed, even socially beneficial, to discriminate against and lambaste lawyers and blonds!).

Anyway, I figured the program needed at least a dozen good jokes to start with, which would be quickly replaced by jokes left by the callers to the program, in their own voices. It would be a self-perpetuating type program, where the program callers/participants, in this case those leaving the jokes, provide the basic program content. The menu was simple, consisting of three options:

1. Press one to hear all the latest jokes.
2. Press two to record your joke and to enter the contest for a shot at winning the $500 prize. A slot was also provided for recording the caller's name and address.
3. Press three to hear last month's winning joke, plus the name and hometown of the lucky winner.

Because my own voice is about as appealing a fingernails on a chalkboard, and because I wanted more than one person reciting the initial jokes, I decided to take advantage of the voice talent offered by West Interactive, and the initial jokes were recorded in its sound studio by a male and a female with excellent DJ-like voices.

AT&T at the time didn't have any NXXs that spelled anything relating to jokes or humor, so the best I could do was to spell "JOKE" with the last 4 digits of the phone number, which was 1-900-737-JOKE. The call charge was $1.95 the first minute, $1.00 each additional minute.

Of particular interest was how the program was updated with new jokes. A separate program editing line was designed and created by the programmers at West Interactive, which I called via an 800 number, with access using a private code number (so a hacker -- or anyone dialing a wrong number -- couldn't get into the program and screw it up). The editing line allowed me to manage the program using the following options:

1. Press one to review the program. This allowed access to the exact same program as heard on the 900 line, so I could review the program without incurring a charge. Whenever appropriate, I used this option to input jokes of my own into the program, following the same procedure any other caller would follow.
2. Press two to hear new jokes left by the latest callers. Because I had to screen every joke for suitability (i.e., not too salacious or

ethnically demeaning) before transferring them to the program, this feature gave me the following options:

    a. Save the joke and go to the next one. This allowed me to give some thought to marginal jokes before making a final go or no-go decision.

    b. Transfer the joke to the program.

    c. Delete the joke from the system

    3. Press three to edit the jokes on the program. This feature allowed the following options:

    a. Delete a joke from the program.

    b. Transfer a joke to the winner's slot.

    c. Save the joke and continue to the next one.

    4. Press four to declare a new winner. This option allowed me to record a new introduction for each new monthly contest winner, giving the name and hometown of the lucky jokester. This was followed by the joke itself, in the caller's own voice, which was accomplished by #3.b. above.

In reviewing the jokes left by the callers, I had to be careful about violating AT&T's standards of propriety (see Appendix H), so I had to kill quite a few good jokes. Almost every day I would call the editing line and add new jokes to the program and delete jokes that had been on it for awhile. Occasionally, whenever I heard or came across a particularly good joke, using the editing line, I would record the joke in my voice or get a friend to call it in. Because I was so attuned to getting good jokes for the program, one of my objectives was achieved very effectively: I was remembering good jokes and contributing to the general hilarity of my social gatherings, much to the delighted surprise and complete amazement of my friends. They couldn't figure out how I was transformed from a social dullard into an exceedingly proficient humorist.

Except for the contest feature, this program was in fact easy to get launched. But I had no idea how difficult it was going to be to give away money to people! I won't get into all the issues related to conducting contests here, because you can get all of that in Appendix

I. Because the legal issues are so complex, I had to hire a law firm specializing in promotion law, and ended up working with Hall, Dickler, Lawler, Kent and Friedman in New York. The bottom line was that AT&T wouldn't allow a contest without a "conformance letter" from an attorney experienced in promotion law. By the way, don't even think about using your local hometown attorney for this work -- you need the specific expertise offered by the law firms listed in Appendix K.

The Joke Exchange was advertised in Rolling Stone, National Lampoon, some of the larger University newspapers, some alternative newsweeklies, and a local radio station. I even used matchbook covers to get the word out. All kinds of people called in leaving jokes, and I think the program went through every single blond joke ever in circulation. We even received a letter from a guy in Moscow, Eugene Vasiliev, who sent along a few Russian jokes, so I recorded them in my voice and gave him credit for the jokes in the program.

Was The Joke Exchange successful? Sort of. It was slowly gaining in popularity, and a lot of people seemed to be enjoying themselves, myself included. What went wrong? I ran out of money long before I could possibly turn the corner toward profitability. I simply didn't have enough capital -- and staying power -- to properly market the program for a sufficiently long period of time to establish credibility, to gain a following and to adequately test the effectiveness of my marketing options. A classic mistake for many IPs, and you'll hear a lot more about this later in this book.

Granted, the purpose for launching the program wasn't so much to make tons of money, but that would have been nice! Nonetheless, I did learn the business fairly quickly, and I pulled the plug on the program after about six months without losing too much money.

In retrospect, after having researched and written this book, I should have done several things differently. First, and most important, you don't go after a huge national, homogeneous market with a tiny advertising budget. It was simply way too ambitious an undertaking.

Second, a lot more could have been done to promote the program and to generate free media coverage. I should have enlisted a reasonably well-known comic or comedy club to be affiliated with the program in some manner, lending name recognition and credibility to the program. And I could have been much more aggressive about sending out news releases for free publicity.

Third, the game of skill featuring a $500 prize was too complex and possibly unnecessary. On the direction of my attorneys, the contest had to be advertised as void in nine states, limiting the usefulness of the contest in those states, not to mention taking up valuable ad space for the list of states.

One month the prize was awarded to a guy in Florida, whereupon we sent out our standard release letter, which had to be signed and returned to get the $500 cashier's check, giving us permission to mention his name and hometown on the program in the winner's slot. Well, we never heard from the guy (and our letters weren't returned). We actually had trouble giving away $500! I don't know, but it seems likely that many people simply didn't believe we were giving away that much money, and perhaps such a large prize wasn't even necessary.

It would have been a lot simpler to give away a promotional prize of nominal value, such as a joke book or tickets to a comedy club. I wouldn't have had to worry about all the complexities of running a full-blown contest, and more prizes could have been awarded more frequently.

As they say, hindsight in 20-20. The Joke Exchange was a valuable hands-on experience for me. Although I wasn't spectacularly successful with the program, that doesn't mean such a program is a bad idea for someone who avoids my mistakes. That's one of the reasons for my writing this book. And a very good reason for you to read this book and heed my advice, and the advice of the other veterans who have contributed to this effort.

Chapter 2
Services and Applications

Delivery Options

Before jumping into the scores of possible applications that are suitable for 900 programs, we must first understand the different 900 delivery options:

Passive. The caller simply listens to a recorded message of a specific nature and duration. Many of the early 900 programs were passive in nature, however few programs continue to be passive due to the limited information that can be offered. Many polling applications are passive, where the call is simply tallied as a vote by calling the 900 number that corresponds to the vote to be cast.

Interactive. This option is generally available only to callers with a touch-tone telephone. The caller is given a menu of selections, to be chosen by pushing the appropriate number on the telephone keypad. There can be numerous sub-menus within the main menu, so that the caller can quickly zero-in on specific recorded information. For a game application such as a trivia quiz, the keypad is used for answering multiple choice questions. In some applications, the caller may be able to leave verbal information, such as name and address, when ordering merchandise or entering a contest.

Interactive is by far the most prevalent 900 delivery option, and most of the 900 applications we will be talking about fall into this category. It should be noted, however, that more than 38% of the U.S. population is still using rotary telephones, which effectively prevents these people from using interactive information or entertainment services. This is a very large segment of the population. Nonetheless, the fact that these people haven't joined the modern electronic age may be indicative that they would be poor prospects for 900 services anyway. Old-fashioned, conservative people do not currently call 900 numbers.

Live Operator. There are some applications where recorded information is inappropriate, such as legal, financial, medical, or customer service advice. Because it is expensive to hire such professionals as operators, the charges for these calls are typically much higher than the recorded passive or interactive services.

Facsimile (FAX). This is a promising new interactive application whereby a caller with a FAX machine can receive a hard copy of the desired information. This service is also known as fax-on-demand or fax-back. Any information with long term-value, or that is difficult to convey verbally -- such as charts, graphs, or detailed financial reports -- is a good candidate for an interactive FAX program. Business-to-business services are the most logical fax applications because few households are as yet equipped with fax machines.

Hybrid. Many interactive programs have a "default" option for rotary telephone callers that results in a passive call where the caller hears the main message. Or, an interactive program may offer a live operator on the menu of choices should the caller be unable to get the information he or she needs on any of the recorded menu options.

Applications

What follows are numerous examples of 900 programs in various categories. It should be noted that many programs are short-lived, and that some of these programs may have been discontinued, the telephone numbers changed, or the stated call charges may no longer be accurate. Nonetheless, all of these programs were operational at one time, and the fact that any particular program is either discontinued or still operational will tell you something about the viability of that specific program.

Timely Information

What types of services and applications are suitable to the 900 delivery medium? Timely information is probably the most obvious application. Any information that changes quickly or continuously falls into this category. Instant access to this information is very useful to the caller. Stock market quotations, foreign currency exchange rates, commodities prices, sporting results, and weather forecasts are some examples of timely information. All of this information will eventually be available later in print or on television, but many people need this information quickly, and will pay a reasonable fee for instant access, because it satisfies a fundamentally important need of the caller.

Currency brokers Noonan, Astley & Pearce provide real-time currency exchange rates by dialing 1-900-288-5858 for $2.95 per minute.

The *Associated Press* offers AP900 Sportsflash, for up-to-date sporting results worldwide, at 89 cents per minute.

Surfing enthusiasts can call 1-900-USA-SURF, and for 75 cents a minute, get up-to-date conditions for just about any beach in the world. The forecasts are up-dated by using satellite pictures, computer models, oceanography, and eyewitness reports.

Get the latest stock market quotation by calling Dow Jones Quick Call at 1-900-246-4444 for 95 cents per minute.

If you need specific, up-to-date news on what is happening in India, Pakistan and Afghanistan, call 1-900-737-0733 at 95 cents a minute.

Knight-Ridder offers its *CRB Blue Line* for commodities investors. Callers to 1-900-454-BLUE get up-to-the-minute commodities prices, trade recommendations and forecasts from the analysts at the Commodity Research Bureau, for $1.33 a minute.

Call the CD Rate Line at 1-900-BANKCDS for up-to-date CD interest rates for $1.95 the first minute, 95 cents each additional minute.

The Weather Channel offers a 900 service for national and international forecasts, plus a weather trivia game, Thunderstruck, where you can win a Weather Channel beach bag or umbrella. For 95 cents a minute, dial 1-900-WEATHER.

Call the Football Results Line at 1-900-420-5888, and for 75 cents per minute get not only the latest scores, but also the latest Las Vegas betting lines, stadium weather forecasts, and *College and Pro Football Newsweekly's* winning picks.

Looking for concert information about your favorite musician or performer? For $2.99 per minute call 1-900-773-STAR, sponsored by Star Quest, Inc.

Bettors can call for instant racing results at the Meadowlands and Monmouth Race Tracks in New Jersey by dialing 1-900-990-2800.

Other serious bettors can call *Pete's Picks* at 1-900-776-5353 for $2 per minute for the latest picks in numerous college and professional sports, or for $10 per call, they can call *Billy's Power Parlays* at 1-900-454-4667.

Fishing enthusiasts in the midwest can call *Discoveries in Fishing* at 1-900-454-5555 to get the latest scoop on the best fishing spots, plus tips from the pros and updates on several fishing tournaments. This program is updated weekly and costs $1.25 per minute.

Penn State fans can call the Blue White Hotline, 1-900-860-4778, for the latest football or basketball results, plus interviews, previews, and game summaries.

Has your pet just ingested some poisonous substance? Get quick help from The National Animal Poison Control Center by calling 1-900-680-0000 and talk to NAPCC licensed veterinarians and toxicologists for $2.75 per minute.

For 99 cents a minute, dial 1-900-976-SNOW for the latest ski conditions around the country.

Or, for ski conditions, food and lodging information in Michigan and Wisconsin, call 1-900-988-9086 at $2 the first minute, $1.50 each additional minute.

Get the latest airline flight status covering 14 major U.S. airports by calling OAG Flight Call at 1-900-786-8686.

Specialized Information

Another type of information that is suitable for 900 applications relates to specialized information which, although available elsewhere in publications or from experts in the field, can be better delivered through the use of a 900 service. A 900 number may be more convenient, permitting the user to call at his or her convenience when he or she needs the information, instead of waiting for an appointment or driving to the library. A 900 number can be significantly less expensive, allowing the caller to get very specific legal advice, for example, without having to schedule a minimum one hour appointment with a $100-per-hour attorney. A 900 number offers the caller complete confidentiality, so the caller can avoid the embarrassment of talking about his or her substance abuse problem face-to-face with the counselor.

Other logical examples are medical advice, customer service assistance, income tax preparation, movie reviews, or even Tarot Card readings.

Customer service help is one specific application with a great deal of promise. We all hate to be put on hold indefinitely, play telephone tag, or get shunted around to various people before getting our question answered or our problem addressed. We're too busy, and life is already stressful enough without such barriers and inconveniences. Customer support is one of the fastest-growing 900 applications, particularly the computer software support lines. According to Kathryn Sullivan, AT&T's marketing vice president for business applications and information services, "Computer software companies have been among the pioneers in the innovative use of 900 service to improve customer support and satisfaction with pay-per-call technical support." Among the companies using AT&T's MultiQuest 900 service are industry heavyweights Microsoft Corporation and Lotus Development Corp.

I recently purchased a top-selling computer software program, the name of which shall remain anonymous, and had a few questions that were not answered adequately in the manual. Not surprising, for most software manuals are apparently written by computer techies who simply have no grasp of the english language, and certainly have no clue as to how to explain anything in a simple, straightforward manner.

Anyway, I dialed the number, which was a regular long distance toll call. Imagine my horror and consternation when I was informed, by a recorded voice, that the current wait for live assistance was 20 minutes! Needless to say, I didn't stay on the line, and I didn't get my question answered. I ended up calling back later when the wait was down to 10 minutes. I was not overwhelmed by the quality of customer service offered by this company, and wonder how this might affect its future profitability. I would have been very happy to pay $1 or $2 per minute to have my questions answered right away, so I could have gone on with the work at hand. Instead, my work schedule was disrupted and I became an unhappy customer, a lose-lose situation for both parties.

Because of budget cuts, the Market News Branch of the California Department of Food and Agriculture was faced with discontinuing its free information services for farmers and the agricultural community, until this service was converted into a self-funding pay-per-call program. Now farmers can call 1-900-555-0923 at $3 a minute for the latest farm commodity prices or specialized weather information for better crop management. When faced with either losing access to valuable information that was once free, or paying a reasonable fee, the farmers have opted for paying.

Computer junkies can call Novell Netware's 1-900-PRO-HELP hotline for technical support services, 24-hours-a-day, for $4.99 the first minute, $2.99 each additional minute.

Entrepreneur Magazine's Entrepreneur Info Line offers advice in starting and operating a successful small business. Call 1-900-288-8890 for an interactive touch tone menu which includes a quiz to determine what type of business best suits your personality. The cost is $2 for the first minute, $1 for each additional minute.

Having trouble with the bureaucratic maze in finding out about your Social Security benefits? Con-Cur Consultants offers trained live operators who can help at $3 per minute by calling 1-900-446-4583.

Consumer Reports Magazine offers a used-car buying service with price and repair trouble information, 1-900-258-2886, for $1.50 per minute.

The CinemaScore Movie Report offers a wide range of information concerning current movies. Call 1-900-288-FILM to find out what movies are drawing best at the box office and how they are rated with other moviegoers, at $1.95 the first minute, 95 cents each additional minute.

Job seekers can call Rauch & Associates' *Media Grapevine* at 1-900-787-7800 for $1.95 a minute, and get a run-down on available jobs in the newspaper industry.

Technical Software, Inc. offers AutoCad Helpline, a $3 per minute 900 line staffed by experts in AutoCad.

The Better Business Bureau is offering a 900 service in New York City. For 85 cents per minute, call 1-900-INFO-BBB to file a complaint or to find out about the reliability of a business.

Need to kick a nasty addiction? Call 1-900-896-HELP and for $1.98 per minute you can get help concerning drugs, alcoholism, or gambling.

Whitehall Laboratories, manufacturers of Anacin®, offers a stress relief line with tips on how to manage stress in this hectic day and age. Call 1-900-329-STRESS at $1.50 the first minute, 75 cents each additional minute, and you can also receive a helpful brochure and samples of Anacin.

The American Automobile Association offers its *AAA Auto Pricing Service* by dialing 1-900-776-4AAA, at $1.95 per minute, giving up-to-date pricing information for both new and used cars.

For $1.75 per minute, call *The Medical Information Line* at 1-900-230-4800 for confidential recorded information on over 300 medical topics.

The National Parenting Center offers advice from experts for those trying to cope with parenthood. Call 1-900-535-MOMS and select from 35 topics of concern to parents ($1.95 for the first minute, 95 cents per additional minute).

Want to make sure your phone call cannot be traced back to you? Private Lines offers 1-900-STOPPER, which gives you a second dial tone so you can place an untraceable call, for $2 per minute.

The American Civil Liberties Union just introduced 1-900-288-ACLU, at $1 the first minute and 75 cents each additional minute, so you can listen to its analysis of Supreme Court decisions or receive updates on relevant issues before Congress.

Now you can do your classified advertising and shopping by phone. Save Now, Inc. offers a 24 hour classified advertising menu by calling 1-900-860-SAVE. The charge is $5 per minute.

For medical advice from licensed physicians, call Doctor's TeleCare at 1-900-933-3737 for $4 per minute (first minute is free).

NeXT Computers is using AT&T's flexible rate service, Vari-A-Bill, charging $2 a minute for technical questions or $0 for hardware problems, at 1-900-555-NEXT.

The Pet Lover's Helpline, 1-900-776-0007, offers over 300 recorded topics on pet health care for 97 cents per minute. Or, for $3 per minute, call 1-900-PHONE-A-VET for live advice from a licensed veterinarian.

Detroit Monthly magazine sponsors three 900 numbers, all priced at 99 cents a minute, including personal classified ads, restaurant reviews, and horoscopes with a local flavor.

Call Adobe Systems at 1-900-555-ADOBE for technical questions about its new Acrobat software, at $2 per minute.

It's pushing midnight on April 15 and you need help finishing up your tax return. Call H&R Block Tax Hotline at 1-900-226-1444 for $2 the first minute, $1 each additional minute.

Here's one designed specifically for you ambitious souls planning to jump into the 900 business: Call Tele-Lawyer, Inc. at 1-900-835-5252, at $3 per minute, for consulting services relating to the 900 industry.

Prospective brides can call 1-900-884-GOWN for $1.99 per minute and speak to a bridal consultant about bridal gowns.

A.M. Best offers its insurance company rating information for $2.50 per minute by dialing 1-900-420-0400.

Dog and cat breeders can use a 900 program for placing or listening to ads for the breeds of their choice. Essentially a voice mail classified advertising application, callers dial 1-900-288-DOGS or 1-900-288-CATS for ads about 30 dog breeds or 10 cat breeds, at a cost of $2 a minute.

Call the Nanny Hotline at 1-900-446-6269 for nanny referrals for parents or placement opportunities for nannies.

Too lazy to write your congressman or senator? Call Tel-A-Letter at 1-900-933-ISSUE, select the current issue you want to address, answer a series of questions about that issue, and Tel-A-Letter will write the letter for you on personalized letterhead addressed to each member of your congressional delegation. $3.95 the first minute, $1 each additional minute.

Entertainment

Another very important 900 application is entertainment. Indeed, entertainment represents a major share of the industry call volume, accounting for more than 20% of the total. Call for the latest jokes in circulation so you can be the life of the party later that night. Enter a sports or music trivia contest and possibly win a prize. Listen to selected recordings of new songs by emerging artists, not yet aired on radio, so you can decide whether or not to invest in the CD. Miss the latest episode of your favorite soap opera? Call to find out whether Priscilla slept with Derek, her ex-husband's son by a previous bigamous marriage. Call and play the telephone version of Jeopardy or Trivial Pursuit for cash or prizes.

Entertainment applications are limited only by the imagination. Many companies are using games and contests to promote their products or services by increasing consumer awareness. Indeed, the use of 900 services for promotions of all kinds is growing, and because most of these applications feature entertainment of some sort, I have categorized such promotional applications under entertainment.

A new game concept can be tested by using a 900 number to evaluate whether the target market truly enjoys playing the game, before investing huge sums in publishing the game or producing a new TV pilot. In many cases, adding a contest feature with the promise of winning a prize will result in much higher participation.

If you've seen all three *The Godfather* movies, call HBO's trivia game, The Godfather Game: The Challenge you Can't Refuse, 1-900-896-0200.

Call 1-900-454-HULK, hear from Hulk Hogan, and play the wrestling challenge by choosing the best wrestling moves. For $1.49 the first minute and 99 cents each additional minute, you have a shot at winning an all-expense-paid trip to Wrestlemania VIII in 1992.

Folk Music fans can call 1-900-740-HEAR to preview new releases for $2.50 before buying the CD.

For 95 cents a minute you can get the full program listings for the *Sci-Fi Channel* by dialing 1-900-773-SFCS.

Do you have a titillating tale to tell? Call it in by dialing 1-900-B-INSIDE for *Inside Editions'* story tip line, and you just might hear from host Bill O'Rielly asking for more details about your torrid tale.

Aficionados of Dungeons & Dragons computer games can call 1-900-737-HINT for playing clues at 95 cents the first minute, 75 cents each additional minute.

Call the Soap Opera Hotline at 1-900-288-SOAP for recaps and previews of your favorite soaps, at $1.30 per minute.

The Detroit Free Press offers a unique fax-back program for its fanatical funnies readers. For a flat $2.50, they call 1-900-740-PLUS and get a week of their favorite comic strips faxed back to their machine.

Planning a trip to Las Vegas? Call the Las Vegas Hotline, 1-900-446-9797 for show schedules, celebrity information, locations, ticket prices, and a hotel directory, for $1.95 per minute.

A new promotion by Silhouette Books will introduce you to its new line of romance novels by calling 1-900-903-DARK for a flat charge of $2, and you will receive a complimentary copy of one of its latest releases.

Not to be outdone, Harlequin gives out two free books in its SuperRomance and Intrigue lines by calling 1-900-97-NOVEL at $2 for the call.

Marvel Comics is sponsoring a game promotion called the X-Men Adventure Game, 1-900-288-XMEN, where callers battle henchmen and answer trivia questions for prizes, at $1.75 the first minute and 75 cents each additional minute.

Play the *Jeopardy* Telephone Game by dialing 1-900-860-0600 at $1.50 per minute. Or try *Wheel of Fortune* at 1-900-884-WHEEL for $1.95 per minute.

At one time (I think it has since been cancelled) you could play the Massachusetts Lottery using a 900 number from the convenience of home (available for MA callers only). Callers had the option of placing $1 bets on The Numbers Game, Mass Cash, Megabucks or Mass Millions. The $1.95 call charge included the $1 bet.

For 95 cents a minute, you can call *Music Access Monthly's* 900 line to hear excerpts of some 200 music recordings that you may never hear on the radio, including purchase information.

Call 1-900-407-HITS for $1.49 per minute to hear batting tips from Houston Astros catcher John Massarelli.

If you have a tendency toward excessive self-assurance, perhaps bordering on arrogance, and you need an attitude adjustment, call *Dial an Insult* at 1-900-2-INSULT, at $2 the first minute and $1 each additional minute, for a well-deserved heaping of verbal abuse. This program has been around for several years despite the humiliating treatment it doles out to its masochistic customers.

Cheers fans can test their trivia knowledge by playing the Cheers Trivia Game, with a shot at winning a $500 prize. Call 1-900-468-2433 for $2 per minute.

For $2 the 1st minute and $1 each additional minute you can call 1-900-370-7777 for *Alexa's Tarot* line.

Dial-a-Porn

No discussion of the pay-per-call industry would be complete without addressing dial-a-porn, or adult, applications. Before going any further, however, we have to nail down exactly what we mean by the term "dial-a-porn." There is a lot of confusion out there as to what is or is not permissible under current laws and regulations.

For our purposes, dial-a-porn will be defined as containing "indecent" language, defined by the FCC as "the description or depiction of sexual or excretory activities or organs in a patently offensive manner as measured by contemporary standards for the telephone medium." This definition seems to encompass some fairly salacious conversation.

The term "adult" has become accepted in the industry as pertaining to non-indecent communications. Examples of adult services would be the relatively tame chat or romance lines.

Under certain circumstances, indecent language, or dial-a-porn, is allowed on the telephone for commercial purposes between consenting adults. A brief review of the legislative history leading up to the current dial-a-porn laws will help put it all into perspective.

Back in 1988 Congress tried to ban both obscene and indecent speech by passing The Helms Amendment to section 223(b) of the Communications Act of 1934, the major federal law governing the telecommunications industry. Shortly thereafter, in *Sable Communications v. FCC,* the U.S. Supreme Court held that the Helms Amendment was too broad in limiting indecent speech along with obscene speech, so Congress went back to the drawing board and came out with another amendment in 1989, banning:

"any obscene communication for commercial purposes to any person," and,

"indecent communication for commercial purposes which is available to any person under 18 years of age."

Where's the line between indecent and obscene speech? After all, the definition of indecent would seem to allow for some pretty lascivious communication. I'm not sure anyone really knows the difference, and any attempt to find out would be a pointless exercise in futility, and way beyond the scope of this discussion. Suffice to say that there's an arcane legal distinction that promises to ensure the livelihood of countless obfuscating lawyers and legislators.

Anyway, in response to this latest legislation by Congress, the Federal Communications Commission (FCC) issued its Report and Order Concerning Indecent Communications by Telephone (FCC Indecency Rules, now the current law), which prohibits indecent communications except under the following conditions:

A. Reverse blocking must be provided by the carrier, where the subscriber must request such indecent services in writing before gaining access to such services, when payment for such services are through the carrier's premium billing services; and,

B. Take one of the following actions to restrict access to persons under 18 years of age:

1. Require payment by credit card before transmission of the message; or

2. Require an authorized access or identification code before transmission of the message; or

3. Scramble the message using any technique that renders the audio unintelligible and incomprehensible to the calling party unless that party uses a descrambler.

As a practical matter, reverse blocking is a non-starter because it's nearly impossible to implement in an effective manner. According to Edwin N. Lavergne, an attorney with Ginsberg, Feldman & Bress in Washington, DC, "the person who wants to provide the (indecent) communication is also under the obligation to tell the carrier that that's what he's going to do, and the reality is that nobody is going to tell the carrier that they are providing such communication." There is no practical way for the long distance carrier to identify and block indecent lines when the IPs are willing to dissemble about the nature of their services.

Because reverse blocking is required only if the telephone company bills and collects for the service (i.e., premium billing services), and virtually all carriers have elected to deny premium billing services for indecent programs, these new rules effectively ended the use of 900 lines for dial-a-porn. The vast majority of indecent adult programming has migrated over to 800 lines, using credit card billing or pre-subscription personal identification numbers (PIN numbers) along with third party billing. Indecent services are still technically possible over 900 lines, but without the benefit of premium billing services, so that a third party billing system must be used, along with pre-subscription to such services in writing. Because it's so much easier to offer adult services via an 800 line with credit card billing, with no requirement for pre-subscription in writing, few indecent programs are carried on 900 lines anymore -- at least legally.

Another compelling reason for an adult IP to use 800 lines and credit cards is purely economic: less lost revenue from chargebacks. According to Jeff White, director of marketing at R.j. Gordon and Company (this is not a typo, the "j" is lower case on purpose), a consulting and financial services company with many adult IP clients, "credit card billing is by far the most effective alternative billing method (for adult services). When we first started in the business, credit card chargebacks were 20% or so, and we started implementing different fraud control and data base systems, and we eventually got it down to 3%. Then VISA mandated 1% as the maximum allowable chargeback rate and we had to become very aggressive in our fraud control systems, and now we operate at a rate of about 0.7%."

It's actually quite interesting how R.j. Gordon and Company's fraud control system functions. The caller dials an 800 number adult program and is asked by a recorded message to input his credit card number and expiration date via the telephone keypad. This information, along with the callers' telephone number, that was captured with Automatic Number Identification (ANI), is sent immediately by separate phone line to Shared Global Systems in Houston. SGS searches its database and scores the caller according to his past calling and payment history, resulting in either accepting or rejecting the call. All of this takes about two seconds, and if approved, a preliminary authorization is issued, and the caller is connected to the adult service. At the conclusion of the call the call charges are totalled by the service bureau and again transmitted to SGS for final credit card authorization and crediting to the IP's merchant account.

With such a sophisticated and effective fraud control system for credit card billing on 800 numbers, it's hard to imagine why any legitimate adult IP would use anything else, unless he cannot get credit card merchant account status.

Why then, do we still see a lot of advertising a for what appears to be dial-a-porn on 900 numbers? Very good question, and there are a couple of possible answers. First, the salacious advertisement may in fact be quite misleading about the actual program content: what you see isn't even close to what you get or expect. Instead, you talk to a woman with a sexy voice, but the actual conversation is rather innocuous and only mildly suggestive, characterized by innuendo. The female operator is instructed to keep control over the conversation, preventing it from getting out of hand and straying into the realm of indecency. These types of tame adult services are also known as "romance" or "chat" lines, and they remain popular with people whose main reason for calling is to cure loneliness.

The second explanation for salacious 900 advertising is that the ad is quite accurate, and you get to talk down and dirty, getting as nasty as you wish, because the IP is willing to risk breaking the law. In this instance, the IP would have to mislead both the service bureau and the long distance carrier, lying about the type of program and its content, and then hope he isn't caught and unceremoniously shut down. This kind of IP risks losing a lot of money invested in advertising, not to mention as much as $50,000 per day in civil fines and/or up to six months in prison.

The third reason would be that the IP is using a third party billing service along with pre-subscriptions for the adult service. By the way, third party billing is simply a service provided by an independent company, some of which have established relationships with the telephone companies (LECs) to permit it to include it's bill in the same envelope as the regular phone bill. This method, when combined with pre-subscription, is quite burdensome, and it is doubtful that many IPs would elect to do business this way when better alternatives are available to them.

In the first case, where the IP is trying to stay within the bounds of decent language, the program may be legal, albeit borderline, but the advertising may be quite deceptive, running afoul of the Federal Trade Commission (FTC) regulations governing fair advertising. In the second case, the IP is again violating federal law, this time under the aegis of the FCC, which governs what can be transmitted over the telephone lines.

Does this mean that all adult programming is offered by sleazy IPs, or that adult programming is pervasively non-legitimate? Of course not. Are *Playboy* and *Penthouse* magazines non-legitimate publications, or do they deliver exactly what you would expect from them? Does the fact that these adult magazines exist taint the entire magazine publishing industry? Honest answers to these questions demonstrate how unfair it is to continue equating the pay-per-call industry with sleaze.

Indeed, now that indecent adult programming is, for all practical purposes, unavailable on 900 numbers, but widely available on 800 lines, the 900 industry gets a double whammy when it's still exclusively associated with dial-a-porn. Ironically, the argument can now be made that 900 lines are the cleanest of them all. And it's real hard to believe that 800 numbers will ever get a bad reputation, despite the volume of indecent intercourse transmitted over such lines.

Early in the game, when there were few controls and no legislation in place to control the industry, adult programming was available to anyone who picked up the telephone, including children. This uncontrolled access is what really caused all the problems. Parents, or the people who paid the phone bill, were getting completely unexpected charges, often for huge sums, for dial-a-porn services. For good reason, these outraged parents complained vociferously, and a lot of people paid attention, as they are wont to do when sex is the topic, and among them were members of the media and the political establishment. A heated debate ensued, resulting in the legislation discussed earlier. Lost in the debate was the fact that these programs were usually quite honest about what they delivered, and that most of the callers were consenting adults, who, for whatever reason, were willing to pay for the services rendered.

We would be faced with the same outcry if *Hustler* magazine were widely available to our children, particularly if they could automatically charge the cost to mom and dad, and then took advantage of the opportunity with alarming frequency.

Another reason for the fast proliferation of adult programming was the easy money involved. The early adult IPs were raking in a lot of money, owing to the novelty of such services and an apparently unquenchable demand. Let's face it, the three most lucrative ways to make money are selling health, wealth or love/sex. These areas cover the most fundamentally important human needs. Satisfy one of these needs and the cash will flow.

Not surprisingly, unregulated access to adult services eventually claimed its first victim. Telesphere, a major long distance carrier accepting "adult lines," terminated all 900 services on September 10, 1991, and then filed for Chapter 11 bankruptcy protection the next day. This action instantly ended many adult 900 programs. Indeed, Telesphere's financial difficulties resulted from abnormally high chargebacks from local exchange carriers, or in layman's terms, uncollectible 900 charges from callers. Many of these uncollectible charges can be traced to irate parents who discovered that little Johnny was getting his sex education from a sultry voice on a 900 line.

What is the current status of dial-a-porn? Basically, indecent programs are not really feasible on 900 lines, and such programming has almost universally shifted to 800 numbers with credit card billing. Dial-a-porn on 900 is a non-issue, a controversy that will hopefully die a quiet death.

It's too bad that the media, including some well-known commentators who should know better, still don't have their facts straight, and continue to link 900 numbers to dial-a-porn. Think about it, they are really doing their audience a serious disservice, particularly those poor horny guys who actually believe what they hear, and whose expectations are not met when they call such a line. They will be sorely disappointed when they get a tame "romance" line instead of the steamy hot filth they were led to expect from the mainstream media coverage. Now who is being sleazy?

Finally, we should address a new problem created by our emerging global economy along with its convenient direct-dial telecommunications. We're now seeing international dial-a-porn using overseas adult services on lines with 011 prefixes. These lines terminate in several foreign countries, including Israel, Holland, Hong Kong, and a few others. These lines range from tame chat lines to steamy sex lines, and present the same problem that plagued early 900 dial-a-porn: uncontrolled access by minors.

At this point it is uncertain how such access can be controlled, if at all. This is another example of how technology moves much faster than government's attempts to regulate it, and when regulations eventually come out, they often solve yesterday's problems, which are no longer the issue. Maybe it's time to demand more responsibility from parents, and stop turning to an inefficient government to solve all our perceived social problems.

Polling

Opinion polling was one of the first 900 applications, during the Reagan-Carter debates, and continues to be a popular method for getting instant readings of people's opinions on a wide range of topics.

Opinion polling need not be limited to simply casting a vote by calling the appropriate 900 number. *Newsweek* magazine recently initiated a 900 letter-to-the-editor service for those opinionated souls who are too lazy to sit down and compose a letter.

CNN uses a 900 number so viewers can select stories that will be covered later in the program. *Sporting News* used a 900 number during the 1990 spring baseball lockout so its readers could call in and express their opinions.

WTBS recently asked its viewers to vote for the best Robin Hood - Errol Flynn or Kevin Costner. The respective 900 numbers cleverly corresponded to the release dates of the two movies: 1-900-720-1938 and 1-900-720-1991. A total of 55,000 calls, at 50 cents each, were generated, and Errol Flynn beat out Kevin Costner 59 percent to 41 percent.

The TV show, *A Current Affair*, used a 900 line to solicit viewers opinions concerning the arrest of Pee-wee Herman. The one-day survey resulted in overwhelming support for Pee-wee.

MTV, a real innovator in interactive 900, recently asked viewers to call a 900 line to suggest a name for Paula Abdul's concert tour.

Fundraising

A recent trend in the 900 industry has been the use of 900 numbers for fundraising purposes. The June 1991 issue of *Interactive World* (a now defunct trade magazine) devoted an eight page article to this promising 900 application.

These programs are often flat rate calls, and usually include a recorded message regarding the topic of concern, often by a recognized celebrity who champions the particular cause. Some organizations which have already experimented with 900 fundraising include World Vision, Leukemia Society of America, March of Dimes, Amnesty International, and Mothers Against Drunk Driving.

What makes 900 fundraising so promising is the convenience, to both the donor and the fundraiser. It's much easier to dial a phone number than to write a check and address an envelope. The fundraisers' collection costs go way down, and the problem with generous pledges who never come through with the cash is completely eliminated.

If you're concerned about the welfare of our dolphin friends, call the Dolphin Project's 900 line, 1-900-USA-DOLPHIN, and the proceeds ($5 the first minute, 50 cents each additional minute) support its efforts in protecting these lovable creatures.

The United Way of New York allows generous New Yorkers to contribute $10 per call by dialing 1-900-820-NYC1.

Using AT&T's Vari-A-Bill service, the Easter Seal Society's Utah chapter is collecting donations of $50, $75 or $100 at the option of the caller, by dialing 1-900-884-SEAL. This program is promoted primarily during the Easter Seals Telethon.

You can help the victims of the war in Bosnia-Herzegovina with a $14.95 donation to the International Relief Committee by calling 1-900-40-PEACE.

Public television is jumping into 900 fundraising because it already owns the media time necessary to make the campaign work. WGBH in Boston raised over $50,000 with a recent campaign featuring an Auction Game.

Trends for the Future

You probably noticed that many of the preceding examples of 900 applications are by well-known companies, and in some cases, by state or local governments. Established companies are turning to 900 applications, in rapidly increasing numbers, to enhance their profitability. Governmental entities can often improve the way they deliver information to their constituents.

Media companies in particular are embracing pay-per-call, because they have ready access to the most expensive component of any 900 application: advertising. *USA Today* sponsors several in-house 900 lines; including weather, sports, and financial information. Many sports publications have their own 900 sports lines. Major newspapers offer 900 movie reviews because they already have an in-house critic on the payroll, and it's a logical extension of their existing service. Many newspapers offer 900 clue lines for their crossword puzzles. Most of the alternative weekly newspapers feature a 900 personals classified dating line.

This trend will continue with non-media companies too, with more and more established businesses offering 900 services that are related to, or are compatible with, their current operations. As the 900 industry gains respectability, this trend will accelerate. Law firms will offer legal advice, hospitals will offer medical advice, travel agencies will offer specialized travel information, and accountants will offer tax advice.

Does this mean that the small, independent information provider will be squeezed out of the picture? Not necessarily. Although it will be difficult to compete head-to-head with well-established companies with wide credibility, name recognition, and media access, there are always specialized niches in any industry. Find a need, and then fill it. Whether it's a unique or specialized information service, or an untapped market segment, there will always be opportunities for those with the imagination and drive to make it work.

Or, as I mentioned in Chapter 1, you don't necessarily have to go it alone. You may be able to sell your unique 900 idea to an established company, combining your entrepreneurial creativity with the financial resources of a large company for the benefit of both parties.

This type of relationship can be established in several ways. You could sell licensing rights, become an equal partner, or simply serve as an independent contractor for such a company. Before you approach such a company, however, you must do your homework very diligently. The program should be operational, if not already successful, because an actual demonstration of a working program is much more effective than simply a concept on paper. And you must have your attorney review every document and every facet of the proposed business relationship.

Later in this book we will discuss partnerships with media companies as a means for reducing advertising costs. But this is only one way to work with an established company. Put your imagination to work and try to identify other kinds of businesses that would benefit from a well-conceived 900 program, and then design a program concept that you can sell to a specific company. Your chances for success will be much improved if you can share marketing costs with an established business.

Chapter 3
What Makes 900 Unique?

Launching a 900 program couldn't be much easier. That's not to say that every program will necessarily be successful. We'll talk a lot more about that later. But the fact remains that it is quite easy to get a program on line, fairly quickly, with a minimal investment of capital.

Start-up costs can be kept minimal - in the hundreds, not thousands, of dollars. By using a service bureau (Chapter 7), it is not necessary to purchase any special equipment. This is a perfect part-time business that can be operated easily from home. The working hours are quite flexible, and need not interfere with family, a full-time job, or playtime. With recorded interactive programs, because program up-dates are often accomplished from any remote location with a touch-tone telephone, business can still be conducted even while on a prolonged vacation.

Assuming the program is successful, revenues can be generated 24-hours-a-day, seven days-a-week, while you are asleep or out fishing. If you're really successful, you can easily move yourself and your business to Florida, Hawaii or Aspen. Few other businesses are quite so portable, with no lost revenue or business interruption.

The industry is open to anyone with a good, workable idea. It doesn't require any special education, training, or an advanced degree.

It does require knowledge, however, particularly in marketing. More about this later.

The industry is still new and growing, with plenty of potential for further growth. Lots of ideas haven't even been tried yet. Except for very specialized programs, the size of the market is potentially unlimited, and growing all the time as more and more people accept 900 programming as legitimate and useful.

These are some very powerful advantages to the 900 industry. These characteristics are extremely attractive to entrepreneurs who want to start out with a part time, home-based business. The only other type of business that comes close to 900 with similar advantages is mail order.

A good analogy is to compare a 900 business with operating a tavern, a business most of us are familiar with (hopefully, not too familiar!). Let's assume that your 900 program nets $2 per call after all long-distance carrier and service bureau charges, about the same you would net selling a mixed drink in your tavern. Let's further assume your 900 business is operated from home, with very low overhead, and the total fixed monthly costs, excluding advertising, are $400.

Now, using the tavern analogy, you need to sell 200 drinks a month to cover rent, insurance, utilities, payroll, and all other overhead. To break even on fixed costs, you must sell about seven drinks a day to your customers. To make a profit, you simply have to sell more than seven drinks a day.

Now this is a really unique tavern with some magical characteristics. It's absolutely enormous in size, with no limit on its capacity. If you can get them to come, you can cram hundreds or even thousands of people into your establishment. And you don't have to rely on your local market, people within a short driving distance. People from any part of the country can be inside your tavern instantly without actually leaving home, as if by some kind of magic tele-transporter.

Finally, your tavern has a special license to stay open 24-hours-a-day, seven-days-a week, and never needs to shut down for maintenance or cleaning. It operates automatically, completely by itself, with no employees or supervision, so you can be out on the golf course even when it's mobbed with merrymakers!

Sound too good to be true? Not necessarily. These are very real advantages to the 900 industry. Getting people to come to your tavern, however, is the real challenge. To get people to come, and then come back again and again, you may have to offer a unique theme or ambiance that appeals to a specific market. Or unique entertainment that your customers cannot find elsewhere. Or an extremely good value on the drinks, such as oversized specialty drinks with those little umbrellas sticking out of them. Or a tasty buffet to induce more people to come. Or a daily door prize for your patrons.

Just opening the tavern is by no means sufficient. Nobody will show up if they don't know about it. And once they find out about it, you must offer them a compelling reason to visit your establishment. And when they come, you want to treat them really well so that they will keep coming back.

Premium Billing Services

Probably the most unique characteristic of the 900 pay-per-call industry is premium billing. The telephone company collects your money for you. In what other business do you automatically get the services of a large, reputable company for all your billings and collections? The fact that your charges are included on their monthly telephone bills almost guarantees that your customers will not dispute your charges or hold-off paying for a long period of time. This is especially true for legitimate, reputable 900 programs. Most people do not question their phone bills, and they pay them promptly, along with other important utility bills.

This feature may not be very important if you're selling big ticket items like cars or boats to a small number of customers. But what is the average price of your 900 service? Maybe $2, $3 or $5? And if the program is marketed nationally to a broad audience, customers could number in the thousands or tens of thousands. Imagine how costly it would be to collect small amounts of money from thousands of people. You would definitely need sophisticated computerized equipment to keep up with the volume. And a lot of people to run the equipment and handle the mail. And your collection rates would be much lower.

With a 900 line, the telephone company does all the work for you, and then sends out one check once a month. One check for $50,000 instead of 10,000 checks averaging $5 each. You spend a lot less time chasing money you've already earned. You can concentrate your efforts on improving your program or marketing, earning even more money for the telephone company to collect for you in the future.

Premium billing services are actually provided at two levels. First, the LEC collects the money from the customer as part of the total monthly phone bill, which aggregates all the local, long distance and 900 charges. The 900 charges are listed separately as part of the long distance IXC bill, and the LEC basically collects the IXC's money and forwards it to the IXC (getting paid for its efforts, of course, in its capacity as the IXC's collection agent). Second, the IXC forwards the appropriate funds to the client of record, which can be either the IP or the service bureau. If the service bureau, the process takes one more step before the money reaches the IP.

Premium billing services are currently available only for information or entertainment services. The telephone companies will not allow the sale of any physical product in connection with their billing services. Some IPs are getting around this by offering a valuable recorded information program, while also "giving away" a related product to callers. Be careful. If you abuse the privilege, the telephone company might just shut down your program.

Nonetheless, this situation may soon change. The telephone companies earn money for serving as collection agents for other companies, using their established billing and collection systems, which are already in place. The amount of money is quite impressive, and the telephone companies are not blind to the potential revenues that would result if products could be sold using 900 premium billing services. The main problem from the telephone company's perspective is what to do about chargebacks for defective or returned merchandise. If this issue can be resolved to the satisfaction of the telephone companies, product sales on 900 numbers will become a reality. If and when this happens, the use of 900 numbers will explode, and the telephone companies will add a lucrative new revenue source to their operations.

Alternative Billing Services

Premium billing services, as the term vaguely implies, is a voluntary service provided by the telephone companies. The telephone company, whether it be an LEC or an IXC, cannot be forced to collect money for other companies, or for categories of services, it does not wish to handle. The telephone company may deny premium billing services simply because it doesn't wish to sully its corporate image by being associated with a certain type of service. This is often the case with adult services, where even the tame chat or romance lines are denied premium billing despite not being classified as "indecent" in content.

This gap in billing services is being filled by independent third party companies that offer such services to IPs and service bureaus. These alternative billers get call data from the telephone company or the service bureau, including the caller's telephone number (through ANI) and billing address. In some cases, through agreements with the LECs, these company's bills are included with the regular telephone bill.

There are basically two types of alternative billing. The most effective alternative is nearly identical to regular premium billing offered by the IXCs and LECs. The third party billing company's bill is inserted into the same envelope as the LEC monthly bill, often designed and formatted to look like the regular phone bill, and the customer pays the entire bill with one check. Essentially, the third party biller is taking the place of the IXC, while the LEC is still performing premium billing. Like getting half of the regular premium billing service.

But not necessarily half of the benefits. According to the third party billers, there are several advantages to using their services:

1. Flexible reporting using report formats that can be customized to the client's data needs.

2. Fraud control measures (such as those discussed in Chapter 2 under Dial-a-Porn).

3. Flexible payment plans and factoring, allowing IPs to get their cash faster.

4. Billing for adult (non-indecent) programs where allowed by LECs.

5. Variable billing rate options that allow the IP some flexibility in structuring the call charges.

6. In some cases, lower processing fees and lower holdbacks (reserves against chargebacks, or bad debt).

7. These companies are specialists in one narrow field, and can do a better job because they are better focused on strictly billing and collections.

Alternative billing is a relatively new phenomenon, but it is apparently gaining acceptance with both IPs and service bureaus. In some cases, IPs are requesting certain third party billers in preference over the IXCs because of the level of services provided. Service bureaus are beginning to offer third party billing as an additional option in their mix of services.

It should be emphasized that this type of third party billing, also known as LEC or Telco billing, must meet the standards set by the pertinent LECs. Except for adult programming, which most LECs are still willing to bill for, most of the other standards are quite similar to those promulgated by the IXCs (see Appendix H).

The second type of alternative billing is known as private billing or private party billing. The main difference here is that the private biller doesn't include its bill along with the LEC phone bill -- it is sent separately to the customer. This means that no premium billing service is provided at any level, and the IP needn't be concerned with IXC and LEC policies as they relate to premium billing. The program content, however, must still conform to Federal law. For example, indecent programs can be offered on 900 numbers and billed by a private biller, but the FCC rules requiring written pre-subscription to such services must be followed in order to be legal (Appendix G). Also, product fulfillment using 900 numbers can be accomplished with private billing.

The problem with this alternative is obvious: collection rates can be quite poor because the bill is not aggregated with the phone bill. It is much easier for the customer to ignore the bill when it arrives independent of the phone bill. Of course, this is actually how most bills, for virtually any other products or services, arrive at the customer's doorstep anyway, and the problem is only relative, because the alternative (LEC or premium billing) is so attractive. Like any other transaction, it will boil down to how satisfied the customer was with the service. The bill is usually paid if the customer's expectations were met.

The argument can be made that just the availability of private party billing is a unique advantage of the 900 industry, despite its ranking at the bottom of the billing hierarchy. What other industries have third party billers already in place who are ready, willing and able to perform such a valuable service? Unless the LECs change their policies and allow product sales, private party billing may indeed become an important product fulfillment alternative for many direct marketers. Chargebacks certainly will not be an insurmountable problem for reputable companies offering good value and services to their customers.

There are currently two leaders in the third party billing arena, listed below. You will find others in the relevant trade publications listed in Appendix A.

> VRS
> 160 Saratoga Ave., Suite 44
> Santa Clara, CA 95051
> 408-296-2740

ITA
1000 Circle 75 Parkway, Suite 700
Atlanta, GA 30339
800-285-4263

Instant Market Testing

Another unique advantage with 900 is instant market testing. Most service bureaus offer instant call-count information. Call at any time of the day to find out how many calls or call minutes have been generated by your program for the day. Many of these services are automated and menu-driven, so you can select specific information you want about call volume to your program. Hourly counts, daily counts, or cumulative counts for the week.

Then, every month you will receive a detailed report summarizing this information, including daily calls, billable minutes, peak call times, average hold time, and just about anything to need to know about the incoming calls. Many service bureaus can customize the monthly reports to exactly suit your specific requirements.

The market testing ramifications of this are obvious: you can instantly measure the effectiveness of your advertising. You know what day your ad hits the streets, so you call in for the next few days to see how many calls it has generated. If the results are good, you commit to the next issue or increase the size of the ad. If the results are way below expectations, cancel the next issue and stop wasting money immediately.

We'll talk more about market testing later. Suffice to say that the 900 industry offers the unique capability to instantly measure marketing effectiveness. And in an advertising driven business, this is no small advantage. You will quickly learn how to most wisely spend your advertising dollars, achieving maximum efficiency quickly and cost-effectively.

Direct Response

How do your customers actually purchase your service? It couldn't be any easier. They pick up the telephone and dial your number. No credit cards, no checks, no mailing. All they need is a telephone. If you offer information they need on a regular basis, they might just slip your phone number into their wallets and become regular customers.

Your customers have instant and easy access to your service from virtually every residential telephone in the country. You have a business with a national market that can be operated out of your home. Very low overhead, very high income potential.

It's called Direct Response. Someone sees your ad, which offers something they want, and they call your 900 number. The cost of your service is simply added to their telephone bill. And they didn't even need a credit card because their local telephone company automatically gives them credit for up to 30 days. They don't have to send away for anything, or talk to an operator to process an order. It couldn't be any easier to purchase your information or entertainment service.

Direct response has been around for quite awhile. You have probably used it many times with an 800 number. Records, cassettes and CDs have been big direct response sellers. Direct response is the only way you can order those melodious Slim Whitman albums! Or those incredible Ginzu knives!

With direct response, you usually have to advertise every time you want someone to call. It is very often an impulse purchase. If they don't call the first time they see, read or hear your ad, you have probably lost them as a customer. Advertising drives calls. Stop your advertising, and calls quickly dry up.

Yes, this is a really easy business to launch, but success is by no means guaranteed. Pay very careful attention to the rest of this book, and avoid some of the pitfalls associated with the 900 industry. Be completely prepared before you jump headlong into launching a 900 program.

Chapter 4
The Disadvantages

To be completely fair and objective, we must address some of the shortcomings and pitfalls surrounding the 900 industry. The industry is not without its special problems, just like any other industry, particularly one that is still experiencing growing pains. Indeed, it's not even clear that the industry will be able to eventually shake off its slimy image, and radical measures could become necessary, like getting rid of the 900 exchange and starting fresh with a new number (which will also require a new title for this book!).

Public Perception

I've already mentioned the August 1991 *Reader's Digest* article, titled "Dial '900' For Trouble," as being typical of the media's early coverage of the 900 industry. After citing several rip-off examples, Remar Sutton, the author, states, "Welcome to the Pandora's box of the 1990s: let a too-good-to-be-true ad entice you to dial a 900 number and you'll likely find yourself ripped off, knee-deep in sleaze or hounded by bill collectors." This five page article is completely devoted to the seamy underbelly of the industry, including only one short paragraph about legitimate 900 programs.

In 1990 the Consumer Action Group out of San Francisco

conducted a "spot check" survey of 144 pay-per-call programs, concluding during an interview on *Good Morning America* that, "many are unfair at any price" and that "they make outlandish promises." Of course, no mention was made how the 144 programs were selected, and it is very unlikely that this was a scientifically defensible random survey of the some 10,000 pay-per-call programs in existence at the time.

As we all know, the media has an unfortunate penchant for sensationalizing the news with the most titillating slant on any given story. The 900 industry is particularly vulnerable to this kind of reporting as long as dial-a-porn or rip-off programs are even a small part of the overall industry.

The January 20,1992 issue of *New York* featured a blatantly biased article, titled 900-DIAL-NOW, by Bernice Kanner, who admitted that her "warm-up was to chose from among 970 hot lines with DYKE, PERV, TOOL, and GENT in the suffix." Her inevitable conclusion was that "many lines are dial-a-porns that hook the caller for long periods while the meter runs." We dare not ask whether she was one of the callers who was hooked! From the overall tone of the article, and the selection of 900 numbers sampled, it appeared that her source for the 900 numbers came from the pages of Al Goldstein's *Screw* magazine or some other equally salacious periodical.

In January and February, 1991, Multi-Sponsor Surveys of Princeton, N.J., conducted a national survey (this one was conducted properly and scientifically) of 2,049 adults, titled "The Gallup Study of Consumer Attitudes and Response to 900 Numbers." The results, although not surprising, paint a fairly dim picture of the public's attitude toward pay-per-call services.

In the sample, nearly 70% of the respondents agreed with the statement, "I never considered calling a 900 line," and only 12% had ever used 900 services. Very few of the respondents agreed with the statements, "For the money you pay, 900 numbers offer useful and valuable information," or, "Most 900 numbers offer legitimate products and services."

Leonard Wood, president of Multi-Sponsor Surveys, stated that "a relatively large proportion were unable to either agree or disagree with each statement. This is likely due to the low level of familiarity with and usage of 900 numbers." He goes on to say that, "those respondents most familiar with 900 numbers and those who have dialed 900 numbers are the groups most likely to have positive attitudes toward caller-paid services."

What all this means is that the 900 industry has an enormous credibility gap to get over. When most of the population won't even consider using 900 services, the potential market size is slashed very dramatically.

Yes, things are changing, but very slowly. Some of the more responsible media, such as *U.S. News & World Report*, have featured positive, well-balanced articles about the industry. As you saw earlier in Chapter 2 about 900 services and applications, many reputable companies and media sources have recently joined the 900 industry with useful, valuable information programs. This helps the legitimacy of the whole industry. *Money* magazine ran a recent article titled, "When It Can Pay To Dial 900 For A Pro's Help," which profiled several helpful live 900 programs featuring legal, financial, and insurance information. I noted in Chapter 2 that *Newsweek* magazine is now using a 900 number for callers to express their opinions in the letters-to-the-editor section.

The December 7, 1991 issue of *The New York Times* carried an excellent article by Leonard Stone about live professional services, titled "Pay-per-Minute Phone Advice Gets Personal and Professional." Similarly, the March 1993 issue of *Home Office Computing* featured an objective article by Alan Rider, titled 1-900-BUY-INFO, that discussed selling professional advice over a 900 line and profiled a Los Angeles attorney who was doing just that.

And finally, the July 28, 1993 issue of *The New York Times,* in discussing the new FTC regulations governing the 900 industry, stated, "Since their introduction about five years ago, '900' services have proliferated into a vast collection of offerings, from news headlines and sports scores to astrology advice, recorded messages from celebrities, 'adult' chat lines and contests offering money and prizes. Many newspapers use them to complement their published product, and some nonprofit organizations use them as a method for soliciting contributions."

It is apparent from the sequence of these articles that the coverage of the 900 industry is gradually getting fairer, if not downright positive. Honest commentators who do their homework can no longer accuse 900 numbers as the sole purveyors of filth and sleaze. Public perception has no place to go but up.

And don't forget, the demographics of the adult population is continually changing as more and more teenagers reach adulthood. These young, electronically literate adults are much more likely to embrace all kinds of convenient 900 services, and their numbers increase daily.

Regulation and Oversight

The legal environment surrounding the 900 industry is, to put it mildly, a veritable quagmire. The FTC, the FCC, Congress, and many state attorneys general have all jumped onto the regulatory bandwagon with uncommon zeal. In some cases, conflicting regulations make it almost impossible to comply with everyone's rules at the same time.

Particularly problematic are the efforts of individual states to regulate what is effectively an interstate industry. Here are just a few examples:

Louisiana. Effective September 1991, HB1007 requires advertising for 900 programs to contain the IP's name, address and telephone number. This legislation also requires IPs to register each 900 number with the Louisiana Department of Justice. This law applies to anyone advertising in the state, which would include advertisers in virtually any national publication or television network.

Illinois. H2523 went into effect on January 1, 1992, and requires all 900 programs with a potential cost over $5 to have a minimum 12 second preamble containing an accurate description of the program and full disclosure of the cost, allowing the caller to hang up without being charged. The price threshold triggering the preamble requirement is inconsistent with recently adopted FCC rules, which will be discussed later.

Missouri. A bill was recently introduced in the state senate that would prohibit 900 contests, games of chance or sweepstakes promotions. The bill also requires a preamble for all calls for which charges may exceed one dollar, and requires an audio signal designating the commencement of charges.

New York. A recent 900 law requires, among other things, that price disclosures in all print advertising to be in at least ten point bold type. If applied to classified advertising, this requirement effectively precludes advertising in many publications which print their classified sections in type sizes smaller than ten points, and several national publications fall into this category. Is the State of New York telling us that we cannot place a classified ad in a national weekly newspaper because the publication is sold within their borders?

New Hampshire. The state PUC has proposed rules that would require, among other things, a periodic tone to note the passage of time on all pay-per-call programs.

Oregon. SB1188 went into effect January 1992, and imposes some of the most stringent advertising standards yet enacted by any state. One provision, for example, requires that the price of the call and the 900 number must be displayed together in the same size and typeface each time the 900 number appears. This applies to both print and television advertising.

Iowa. Effective July 1, 1991, legislation was passed that requires a preamble message for calls costing more than one dollar.

New Jersey. Legislation is currently pending which would require a preamble on calls that may cost over $5, and calls for registration and a fee for operating 900 services in New Jersey.

South Carolina. In 1992 the South Carolina Public Service Commission instituted reverse blocking regulations requiring consumers to pre-subscribe with the local exchange carrier for access to **all** interstate and intrastate 900 services, and is currently engaged in an ongoing battle with the FCC over jurisdiction.

California. In January 1993 a new bill went into effect that regulates the use of 900 numbers as a means of entering a sweepstakes, requiring, among other things, that the cost disclosure be of the same type size as the predominant size used in the ad.

These examples are by no means complete or even up-to-date. Many other states have already enacted or are considering legislation regulating the 900 industry. The National Association of Attorneys General (NAAG) recently issued 900 Legislation/Regulation Model Provisions, which states may use as a basis for new 900 legislation.

The most onerous requirement in the Model Provisions calls for registration of all IPs with the state, similar to Louisiana's existing statute. Such registration would require certain corporate documents, personal information on the owners or managers, and copies of all promotional materials. Also, it wouldn't be unreasonable to expect that a registration fee would accompany the registration requirement by those states that adopt this legislation.

Fortunately, this regulatory mess has been improved somewhat by the recent enactment of Federal Law. On October 28, 1992, President Bush signed into law The Telephone Disclosure and Dispute Resolution Act (Federal 900 Law, or the TDDRA), which was a compromise between the U.S. Senate's "900 Services Consumer Protection Act of 1991" (S. 1579) and the House bill, H.R. 3490, the "Telephone Disclosure and Dispute Resolution Act."

The Federal 900 Law required both the FCC and the FTC to promulgate rules for enforcement of its provisions, which both agencies completed by August of 1993. See Appendix G for a detailed discussion of the Federal 900 Law and the ensuing regulations promulgated by the FCC and the FTC.

Besides outlawing obvious illegal practices, the most important provisions of the new regulations set standard preambles requirements, allow free one-time blocking of 900 services by residential subscribers, and prohibit disconnection of telephone services for non-payment of 900 charges.

The preamble is required on all programs costing more than $2 for a flat-rate call, or for all calls that are usage priced (per minute). The caller cannot be charged for the time it takes to listen to the preamble message, so the call charges must begin after this message. The preamble must contain the following information:

1. Name of the Information Provider.

2. Brief description of the service.

3. Price of the call, including average length of call for per-minute charged calls.

4. Notice to the caller that billing will not start until 3 seconds after the preamble and that they may hang up before the program begins without charge.

5. When a 900 program is marketed to or could be of interest to minors under 18 years of age, they must be warned to hang up if they don't have parental permission to call.

A significant benefit with these new Federal rules is that states are now dissuaded from imposing preamble requirements or other restrictions on interstate calls which are inconsistent with those adopted by the FCC and FTC.

Although many in the 900 industry dread the prospect of federal regulation, reasonable federal regulation of interstate 900 services is surely preferable to the confusing tangle of state legislation that is continually popping up with frightening regularity. One set of fair rules for everyone to play by will make life a lot easier for everybody.

By its very nature, the regulatory environment for the 900 industry may be quite fluid for a few more years, at least until the dust settles a little more. Some of the publications and organizations listed in the Resource Guide stay up-to-date on industry-related legislation and will be good sources for keeping current.

Snake Oil Hucksters

There are still plenty of fast-buck artists and less-than-reputable players in the 900 industry. As government legislation and industry self-regulation begin to clean up the industry, some of these individuals appear to be shifting their focus from ripping off the calling public to picking the pockets of would-be IPs.

Maybe you have seen an ad or attended a seminar with statements like, "acquire your own 900 number before the government limits the amount of numbers," or, "purchase the rights to one or more 900 numbers and lease the rights to others for monthly profits." These statements are generally accompanied by a hard sell for you to part with a substantial sum of money before it's too late.

These kind of statements are pure snake oil, and you will be wise to disbelieve everything these people tell you. Beware of significant up-front fees. Stay away from seminars where they push you to "purchase" 900 numbers before they let you out the door.

Here's a verbatim statement from an actual seminar flier: "Ordinary people like you and I are making billions of dollars from 900 numbers." The entire 900 industry hasn't yet reached the billion dollar mark, so it's kind of unlikely that any one individual is doing quite so well. Also, these seminars rarely mention the advertising expenses that would be required to achieve the call volume they proclaim is so quick and easy to get.

You have to ask yourself, "If it's such an unbelievably fantastic opportunity, why in the world would the speaker be wasting his or her time conducting seminars?" The old adage applies, "If it sounds too good to be true, it usually is." Also, watch out for hard sell 900 infomercials, which are nothing more than the up-to-date electronic version of the snake oil business.

Back in July 1993 I received an invitation in the mail to attend a 2-day Home Business & Technology seminar at the Marriott hotel in Providence, Rhode Island. Because I publish a catalog along these lines, *The Entrepreneur's Business Success Resource Guide* , I set aside the time to attend. Perhaps the seminar sponsors had some materials that could be featured in my catalog; or, if nothing else, I could distribute some catalogs and make a few sales. After all, the attendees were interested in starting home businesses, and should have been interested in the contents of my catalog. Or so I thought.

Anyway, I sat through two presentations on the first morning. There were probably 300 people in the audience. The first segment was about joining an organization where you could purchase distressed or close-out goods at a fraction of the retail cost and re-sell them at a huge profit. It sounded pretty interesting, and they managed to sign up at least 50 people at $495 each.

The second presentation was about a new way of teaching math to kids, and the business opportunity was to hold classes in your home using this system. This system was very interesting, fascinating actually, but no mention was made about zoning, licensing, insurance or any other hurdle to teaching children at home. Again, the cost for this system was around $500, and another 50 people or so rushed to the table at the back of the conference room to sign up.

I was beginning to get the uneasy feeling that these people could make a septic tank cleaning business sound like the most glamorous business opportunity of the century. These guys could sell sand to a Saudi or ice to an Eskimo.

After lunch, I was convinced. The third presentation was about making a fortune in 900 numbers. Well, I thought, now they're talking about a topic I know something about, so we'll see how accurate they are.

I honestly can't say that there were a lot of blatant lies in the presentation. Some of their statistics were wrong, like saying the 900 industry revenues had exceeded $2 billion dollars in 1992, when in fact the actual number was less than half that amount. Nonetheless, it's possible that some of these inaccuracies were not intentional misrepresentations.

But oh boy, did the truth get stretched to the limit! Like giving an example of a program that generated a zillion calls, but leaving out a minor detail on how much advertising was spent to generate that call volume. I guess they didn't think the audience was smart enough to understand the difference between gross revenue and net profit, so they just kind of skipped over such an inconvenient detail. IBM has gross revenues in the billions of dollars, yet it has still managed to lose millions of dollars lately. Few of us can afford to lose hundreds of dollars, let alone millions.

Anyway, they were offering a package of three passive 900 lines where you had to charge $2 or $3 a minute for your recorded message. Not even a program sharing arrangement where you can use an established dating or sports line. No, the IP had to come up with a recorded message that would be sold for $2 or $3 a minute, an impossibly high amount, and then the speaker had the temerity to say that passive lines were the best, and that interactive programs were with live operations. Maybe he was tired and confused at this point. So many important and often inconvenient facts to get straight!

To create a sense of urgency, the audience was warned that they had better buy their 900 numbers before the government placed limits on them, and another 50 or more people rushed back to sign up for a $500 package of 3 lines (passive program only) and an instruction manual consisting of a 3-ring binder filled with information of dubious value.

I was in awe. These smooth talkers were convincing a lot of people to part with large sums of money they could ill afford to spend (this was on a weekday, and I'd wager many in the audience were unemployed and even somewhat desperate). They had refined the art of snake oil selling into an exact science.

First, they established rapport by smiling a lot, talking about their families, and complimenting the Providence area on its beauty. They ask a lot of questions like, "Would you like to make $10,000 a month?" The audience gets involved by enthusiastically answering such difficult questions, usually in the affirmative, or the obvious skeptics get a playful follow-up, "You're holding out for $20,000 a month, right?"

The audience warms up to the speaker, getting involved in the presentation, and really wants to trust this friendly fellow who is telling them what they really want to hear.

Maybe I'm a real cynical guy, but I wonder if I was the only person to notice that none of the presentation was supported by anything in writing. None of the claims made were repeated in any written form, and tape recorders were strictly forbidden (there was even a mean-looking guy walking around trying to spot tape recorders).

The whole spectacle would have been quite amusing had it not been so sad. A lot of desperate people were being relieved of money they needed for food and rent. They were being promised easy riches, something they desperately wanted to believe they could achieve. They let greed cloud their judgement, and now they are paying for it.

Here's what Bob Bentz says in his new book, *Opportunity is Calling* (See Resource Guide), about the snake oil business: "I've heard of some travelling carpetbaggers who sell 900 line extensions at seminars in local hotels for as much as $695! Part of the pitch is that 900 numbers are in short supply so you'd better buy one now. Not! There are currently 10,000 900 lines operating and AT&T alone has over 170,000 different 900 numbers available! They are not in short supply. And, if they ever get close to running out, they'll surely make others available."

There are plenty of variations of this kind of snake oil seminar out there, so be very careful if you decide to attend one. Leave your wallet at home, and be very skeptical about claims that seem to stretch the limits of credibility.

This is not to say, however, that all 900 seminars are worthless. The publishers of *Audiotex News*, Jerry and Carol Ginsburg, put on an excellent educational seminar through the Learning Annex in Hampstead, NY and in Washington, DC. Antoinette (Toni) Moore, a 900 consultant and author of *Dialing For Dollars*, conducts valuable seminars for serious IPs in the San Diego area. See the Resource Guide for further details about the products and services offered by these experts in the 900 industry.

We will be discussing service bureaus later, but it should be mentioned here that a disreputable service bureau can cheat an IP out of a lot of money. They do exist, and you should obviously avoid them. This is particularly problematic if there is no independent or automated means of verifying call counts. If your call count information is limited to a weekly or monthly written report generated by the service bureau, there is no way you can independently verify the accuracy of the numbers.

The better service bureaus generally offer automated 24-hour access to call counts, often with a toll free 800 number. Also, they will often include a copy of the monthly long distance carrier report (i.e., AT&T, MCI, Sprint) of call volume to the 900 number. These are obviously good features to look for in selecting a service bureau.

Also, be somewhat wary of service bureaus that sponsor their own turn-key 900 programs, particularly if one of their programs will be in competition with yours. They will be competing with you and serving you at the same time - a classic conflict of interest. Nevertheless, some service bureau program sponsors offer attractive programs, so don't be quick to discount this option yet. We'll talk more about this later.

900 is No Free Lunch

First, let's look at some numbers. According to Strategic Telemedia, a market research and consulting business in the 900 industry, the total 1991 revenues for 900 services was 975 million dollars (by the way, Strategic Telemedia's numbers are somewhat different from those of Link Resources, reported in Chapter 1, likely due to statistical variations. Nonetheless, the overall trends are the same, and the differences are relatively unimportant). This was the total spent by consumers calling 900 numbers. These revenues were earned with 273 million calls, totalling 780 million call-minutes, to roughly 10,000 different 900 programs. Of the total call revenue, 55%, or 539 million dollars, went to the IPs. The balance went to the long distance carriers and the service bureaus. By simple division we can calculate the average annual revenue for each IP/900 program:

$539,000,000 / 10,000 = $53,900

This number represents the average gross revenue for an IP/900 program, so we still need to subtract operating and advertising expenses. You can readily see that the average numbers involved aren't quite as exciting as you may have been led to believe. The advertising costs alone, required to generate 27,300 average annual calls per program, could very easily exceed the total revenue. Earning a respectable profit isn't necessarily easy in this business.

According to Bruce Kushnick, the former president of Strategic Telemedia, "80% of IPs do not make their money back. 900 services have attracted entrepreneurs and IP wannabes who see a pot of telecom gold at the end of the phone line. The entry costs to 900 programming are low, and the false promise of getting rich quick has been perpetuated by the industry itself. In most cases, basic marketing principles are often ignored by the entrepreneur."

I've said it before and I'll say it again: Success in the pay-per-call industry is by no means guaranteed. You must know what you're getting into, and it will be just as challenging as launching any other kind of business. Sure, there are people making good money in this business. But no one is raking in millions of dollars without expending any significant effort. There is no free lunch with any business, and pay-per-call is no exception.

Chapter 5
Getting Started

Research

When you start any new business you begin by collecting as much information as possible about the business field you are entering. Starting a 900 business is no exception. The Resource Guide lists several publications that you should purchase. *The Power of 900* by Rick Parkhill is a comprehensive, 156 page book about the pay-per-call industry. *Opportunity is Calling* by Bob Bentz is written from the perspective of a service bureau marketing director who has seen thousands of 900 applications, from the success stories to the failures. *The Audiotex Directory and Buyer's Guide* is another invaluable resource, including lists of service bureaus, 900 advertising agencies, 900 consultants, and other sources for audiotex products and services.

You should also subscribe to one or more of the leading trade magazines or newsletters in order to keep current with what is going on in the industry. Also, attending a trade exhibition is a quick way of making contacts and learning about the business. You will meet and talk to people from service bureaus, long distance carriers, equipment vendors, 900 advertising agencies, and program sponsors, to name just a few. You will make valuable contacts and learn about what is currently happening in the industry: what kinds of programs are out there, how are they marketed, and where to go for specific help or advice. This will be your fastest and most direct method of gathering valuable information about the 900 industry.

At the same time, pay attention to media advertising for 900 programs. Get a good feel for the types of programs being offered and what media they are being advertised in. Vary your TV viewing and radio listening habits, perhaps even recording a good sampling of 900 commercials. Make a habit of buying different publications and clipping out print advertising. Develop a file of 900 advertising, paying particular attention to repeat advertising, because this usually indicates a successful program.

Study what appear to be the most successful ads - how are they different? How did they grab your attention? For radio and TV, what time of day or night do they normally appear, and on what networks or stations? We'll talk more about this later in the next chapter about market research, but suffice it to say, pay close attention to the ads which are repeating regularly over a long period of time. The advertiser has already spent a considerable amount of time and money testing different media and ads, so you might as well learn something from his or her experience and investment of advertising dollars.

Call several kinds of 900 programs. Hear what type of information they offer, and how they handle the interactive menu selections. No amount of writing in a book like this will give you a true picture of how these programs can work. Call them, and you will get valuable ideas on how interactive programs can be designed.

It is probably not a good idea to zero-in on, or make a hard commitment to, any specific 900 application until after you have completed the preliminary research we have outlined up to this point. Having some general ideas is fine, but financial commitment might not be. Finish reading this book, then get some of the other publications listed in the Resource Guide. Talk to people at service bureaus, and attend a pay-per-call conference. Then read this book a second time - some parts may have an entirely different meaning to you after you have learned more about the 900 industry.

Your 900 Idea

What if you have this great idea, and after reviewing all the most logical media sources for possible competitors, you find none. No competition. This could mean one of three things. First, your idea is so unique and revolutionary that no one else has thought about it yet, or at least their programs haven't yet hit the streets. Second, your idea simply won't work or has been tried and failed. Or third, you idea is in fact already being used, but it's being advertised in specialized media that you haven't been exposed to yet.

Be real careful about reaching the first conclusion. There are lots of very imaginative entrepreneurs in this industry, and the fact that your idea hasn't been tried should be a danger signal, not an invitation to plunge headlong into a program that might flop miserably. This does not mean, however, that you should discount any novel application simply because there's no competition. That's not being very entrepreneur-like! It simply means that you need to do some further digging until you are completely satisfied that there is no good reason for the lack of competition.

Make sure that your idea is suitable for a 900 application. Is there an easier or cheaper way for your target market to get the information? Will someone actually pick up the phone and pay his or her hard-earned money for your information or entertainment service?

As mentioned earlier, weather information is timely, and seems to fit the criteria for a successful 900 application. But what are the potential caller's other sources for this information? If he has cable TV, he can tune into the Weather Channel. If he is a boater, he tunes his radio into the marine weather frequency. Or maybe he simply calls his local weather bureau. If he's travelling by car, he listens to the radio. It is doubtful that you can compete with those free sources of information by offering general weather information.

But how about some truly unique or specialized weather information? In California, you can call a 900 line to get the latest surf conditions at the beach. Now, if you're an avid surfer who lives 50 miles from the beach, this is very valuable information. It can save you a wasted trip, consuming valuable time and gas, only to find out that the surfing conditions are pathetic.

Windsurfing is another sport with a following of hard-core fanatics who need to know precise conditions. Wind conditions can vary significantly within any given area, and the windsurfer needs to know what size board and sail to load onto his vehicle to match the conditions he will find at his destination.

Offering specialized weather information to a small specialized market is not going to work in a small town. There just aren't enough people to generate sufficient call volume. But it will certainly work in a large metropolitan area such as Los Angeles or Miami. And it's pretty easy to get the word out to your market through the area surf shops or radio stations.

How's this one for a great idea: a specialized 900 service which offers up-to-the-minute information on nightlife, restaurants, tourist attractions, sporting events, and cultural activities for travellers to your city? Great idea, right? Wrong! People who visit your city stay in hotels, which do not offer 900 calling services from the rooms. And trying to get them to call from home prior to leaving on the trip will require extensive regional or national advertising to reach them, and then it's unlikely they will want to plan that far in advance.

This is an example of a good idea, with a good targetable market, but with a fatal flaw: no way for the target market to purchase your service when they are most likely to need it.

Good ideas are both plentiful and cheap. It's the execution of a good idea into a successful program where the real challenge and talent come into play. This is what separates the dreamers from the doers.

Program Sharing

Instead of investing lots of time, money, and effort in developing a brand new un-tested program, the budding infopreneur has many opportunities to share existing programs that are already established and successful. For a share of the call revenue, the infopreneur is given an exclusive 900 number (or extension) to promote as he or she sees fit, which taps into the existing 900 program owned by the sponsoring IP, or program sponsor. Many service bureaus offer in-house packaged programs in this manner. Such established programs are also known as "turn-key" programs.

Calls to each number are separately accounted for, and revenues are split on a pre-determined basis between the infopreneur and the program sponsor. The program sponsor may require a minimum monthly fee to cover the incremental costs associated with adding another 900 line to the program, but this amount is usually much less than what the infopreneur would pay by going it alone.

The program sponsor may also help with marketing efforts or advice. After all, it's a win-win situation for both parties, and higher call volumes benefit both parties. The program sponsor already has a great deal of experience in promoting the program: what type of ad copy works best, and which media pulls in the most calls at the lowest cost-per-call.

There is also strength in numbers with many people promoting the same program. This is particularly true if the program has a recognizable name and everyone uses similar, standardized advertising copy. For example, "Madam Zarra's Horoscopes" or "The Ski Connection" could become well-recognized programs if they are promoted widely in various media by many infopreneurs. The promotional efforts of the combined group benefit each individual infopreneur, because repetition breeds credibility and legitimacy. The fact that the telephone numbers are different is of little consequence. The caller isn't likely to notice, and will simply dial whichever number is immediately at hand.

Program sharing opportunities cover the entire gamut of 900 applications, including weather, sports, games, jokes, soaps, and horoscopes. This is a trend that will continue to be popular, because everyone wins. The program sponsor is able to inexpensively broaden his market while spreading out his program and marketing costs, reaching a much larger audience than what he could possibly afford to reach alone. For the participating infopreneur, it's a simple, inexpensive way to get started in the pay-per-call business, while benefitting from the marketing knowledge and experience of the program sponsor, saving a lot of money on potentially ineffective advertising.

Where can you find out about program sharing opportunities? Check out the ads in the relevant trade magazines or the Business Opportunity sections of major newspapers or business magazines. Many of the service bureaus listed in Appendix F offer turn-key programs, so ask what types are available. Indeed, many of the smaller service bureaus are nothing more than IPs who own their call processing equipment, with excess capacity that will handle additional programs or IPs. Most of these companies actively seek IPs to help promote their programs.

Beware of significant up-front costs. The cost of adding a separate 900 number to an existing program is quite modest. It would not be unreasonable to charge something to cover programming, administration, and accounting costs, so a modest monthly charge would be reasonable.

On the other hand, if the program sponsor is simply offering a separate extension to the 900 number, this normally costs the program sponsor nothing, and a set monthly charge, if any, should be minimal. Although less expensive, the use of extensions cheapens the product, and may not be the best way to promote the program.

Another consideration is call count verification. Most major service bureaus offer automated access via telephone to current call counts to the program, often with a toll free 800 number. The service bureau can be a separate, independent entity from the program sponsor. If the infopreneur is given access to call counts to his or her 900 number, through the use of an exclusive access code, it serves as an independent verification of the call volume from the service bureau. This is easily achieved if each infopreneur is assigned a discrete 900 number, but is not generally available when extensions are used. With extensions, you usually rely exclusively on the honesty of the program sponsor in accounting for calls to your extension.

Besides independent call count verification, instant telephone access to call counts is very helpful in measuring the success of advertising strategies. Waiting for a two week old written call summary report can result in expensive marketing mistakes or lost opportunities.

In general, it is probably best to avoid programs where call counts cannot be accessed instantly by using an automated interactive telephone program. The notable exception would be where the 900 number spells a highly recognizable word or phrase. In this case it would benefit the infopreneur to use the same 900 number with a separate extension. Just make sure you check out the program sponsor.

The revenue sharing arrangements can be structured in many ways. The program sponsor will be interested in covering his incremental costs for each additional line or extension, but should also want to give the infopreneur sufficient incentive to aggressively market the program. For example, the monthly fee could be "$250 or $0.15 per call minute, whichever is greater." This way the program sponsor receives 100% of the call revenue until his $250 cost is covered, then $0.15 per minute thereafter. Or a sliding percentage scale could be used based upon monthly call-minute volume, with the infopreneur receiving a greater percentage as volume increases. Regardless of how it is structured, the party doing the marketing - the infopreneur - should receive the largest share of call revenue because marketing is the largest cost component of any 900 program. Be careful with any program that offers a 50-50 or worse split, because it may not be a fair division of revenue, unless the program sponsor is also providing significant marketing assistance.

What Works for 900?

As discussed in Chapter 2, the most obvious kinds of information that can be sold via a 900 program are timely information and specialized information. Timely information changes quickly: weather forecasts, stock prices, sports scores, horse races, currency exchange rates, or flight information. Existing 900 programs already cover the gamut of timely information applications, and you will really have to use your imagination to come up with original applications in this area.

Specialized information, on the other hand, is still wide open with opportunities. Possible information categories are essentially unlimited. Here is a short list of only a few broad categories of specialized information, and each of these will have its own extensive list of sub-categories:

LAW	HORTICULTURE
ACCOUNTING	COMMUNICATIONS
INSURANCE	TRAVEL
MEDICINE	ENTERTAINMENT
FINANCE	LITERATURE
MANUFACTURING	DIPLOMACY
TRADE	HISTORY
MARKETING	BANKING
CONSTRUCTION	HOBBIES
REAL ESTATE	SPORTS
ENERGY	EDUCATION
POLITICS	RETIREMENT
MUSIC	BUSINESS
CINEMA	TRANSPORTATION
PUBLISHING	APPAREL
INVESTING	FASHION
CHILD CARE	FOOD
FITNESS	SPIRITS
WEALTH	HOME
COMMERCE	ENGINEERING
AGRICULTURE	ARCHITECTURE

Again, this is only a brief listing of some possible information categories that might be suitable for a 900 program. And there are hundreds of sub-categories under these headings. Try this for an exercise: go to the reference section of your nearest large library (or college library) and browse through the reference books. You will find hundreds of information classifications that are obviously useful to someone -- or books would never have been published about them!

Now, going to the library to dig out a reference book to look up specific information is a time-consuming chore. This is where a 900 program can excel. It's a whole lot more convenient to pick up the telephone, from the comfort of home or the office, at any time of the day or night, and get exactly what you need, when you need it. Immediate, efficient, useful, and quite valuable for the potential customer.

Don't forget about business customers, particularly small businesses. Many small businesses lack the staff or resources to have easy access to the wide range of information they need every day. Business customers are easy to target, and they will pay a reasonable fee for convenience.

Live or Recorded?

If you're going to offer expert advice on WordPerfect® software, you will have to talk to your customers. You will also have to be an indisputable expert in WordPerfect®, and you will be tied to the phone during business hours (accounting for all 4 time zones if you're offering your services nationally). You will also need a computer at hand so you can walk through the specific problem with your caller.

Callers expect to pay more for live technical advice, so you may be able to charge $2 to $5 per minute. You will probably get repeat calls until that caller becomes proficient in this software, then he or she will no longer need you.

There is a limit to how much money you can earn, at least by yourself. A very high call volume would realistically tie you up on the phone 50% of the time over a 10 hour day. You can't possibly talk continuously for 10 hours, and at 50% usage many callers will be getting busy signals or will have to wait in queue.

Say you're charging $3 per minute. The most you can gross in a day will be $900 (10 hrs X 60 min/hr X $3 X 50%). After telephone company and service bureau charges, your net will be between $550 and $600 per day, before advertising and overhead expenses. Not a bad income, but there's no potential to make any more money unless you hire additional operators with the same level of expertise as you.

With a live program, you miss out on some of the strongest advantages of a recorded interactive program: **the ability to earn money around the clock with no upper limit on the number of calls you can handle**.

Yes, you have to spend time collecting your program information and periodically up-dating the program content. But this certainly won't tie you up for 10 hours a day, and you can choose your working hours as you see fit. And your 900 program can handle hundreds, even thousands, of calls simultaneously. Why limit yourself?

By the way, fax-back and voice mailbox classified advertising applications are types of recorded interactive programs -- there is no need for a live operator. Fax-back programs, where a caller with a fax machine can instantly receive a hard copy of very specific information (charts, graphs, schedules, directories, reports, etc.), is a relatively new development with great promise. Again, small businesses are the prime target market for this application, and most have fax machines.

What are the Best 900 Opportunities?

Most industry experts agree that the best opportunities for start-up IPs will be with specialized information that can be precisely targeted to a specific niche market. Again, the information classifications are nearly unlimited. Virtually any kind of information can be categorized, packaged and delivered in such a way as to be useful to a given target audience.

The future in 900 is in serving easily definable and targetable niche markets. The large, reasonably homogeneous markets are already served by numerous 900 applications: sports lines, weather lines, horoscope lines, classified personal dating lines, stock & commodities lines, and soap opera update lines, to name just a few.

Although the markets for these types of 900 lines are potentially huge, they are not easy to target with cost-effective rifle shot advertising, a topic that will be addressed in detail later. The successful IPs serving these homogeneous markets are spending tens of thousands -- even hundreds of thousands -- of advertising dollars

---

to reach their market. And in many cases, these 900 programs do not offer critically important information that is immediately valuable to the given market -- the advertisers must rely on impulse purchasing, which is very expensive to achieve, requiring big splashy display ads or attention-grabbing TV commercials.

The beginning entrepreneurial IP simply doesn't have the financial resources to go after such a large homogeneous market. You must identify a very specific market with very specific information needs. Ideally, information that is critical to achieving a very important personal goal or objective. You cannot rely on one-shot impulse purchases of your information service. You need your customers to call your service again and again. You need to offer information with high perceived value that your market will need on an ongoing basis.

The point I'm trying to make actually applies to starting any kind of business with limited capital. You don't usually launch a business by taking on your biggest, most established competitor head-on. You will lose. For example, you wouldn't start a mail order catalog operation in direct competition with L.L. Bean unless you're willing to spend/risk millions of dollars. You start by narrowing your focus and your market. Maybe you start with distinctive hunting jackets and outerwear, items that can be targeted precisely toward hunters.

Every successful 900 IP will tell you that his single largest expense is advertising. By far. All other business expenses pale in significance to advertising costs. This is why you need to get the biggest bang for your advertising buck. A well-defined niche market is easy to reach in a cost-effective manner. It will be served by one or more specialized periodicals,or media, and your advertising dollars will not be wasted on people who have no interest in your information service. And hopefully you will have a program that offers information they will need frequently, so they will become steady customers and continue to call your 900 service despite the frequency of your advertising.

How Do You Find
the Right Niche Market?

Begin with your own skills, interests, hobbies, or avocations. In all likelihood, you already belong to more than one niche market yourself. List all of your specific interests, skills or hobbies and the specialized publications you read. You may discover a likely information need that could be better delivered with a 900 information service.

Be careful, however, about choosing a niche market that is too small. For example, collectors of World War II airplane propellers are a very definable market, but they probably number under a dozen people (if, indeed, there are any at all!). You simply cannot achieve sufficient call volume to justify a 900 service for this market. Stamp collectors, on the other hand, number in the hundreds of thousands, and would be an adequate sized niche market for a 900 program offering information these collectors need.

Keep in mind that you are offering a relatively low-cost service, probably well under $10 total, and you will need a fairly decent volume of calls to make your efforts worthwhile. You must know the size of your market and how frequently each person is likely to call. Repeat callers will be very important to the success of your program, so it will be best to offer information that changes regularly. Getting the most up-to-date information available will be the primary motivation for inducing your customers to call repeatedly. Specialized information with an element of timeliness: this is where a 900 program can truly excel.

Where can you get ideas for possible niche markets? Go to the library and look through the following reference volumes. You will find very specialized periodicals and organizations that serve very specific niche markets. Indeed, you will find many publications and markets you never knew existed!

Ayer Directory of Newspapers & Periodicals. Includes newspapers, magazines and periodicals published in the U.S. and Canada, including circulation and advertising rates.

Encyclopedia of Associations, published by Gale Research. Includes thousands of associations and organizations by subject category, many of which publish newsletters for their members.

Hudson's Subscription Newsletter Directory. Lists thousands of specialized newsletters covering every conceivable subject.

The Standard Periodical Directory, published by Oxbridge Communications. This is the largest annual directory of magazines, trade journals, directories, newsletters, etc.; published in the U.S. and Canada.

Ulrich's International Periodicals Directory, published by R. R. Bowker. Includes 65,000 periodicals published internationally.

Directory of Directories, published by Gale Research. Includes directories and databases.

Gale Directory of Publications and Broadcast Media. Lists 35,000 magazines, newspapers, radio and TV media.

Standard Rate & Data Service (SRDS). A multi-volume reference series including business & consumer magazines, newspapers, TV, radio and mailing lists.

A Working Example

I have always felt that the best way to illustrate a process is to use a specific example. Something we can really get our teeth into. So I'm going to use my own knowledge and come up with a 900 program that relates to my background in writing and publishing.

It will be a program that, as far as I know, has never been attempted. We don't want to copy an existing program, we want to conceive and design a unique new 900 information service that doesn't yet exist. You can follow the exact same process in coming up with your own idea for a 900 program. The process of conceiving and designing any 900 program will follow the same steps we outline here.

Conceiving the Program

In conceiving our 900 program, we must first answer the following questions:

1. Who is our target market?
2. What size is the market? Will it be large enough to support a specialized 900 information service?
3. What are the market's specific information needs? Better yet, what kind of information does the market need to help achieve its most important goals?
4. How is the market currently getting this information?
5. Can a 900 program better serve these needs, with more timely or better organized information?
6. Can this market be easily reached through well-targeted media?
7. Where do I find the source information necessary for the 900 program?

In answering the first question, let's start with *writers*. However, simply *writers* may be too broad a market. After all, there are fiction writers, poetry writers, mystery writers, lifestyle writers, article writers, how-to writers, novel writers, textbook writers, technical writers, aspiring writers, veteran writers and so on. And there are literally thousands of information categories that writers write about.

Should we narrow down our market to a more specific niche? If so, what is the size of this niche? Before we make this decision, lets go through the rest of the questions.

What are some specific information needs of writers? Well, writers need all kinds of information in order to produce their work. Many writers spend a lot more time on research than on writing. But the information categories they need are virtually unlimited. It may be way too ambitious to consider offering research type information.

What other information might be even more important to writers? What will help them achieve their most important goals? Well, getting published and getting paid for their work is certainly important. Few writers enjoy slaving away for little compensation. Can we offer timely, helpful information that will help them sell their work? Of course we can.

Where do writers now turn for this information? *Literary Marketplace, Writer's Market,* and some of the reference volumes listed earlier are some of the sources they would use. Most of these are fairly expensive publications, however, and few writers actually purchase them. They go to their local library. And, although most of these publications are up-dated annually, they cannot keep up with the fast-paced changes always taking place in the publishing industry. And all libraries are on tight budgets, so they may not even have the latest editions available, if they have them at all.

Can a 900 program better serve the writer's needs by offering more up-to-date information that is more easily accessible? Absolutely! Indeed, we might be able to improve upon what already exists by making timeliness our strongest advantage. For example, we could get publishers involved in the program by giving each participating publisher a voice mailbox slot, with access via a toll-free 800 number, so that each publisher can leave a message soliciting the exact types of books or articles he is seeking at any given time. The publisher could change his message daily, weekly or monthly. We have created a true information exchange for publishers and writers to connect with one another.

This is how to use the awesome capabilities of voice processing equipment. We can be much more responsive to the immediate needs of our market than any annual printed publication could ever hope to be. And the best part is that one of the most unique and helpful features of our program, the publisher's message, is automatically input into our program directly by the publisher. We simply start the program and let the publishers help us keep it up-to-date.

There's no question about it -- a 900 program can be designed that would be highly useful to writers. Publishers too. And it could incorporate features that would be both unique and timely. Very possibly a real winner.

Can our market be easily reached? *Writer's Digest* is a monthly magazine that no aspiring writer worth his salt can afford to ignore. It has a circulation of 234,000 mostly writers who need to sell their work. And if we go through the reference sources listed earlier, we will be sure to find other periodicals that are also targeted to writers. It appears, therefore, that we will have little difficulty reaching our market through well-targeted publications and media.

And to keep the information truly timely, we could run small ads in *Publishers's Weekly, Folio Magazine,* and *The Newsletter on Newsletters,* asking all publishers to keep us up-to-date. Indeed, publishers can get very specific about the books or articles they are looking for, making it very easy for writers and publishers to communicate with one another.

Where do we get the source information for our 900 program? The same place our aspiring author would go: *Literary Marketplace, The Writer's Market,* and the listing of directories mentioned earlier.

However, we soon discover that there are tens of thousands of publishers and periodicals. It would be a herculean task to input all this data into our program. The voice storage requirements would be enormous. We need to further narrow our market to make this a more manageable task.

We return, therefore, to defining our market. We know that repeat callers will be important for us, so what kinds of writers will need our services on a regular basis? Writers who create articles or short stories for periodicals. Thousands and thousands of periodicals publish tens of thousands of articles every month. This is obviously a good place to start, and we can immediately eliminate book writers and publishers from consideration.

Many periodicals don't use outside, unknown or freelance writers for their articles, so we needn't concern ourselves with these. And many experienced writers already know how to sell their work, or it's sold before it's even written, so our target market can be further narrowed to aspiring, beginning writers in search of receptive publishers. We can eliminate highly specialized technical writers and their journals, because they already know who is going to publish their learned yet often incomprehensible writings.

We are actually talking about two potential markets here: aspiring authors and those publishers who actively want their work. If we can bring the two together we will be helping both achieve their goals. We might even be able to get publishers to call a separate 900 line to up-date their specific message about what kinds of submissions they are seeking. We must be careful about this, however, and remember who is best served by our program. If publishers resist paying for up-dating their messages, few such up-dates will be forthcoming, and the value of the program to aspiring writers will be diminished, perhaps fatally.

An interesting parallel can be found with the personal classified dating lines. Many IPs allow women to advertise for free, via a local number or a toll-free 800 number, because women advertisers generate virtually all the heavy call volume from all those lonely guys out there. Call volume is the name of the game, and these IPs recognize that men constitute the vast majority of their market. The more women advertisers, the more men are going to call. Repeatedly. We don't want to kill the goose that laid the golden egg!

Designing the Program

Okay, now we have an initial concept for our program. It will target aspiring or beginning authors of articles or short stories. The purpose of our program is to help our target market find publishers who will pay for their work. Our objective is to offer a uniquely responsive service that will truly help writers achieve their goals very efficiently, generating lots of satisfied customers and repeat callers.

How do we design such a program? First, we must list all of the specific information our aspiring authors will need to achieve their goals:

1. Which periodicals, by subject category, are seeking submission or proposals. Obviously, periodicals will need to be categorized in some coherent fashion by general content.

2. The current address and telephone number of each publisher.

3. The current names and titles of editors, by specialty, at each periodical (to whom to address a specific submission).

4. A brief outline of submission requirements (subjects, number of words, SASE, etc.)

5. Standard payment terms.

6. Publisher's message. Again, this would be a voice mailbox for the publisher to use for soliciting very specific submissions, or even advising against certain subject categories. It could also be used for alerting authors to address or personnel changes, or for describing a new publication planned to be launched in the future.

The above information is what our caller will receive once she reaches her <u>destination</u> in our program. This is the end product. We can't possibly expect her to sit through a three hour recitation of every publication in our program. She must be able to zero-in on those specific publications that will be most likely to want her article.

This is where the menu tree comes in. This is a unique feature of interactive audiotex services, something no reference book can possibly emulate. We can organize our publications into numerous very specific sub-classifications, and we can quickly guide our caller to the most appropriate grouping of periodicals for her purposes.

Remember, we want to serve our callers as best we can, which means allowing them to reach the information they require as quickly and efficiently as possible. A well-designed menu tree will be essential to achieve this purpose. This is where we have to exercise our creativity in designing the most effective, easy-to-follow pathway to the end-product information.

A menu tree is simply a hierarchy of classifications, beginning with the broadest possible divisions and ending with very specific divisions. The number of menu levels in between these two extremes will depend upon the nature and number of information categories in our program.

In general, the fewer the menu choices at each level, the better, particularly at the beginning menus. We should never exceed 5 menu choices at any level, because once the caller hears the last choice, she may have forgotten the first choices.

Our example menu tree may require up to 6 levels, and might look like the following example, which shows only one possible sequence of selections by our caller (the selection path is indicated by bolded words):

Main Menu:
1. Newsletters
2. **Magazines**

Sub-Menu A:
1. Fiction
2. **Non-fiction**

Sub-Menu B:
1. **Adult**
2. Teens
3. Children

Sub-Menu C:
1. Business/Industry
2. Entertainment
3. **Lifestyle**

Sub-Menu D:
1. **Home**
2. Crafts/Hobbies
3. Travel
4. Fashion
5. Health/Fitness

Sub-Menu E:
1. Cooking/Food
2. Decorating & Remodeling
3. **Gardening**
4. Family
5. Pets

Using this example, once our caller selects the "Gardening" classification under sub-menu E, she would receive the information end-product: a recorded list of magazines that deal with gardening, plus the information, outlined earlier, about each publication.

Remember, this example demonstrates only one possible menu path. The complete menu tree will likely be quite complex, with dozens of classifications at the lower menu levels. In the interest of brevity, however, we will not attempt to design the entire menu tree here. I'm simply illustrating the design process.

Scripting

Now that we have designed our proposed menu tree, we need to write the script for our program. While writing the script, we need to identify what information needs to be exchanged at each level:

1. The Introduction.

a. The preamble. This is a mandatory message giving the name of the IP (company name), a brief description of the service, and the cost of the call:

"Welcome to the Writer's Marketplace, presented by Aegis Publishing Group, where you will locate periodicals in different subject categories that accept submissions from freelance writers. This call will cost $1 per minute, unless you hang up within 3 seconds after the tone."

b. Other instructions. Before stating the main menu, we may wish to offer additional instructions or information. For example, we could offer a customer service telephone number for callers who encounter problems with the program, or offer to send a copy of the full program menu (plus some compelling sales literature!). Or we may want to make it easier for frequent callers to go through the menu levels more quickly:

"If you have any problems with this program, or would like to receive a copy of the full menu of options, please call 1-XXX-XXX-XXXX. You can return to the main menu at any time by pressing the star key. You do not have to wait to hear all menu choices if you know the menu selection, which can be pressed at any time."

2. The Main Menu. The next message heard will be the main menu. The caller will also be returned to the main menu whenever she presses the star key:

"The main menu. Press 1 for newsletters, press 2 for magazines."

3. The Sub-Menus. In our example, it may be advisable to title the sub-menus so frequent callers, or callers with a printed copy of the full menu (sent to them or published in a display ad), can easily follow the menu path. It might also be a good idea to allow our caller to go backwards to the previous menu, and to confirm where she is located within the program:

"Sub-menu B, non-fiction magazines. Press 1 for adult, 2 for teens, 3 for children. Press the pound key at any time to return to the previous menu."

It would be a good idea to repeat the instructions given in the introduction in case our caller has forgotten them; or to allow our caller to hear the menu again:

"Press the star key to return to the main menu at any time, press 9 to hear the menu again."

4. The Information End-Product. Once our caller selects the "Gardening" category, she will hear a list of publications along with address, editors, submission requirements and a publisher's message. Because there could be several publications in each destination category, we should allow her to skip through our listings. Also, because she will be writing this information down, we need to give her the ability to control the pace of the information flow:

"Gardening. You will hear the name, address, phone number and submission information for each publication in this category. Press 2 at any time to skip to the next publication. Press 1 at any time to return to the beginning of the message for each publication. Press 3 at any time to pause, and press 3 again to resume."

At this point the recorded information for each publication is given. If there were 5 magazines under this classification, all 5 would be given, one after the other, unless the caller skips ahead (#2), returns to the beginning of the publication recording (#1), returns to the previous menu (pound key, returns to sub-menu E), or returns to the main menu (star key).

5. The Conclusion. After the caller hears the information about the final publication in the "Gardening" category, we need to tell her there are no further listings, remind her what to do to find other classifications, or conclude the program and thank her for calling:

"There are no additional listings in this category. Press 1 to hear the last publication. Press the pound key to return to the previous sub-menu, or press the star key to return to the main menu. Thank you for calling the Writer's Marketplace."

This same scripting process will have to be followed for every possible menu path in our program. In some cases, there will not be 6 menu levels, or there may not be any end-product information at the end of a certain path.

It is also apparent the sub-menu classification will vary depending upon the menu path. Sub-menus A and B might remain constant, but sub-menu C and beyond must be responsive to the path chosen. For example, the following path:

Main Menu:	2. Magazines
Sub-Menu A:	1. Fiction
Sub-Menu B:	1. Adult

might result in the following sub-menu C classifications:

1. Mystery/detective
2. Science fiction
3. Western
4. Adult
5. Romance

This particular menu path may not require any further sub-menus beyond level C.

By the way, our proposed menu tree is not necessarily the best possible design. For example, newsletters always contain topical news, never fiction, so it would be better to revise sub-menu A, at least after the newsletter path is chosen. Again, a lot of creative effort needs to go into designing the most responsive menu tree, and we might end up going through numerous variations until we get it right.

Although this process may appear somewhat complex and intimidating, don't despair. Your service bureau, if you've picked a good one, will help you every step of the way in designing your program. They will tell you what can and can't be done.

Data Input

Now we need to fill our program up with all the end-product data. This is the meat of our program, the reason callers are paying $1 per minute to hear our information.

How is the information physically put into our program, and how is it updated? A dedicated program editing line. An interactive telephone program, using a local or toll-free 800 number, would be designed along the same lines as our 900 program, except to input the voice data. Using an interactive menu and voice prompts for each information category, we can load the entire program from our telephone. Or revise it after it's up and running.

Now, we have three options as to how the information gets loaded into our program:

1. We input all of it ourselves. This may have to be done over numerous sittings spanning several hours to record all the necessary information.

2. We get publishers to do all the work for us. We give the editing line number to publishers and encourage them to input the information about their publication. The disadvantage to this approach is that we must get the word out to all prospective publishers well before the program is operational, and then we must rely on them to input all the data correctly and on time. And since the editing line will be somewhat complicated, and we have no control over whether or not the publishers will actually respond, this option doesn't have much promise of working.

3. A little of both. We input all initial data to get the program off the ground. Then we provide publishers with a simple editing line for up-dating their information and leaving their "publisher's message." For example, we could assign each publisher a voice mailbox number where they call to record their message and any changes to the other publication data, such as address changes, personnel changes or new submission requirements. Then we control the transfer of this information to the actual 900 program, transferring it directly or by recording it in our own voice.

When gathering your source information, make sure you get all the necessary permissions you need, such as copyright or a license to use the information in your program. Instead of paying for the right to use such information, we might consider proposing a joint venture with one of the leading sources for such information, such as *Literary Marketplace* in this example. The resultant name recognition would be quite beneficial to the program's success.

Will Our Program Work?

Now let's sit back and dispassionately evaluate our proposed 900 information service. Does it truly help our market achieve its goals? Is it responsive or unique enough to generate sufficient call volume? To help answer these questions let's put ourselves into the shoes of an imaginary potential customer -- the exact kind of person we are trying to reach.

Say our caller has written an article about herbal gardening, and wants to identify all possible publications that might be interested in her article. In addition to the menu path indicated, she may also select the "cooking" and "health & fitness" categories as well. She may end up spending 6 or 8 minutes on the telephone.

At $1 a minute (a very common charge for recorded interactive programs), she will spend $6 to $8 dollars. Was it worth it? Well, this information is available at good-sized libraries, but our aspiring author must drive 30 minutes to get there. And then spend another 30 minutes digging through the appropriate reference volumes. An hour and a half, minimum, plus the cost of gas, parking fees, and the babysitter, which could easily exceed the cost of the 900 number call.

And the reference volumes might not be the latest editions. Libraries have tight budgets. Because we can update our 900 program daily, we were able to add a new gardening magazine that was launched only 2 months ago.

Our author certainly appreciated the convenience of the 900 program. With a full-time job and two kids, it is very hard for her to find the time to go to the library. And she would never have learned about a new gardening magazine that is eagerly looking for authors and articles.

She might be so happy with the 900 service that she begins using it in order to find out what topics publishers are seeking before writing her next article. The 900 program is truly helping her achieve her goals: finding receptive publishers, selling her work and getting published.

What, in effect, have we actually done? We have taken existing information that is already available, then we simply re-packaged, sorted, and organized the information in such a way to allow our callers to quickly find the information they need. We have done all the research for our callers, making it instantly available by telephone. And as a finishing touch, we added **value** to the information with the publisher's message.

Now for the most important part. How do we get people to call our program? Fortunately, we have selected an easily definable and targetable market segment: writers. Even more specifically: aspiring writers who haven't yet learned all the ropes or made all the industry contacts. We know we can reach this market very cost-effectively through well-targeted publications and media.

This is just one example of the kind of 900 program that can work. You probably have knowledge or interest in other areas that lend themselves to similar 900 programs. Find an information need within an easily identifiable and reachable target market, then design an information program that is superior to all the other alternatives. Provide information that makes it easier for your callers to achieve their goals. Help them, and they will help you by patronizing your service.

Chapter 6
Marketing &
Market Research

Okay, you have now come up with a promising 900 application. How do you get people to call your number? Simple question. However, this is by far the most important question you must answer. Your success in finding the most cost-effective answer to this question will determine whether or not you will succeed.

First, let's talk about who your market isn't. The conventional wisdom is that the over 40 crowd doesn't call 900 numbers. At least not yet, with few programs appealing to this age group. Back in Chapter 4 you read about the survey that showed that 70% of the respondents wouldn't even consider calling a 900 number, and only 12% have ever used 900 services. This kind of narrows down the potential market. The hip younger generation, who have grown up in the electronic/information age, are the most likely people to call a 900 number.

Because interactive 900 services require a touch-tone telephone, 38% of the population that are still on rotary phones are unlikely callers. Fortunately, they are probably already included in the over 40, 70% segment that wouldn't call anyway, so we shouldn't count them twice. But there are exceptions to this rule, which we will discuss later in Chapter 7.

This should tell you that a 900 program offering valuable advice on Medicare or Social Security benefits would be a miserable failure (remember Con-Cur Consultants back in Chapter 2, who were offering advice on Social Security by dialing 1-900-446-4583 at $3 per minute? It would be interesting to see if they're still in business). Anyway, targeting oldsters is swimming against the tide. At least now, while 900 still has a serious image problem to contend with.

Not all telephones are created equal. Access to 900 dialing isn't available in many college dorms, businesses, hotels, or from public telephones. It makes little sense, therefore, to target anyone who doesn't have ready access to a residential telephone. And now that call blocking is readily available to all residential customers, we will probably see many families with young children elect this option to keep the kids from running up the phone bill.

Who's left? Hip young singles, Yuppies and Dinks (dual income, no kids), to name a few. But don't get mislead by cute titles. Plenty of people who call the soaps and 'scopes lines don't necessarily fit these classifications, yet these kinds of lines can be very successful. In general, however, it is safe to assume that the largest overall market for 900 services is young, fairly sophisticated, and they generally haven't started families yet.

The Target Market

Based upon your chosen 900 application, you now need to further identify your market with as much precision as possible. Why is this so important? Because if you don't know who they are, you will have a very hard time reaching them; and if you can't get your message to them, they are not going to call your number.

Use the following list of demographic questions as a guide for profiling your target market:

1. How old are they?
2. Are they male or female?

3. How much education do they have?
4. Do they live in apartments, or houses?
5. Are they in cities, the suburbs, or out in the sticks?
6. What kind of jobs and income do they have?
7. Are they married or single?
8. What do they do for fun and relaxation?
9. What media do they watch, listen to, or read?

Once you carefully profile your target market and get to know the kind of people they are, you will be better able to identify the most effective ways of reaching them. If you're offering a fairly specialized program, there will likely be specialized media targeted specifically at your market.

Say you're offering a classified advertising program for coin collectors, where callers can either leave recorded ads or listen to ads in various classifications, then make direct contact with each other for buying, selling or trading rare coins. These same people probably subscribe to magazines which specialize in rare coins, so it is very easy to reach this market through print advertising in these publications. This is known as "rifle shot" marketing, because you are able to devote all your advertising dollars in reaching the exact market you need to reach.

The converse is "shotgun blast" marketing. An ad in a general circulation daily newspaper may reach the target market in the circulation area of the newspaper, but you are also paying to reach everyone else who reads the paper, including a lot of people who are not interested in your message. Because advertising costs are based upon circulation, or the size of the audience, you pay a lot of money reaching people who will never respond to your ad.

Of course, rifle shot marketing only works with a very well-defined target market which is served by specialized media. A more general 900 program, such as sports or weather, doesn't permit such precision in reaching the target market. Nonetheless, keep in mind who, in general, calls 900 numbers, and you still may be able to narrow down the media focus to your general target market.

For example, alternative weekly newspapers are well read by the potential 900 market: young, hip, educated, readers. It follows, therefore, that a general 900 application would be more successfully and cost-effectively marketed in such a newspaper than in the major daily newspaper in the same city. The alternative weekly newspaper has a smaller circulation, so advertising costs are lower. Yet the audience is much more likely to call your 900 number because many have probably already used other 900 services. This results in much more cost-effective advertising. The cost per response is much lower. We'll talk more about this later.

The Advertisement

It's beyond the scope of this book to get into the art of creating the actual advertising -- the layout, design and copy. There are many excellent books that are entirely dedicated to the subject, and they do a much more thorough job than I could possibly hope to do here. Nonetheless, there is one simple formula that should guide the creation of any ad: it's called the AIDA principle. Attention, Interest, Desire, Action.

Attention. First you must get your customer to stop and notice your ad. This is accomplished with a headline, a photo, a graphic, a cartoon, or anything that commands attention.

Interest. The only thing that really interests anyone is something that provides benefits that help him or her achieve an important goal or solve a problem. What is important here are benefits, not features. A man buys cologne because he wants to be attractive to the opposite sex. The actual smell is merely a feature of the product, which is quite secondary. If women were attracted by the odor of skunks, you better believe that men would enthusiastically drench themselves in copious quantities of eau-de-lepieau.

Desire. Now you've got him hooked, but you need to do some more convincing so he'll buy your product, and not someone else's. Here's where some features might come in, like the uniqueness of your scent, extracted from only the most virile of skunks. A testimonial or two -- from lucky guys who used the scent and were attacked by mobs of beautiful, lustful women -- would be a nice touch.

Action. You haven't made the sale until your customer actually calls and orders your product. Don't expect him to do that without some encouragement. This is where you use words like CALL NOW, or ORDER TODAY, or WHILE QUANTITIES LAST, or any other method of getting him to act immediately. Incentives for immediate orders are always effective, like BUY ONE GET ONE FREE UNTIL DEC 31st!

These basic principles can be used for guidance in creating any kind of ad, or inducement to buy, whether it be for print, TV, radio, classified, brochures, sales letters or anything else. Forget these principles at your peril! I am continually amazed at how many companies -- and it's usually the biggest ones -- completely ignore the basic AIDA principle in their marketing materials. They are throwing a lot of money down the drain. If it doesn't motivate your prospect to buy your product or service, the cash you spent is gone forever.

The Media Choice

Once your target market has been defined and profiled, you need to find out what types of media best reach your intended audience. If you can get a rifle shot media source, go for it. You should select likely sources and contact them for media kits, which include information on circulation/audience size, advertising rates, and most importantly, the demographics of their audience. Also, make sure they accept 900 advertising. The lingering negative perception about 900 numbers has resulted in the exclusion of such advertising by many media companies.

Print

There are literally thousands of print media sources to choose from, from huge daily newspapers to very specialized monthly magazines. Newspapers are usually read by a broad, general audience and are unlikely to be a cost-effective choice for many pay-per-call programs. Nonetheless, there are exceptions. The national sports newspapers are targeted to sports fans. The national tabloids may be a good choice for horoscope or soap opera lines.

And, as I mentioned earlier, the alternative weeklies are good prospects for 900 advertising. Paul Twitchell, director of marketing at Tele-Publishing, a service bureau serving numerous alternative weeklies with 900 programs, says, "The typical reader is a socially active, college educated professional between 18 and 35 years of age, with a high disposable income. Many IPs are turning to alternative weeklies as a more efficient means of reaching their target audiences."

What makes the alternative weekly unique is that it is often the most comprehensive source for local arts, entertainment and cultural activities, which means it is being read when the reader is in a relaxed, fun-loving mood. This could be particularly auspicious for 900 game, contest or entertainment lines.

The Association of Alternative Newsweeklies (AAN) is a trade organization that represents some 88 member publications with a combined audience of over eight million readers. Because the alternatives are so promising for 900 advertising, I have included a comprehensive listing of such publications in Appendix E of the Resource Guide.

Magazines require a much longer lead time for ad placement than newspapers, often a few months or more, but the variety of specialized markets is truly impressive. There seems to be a special magazine for just about every sport, hobby, profession, or interest imaginable. The potential for rifle shot target marketing is very good with specialized magazines. The reference section of your local library should have some of the reference volumes mentioned earlier in Chapter 5, listing all periodicals published in the U.S. and abroad. You should definitely review some of these, because you will find many magazines you have never even heard about, and some could be good prospects for your 900 advertising.

With any print media choice, the size and placement of your ad will greatly influence the rate of response. First, you must grab the reader's attention, and only then can you induce him to call your number with compelling benefit-laden copy. If the reader doesn't first notice your ad, the best copy in the world can't save it from being ignored. The right-hand page, top outside corner, is generally recognized as the best position for a display ad that isn't a full page.

Classified advertising, although relatively inexpensive, will not generate calls if you need to thoroughly explain your message in order to induce a call. A trivia contest or a music review line will not work with classified. For classified to work, the benefits of calling must be fairly obvious to the reader, without having to explain it in the ad copy, and the cost of the call should be quite low.

People in the mail order business are often successful with a two-step classified ad. The classified ad doesn't ask for money, but offers to send free information. Then, a very detailed mailing piece is sent, which can do a much better job of inducing the purchase decision. This same concept can be tailored to pay-per-call marketing, with the added advantage of compiling a data-base of inquirers for regular follow-up mailings. Indeed, the first step of the classified ad could be to call a toll-free 800 number, where the caller hears a convincing message that motivates him to call the 900 program. A whole lot more information can be conveyed verbally in 30 or 60 seconds than can be printed in a classified ad, and the printed word will never convey a reassuring or enthusiastic tone of voice.

With most publications, you're not limited to just display or classified advertising. Many will accept printed inserts, which can be quite cost-effective. You can print up a colorful insert, on both sides if appropriate, and get better exposure than with a full page ad for less money. Inserts also dovetail nicely with a fundamental feature of the 900 business: if a potential caller doesn't have your 900 number readily available, he or she isn't going to call. An insert can be put aside or stuffed into a pocket for later reference without destroying the publication by tearing out the page. It makes it easier for the potential caller to save your promotional message and telephone number.

Because print media is a relatively low-cost advertising vehicle, often permitting fairly precise target marketing, it is usually the first choice of many start-up 900 programs. Indeed, the ability to rifle shot the marketing with low-cost print advertising should influence the final selection of a 900 program.

Radio

Radio is another medium that can be fairly accurately targeted to a given market. A significant shortcoming, however, is the fact that a very large percentage of radio listeners are in their automobiles, with no access to a telephone. This problem can be partially offset with the use of a very recognizable telephone number, or a vanity number that spells a word or phrase, which can be easily recalled later when the customer is near a phone. Nonetheless, response to 900 advertising is usually immediate and spur-of-the-moment, and many potential callers will be unable to respond to your message. It's not enough to target the market. You also want to reach them at a time and place where they will be most likely to respond to your ad.

This doesn't mean that radio should be ignored as a source of advertising. After all, radio can be quite inexpensive. Talk radio has been effective for some 900 programs, particularly live ads by a popular DJ. Just keep in mind the limitations, and test carefully before making any large financial commitments.

Television

Television is probably the most effective medium for most 900 advertising. TV viewers are a very captive audience, and a good, attention-grabbing commercial will be noticed by a large percentage of the viewers. Tune into various cable channels or the Fox Network, especially after 11:00 p.m., and you will see many 900 commercials.

The fact that many of these commercials have been airing over a long period of time indicates that they have been successful for the advertisers. You will also see many direct response 800 commercials on TV. Direct response works on television, and 900 is a direct response information or entertainment service.

As a start-up IP, you may automatically assume that TV advertising is way beyond your budget. Not necessarily, because you don't have to start by trying to reach a huge market on a national network. Local cable channels, depending on the size of their market, can cost as low as a few dollars a spot. The cost of producing a good commercial will run from $3000 to more than $10,000, but once it is produced it can be used for a fairly long period of time with various cable channels or networks.

The actual conceptual design and production of any TV commercial should not be undertaken by novices. Too much money is at risk. According to Jeffrey Price Michelson, president and creative director of Media Wizard Productions, an experienced producer of 900 TV commercials, "Production values, which didn't matter so much in the beginning, are all important now. I remember the days when just being on TV was enough. There was the novelty factor, fewer players, lots of first-time impulse buyers, and no recession!" Well, those days are over, and to protect your investment and to assure success, you must seek out the help of experts, preferably ones with experience in 900 television advertising.

Direct Mail

Direct mail is the most precise rifle shot marketing available. There are specialized mailing lists for just about any kind of demographic group of people imaginable. There is a lot of valuable statistical science associated with good mailing lists. A direct mail piece allows a comprehensive message which can be exactly tailored to the target market. There is virtually no limit to the length, size, or complexity of the advertising message included with the mailing.

Direct mail, however, is a fairly expensive rifle. A mailing piece can cost up to 35 or 45 cents each including list rental, creative and production, printing costs, and postage. A typical 900 line might net only a couple of dollars a call, so the response rate from the direct mailing would have to be extremely high in order to be successful. Much higher than industry averages.

Direct mail should be considered only for higher priced 900 services. For example, a computer software help line staffed by expert live operators, netting an average of $10 or more per call, could work very well. Particularly if the IP was able to rent a mailing list of all such software purchasers from the vendor. A true rifle shot without a penny wasted reaching the wrong people.

A unique advantage of direct mail is the ease and confidentiality of testing. You can try small mailings without investing a lot of money to measure response rates. You can test different messages, prices or lists. And you can do this while keeping fairly low-key, so your competitors will be less likely to find out about your program or your methods.

Other Media

So far we've talked about the most logical advertising media. It's possible that none of these will be the most suitable or cost-effective way of promoting your particular 900 program. What else is there? Billboards, cocktail napkins, coffee mugs, matchbooks, keychains, or other novelties. Hand out fliers at shopping malls, sporting events, or music concerts. Have your message displayed on the electronic scoreboard at the football game, or have it printed or inserted in the game program, or hire an airplane to tow the message over the stadium!

Contact the manufacturer or mail order distributor of a product that your target market regularly purchases, and see if you can insert a flier in their package. This is called "piggyback" advertising, and can be just as effective as direct mail at a fraction of the cost. See if your local pizza parlor will include your message on its pizza boxes, in return for you helping out with the cost of producing the boxes. If it works, try a national pizza chain next. Promote your 900 program on someone else's related 900 program. This will target proven callers to 900 numbers.

Always think about what your target market is doing when he or she is most likely to call your program. Eating a pizza, watching TV, enjoying a beer, or with a group of friends? Keep your eyes and your imagination open to creative new ways of reaching your target market during these times, or making your message easily accessible when they might need it. Make it convenient for your target market to not only find out about your program, but also to purchase your services. Always keep the needs of your audience foremost in your planning, and they will reward you by patronizing your services.

Advertising Agencies

A good advertising agency, particularly one with experience in direct response marketing, can do all the marketing work for you while saving considerable money by staying away from ineffective advertising buys. These are experienced professionals who can be immensely helpful in designing and executing your marketing strategy. They eat, sleep and breathe advertising, and they know a lot more about it than you do.

Nevertheless, few advertising agencies have a lot of experience with the 900 industry, so you must choose carefully. Also, be careful with agencies that specialize in only one medium, unless you have already decided that this medium is best for you. Don't abdicate your responsibility in evaluating all possible media options, and trust your judgement when considering which is best for you. No one understands your program as well as you, and there are many horror stories around the 900 industry about IPs who have lost a lot of money by starting out with the wrong agency.

Because marketing is the most important part of any successful 900 program, it makes little sense to completely relinquish control to an advertising agency. There is no substitute for the hands-on learning that comes only from doing it yourself. As a start-up IP, you should at least try out the lower cost media and techniques yourself, and perhaps use an ad agency for the more complex and expensive advertising, such as television. Remember, if you are launching a novel 900 program, both you and the ad agency will be going through a learning curve together.

If you can team-up with an agency with extensive 900 experience with programs similar to yours, it will be a source of extremely valuable help. Even if it handles only one segment of your marketing, it will usually be happy to advise you on those areas you plan to handle personally. And after you have learned the ropes in the marketing game, you may wish to turn over all marketing efforts to the agency.

How do you find an advertising agency with experience in the 900 industry? A good place to start is the listing found in the *Audiotex Directory & Buyer's Guide* (see Appendix C). Perhaps a better source would be recommendations from your service bureau. Books and periodicals about direct marketing, such as *DM News,* will list agencies with experience in direct response marketing. In any event, you will be entrusting a lot of advertising money to an agency, so check them out thoroughly before making any commitments.

Although not technically a full-service ad agency, you might want to check out *The "900" Advertising Club.* This company was started by Keith Mueller, an experienced IP with an advertising background who understands the 900 business. He uses bulk purchasing to get better ad rates for members, offers per inquiry programs, and publishes *Teleletter,* a helpful newsletter on 900 number marketing techniques:

> The "900" Advertising Club
> P.O. Box 5048
> Newport Beach, CA 92662
> 714-721-9280

The Competition

You don't have to make all your media selection decisions in complete isolation. Simply check out the competition. Or, if there is no direct competitor to your unique 900 program, there will surely be some similar programs which would advertise in similar media.

As I mentioned earlier, pay real close attention to repeat advertising. The longer the ad runs, the bigger or splashier it is, the more likely it has been successful.

First, identify all the possible media that are most appropriate for reaching the target market. And then get creative and try to identify a few which may not be so readily obvious. Then monitor them all to see what programs are being advertised, and how. Learn from their marketing and then gratefully borrow as much useful information as possible.

Don't automatically assume, however, that because you saw a competitor's ad a few times in a given media, that it has been successful. All advertisers constantly test different media, anywhere from a few weeks to several months. You want to watch for fairly long-term repetition. To save some time, call the media advertising department and try to find out how long your competitor has been advertising with them. Or go to the library and go through several back issues of the publication.

In addition to where your competitor advertises, pay attention to the size, layout, or design of his ads. Try to identify the features that make it successful, then incorporate them in your advertising.

Why does Burger King always sprout up across the street from McDonalds? Because they let McDonalds do all the expensive market research in selecting the best location, and then simply play follow-the-leader. Burger King saves a lot of time and money by just watching and following the competition.

This does not mean that you should never conduct your own market testing. You should, and you will, and we'll talk more about this later. But you have to start somewhere, and you may as well benefit as much as possible from other people's experiences in order

to get the biggest bang for your advertising buck. The more effective
your initial advertising, the quicker you can increase your budget and
multiply your revenue.

Media Partners

Advertising is by far the largest expense associated with any
successful 900 program. What if we could completely eliminate this
expense? Sounds like a reasonably attractive proposition, does it not?
It is often possible to structure a win-win relationship between the IP
and the media company, also known as a "per inquiry" (PI) revenue
sharing relationship. And, not surprisingly, revenue sharing with
media partners fairly common in the 900 industry.

The media partner already has the advertising vehicle, and often
has difficulty selling all its ad space or time spots on a regular basis.
The IP has the program, access to the featured information or
entertainment, and keeps the program up-to-date and functioning. Put
the two together and both come out ahead.

The media partner contributes ad space or time spots which
otherwise may have remained unsold, in return for a predetermined
share of the call revenue to the 900 program. Although the IP gives up
a percentage of potential revenue to the media partner, he doesn't pay
a dime in advertising costs. If the program proves to be successful, the
media partner may in fact earn more per ad with this arrangement
than by selling the space or time to a regular advertiser.

And if the 900 program is compatible with the image of the media
partner, the media partner may lend credibility to the program by
sponsoring it under its own name. As we already know, the 900
industry lacks credibility, and media partner sponsorship can go a
long way toward improving the perception of legitimacy for any given
program.

Revenue sharing with a media partner is a lot like program
sharing discussed earlier. If the IP is using more than one media
partner for a given program, each media partner should be assigned
an exclusive 900 number plus access to independent call count

verification. The media partner may justifiably insist on exclusivity in its market area, particularly if it is lending its name to the program. The IP, on the other hand, has a legitimate basis for requiring a commitment to a certain level of advertising to help cover the cost of adding another 900 number to the program.

The revenue sharing breakdown must be beneficial to both partners. The media partner will want to see projected revenue, at a realistic response level, at least equal what it would otherwise earn by simply selling the space or time to advertisers. Also, the media partner will probably not want to compete with established paying advertisers of similar programs in its media.

Because revenue sharing can be quite lucrative for the IP, you should carefully consider this option for your 900 program. And do your homework before approaching a prospective media partner. It might be prudent to advertise with the company for awhile so that you can unequivocally demonstrate call volume response to advertising in that specific media. You will be dealing with an experienced business person, therefore a well-organized written proposal should be prepared. The subjects outlined in your proposal should include the following:

1. Description of the program.

2. Your target market (It better describe the potential media partner's audience!).

3. The proposed functions and responsibilities of both partners.

4. The revenue sharing breakdown, including details on per minute/call gross revenue, long distance carrier charges, service bureau charges, and net revenue per minute/call.

5. Demonstrated response rates. This can be from prior advertising with similar media or from a test run with the prospective media partner.

6. Call volume and revenue projections. Demonstrate realistic revenue projections as call volume increases with repeated advertising exposure.

7. Anything else that gives you credibility. A paragraph about your background, business references, other successful media

partners, the capabilities of your service bureau, and anything else that makes the potential media partner feel comfortable about doing business with you.

Don't ask the media partner to invest any money, and don't require a minimum monthly fee. Make your proposal as risk-free as possible, which makes it much easier for him or her to accept it. To cover your incremental monthly costs, you may consider dividing the revenue on a sliding scale, with the largest percentage going to you until your costs are covered. And don't tell the media partner that it doesn't cost him anything. It certainly does, if he has to turn away a potential paying advertiser for the same space or time spot. Just make sure you structure the revenue sharing such that there is a realistic expectation for the media partner to in fact earn more than by simply selling the advertising space or time.

It would also be a good idea to prepare the media partner for a realistic trial run of three to six months in order to give the program a fair chance of success. Like any other advertising, it will take time and repetition for response rates to increase to an acceptable level.

Low-Cost And No-Cost Advertising

When you get a media kit or price quote from a media source, don't automatically assume that the quoted advertising prices are set in concrete. Just because the prices are formally printed up on an official looking schedule doesn't mean there's no room for negotiation.

I mentioned before that media companies often have unsold space or time spots. If they cannot sell this advertising in time, they will earn absolutely nothing. They will much prefer to get at least something for the space or air time. It's not unusual to be able to negotiate drastic discounts, often less than half the published prices. Or, get them to throw in some free insertions or time spots for an up-front payment. Nothing works as well as the promise of immediate cash in hand.

With print advertising, a good strategy is to wait until the submission deadline date for a particular issue, then contact the media company at the last minute to see what kind of deal they can give you. Explain that you are just starting your program and would like to give them a try, but you simply can't afford to spend more than X number of dollars for testing your ad in their publication. More often than not you will be able to get a significant price break for your efforts. Yes, you may have to Federal Express the camera ready ad copy to them to meet the deadline, but this will often be worth it. And remember, particularly with print media, their published deadlines are very rarely their true deadlines.

With radio and television you can achieve similar savings by taking advantage of "run of station" (ROS) advertising. You simply contract for a certain number of spots over a period of time, and the station airs the spots wherever they have unsold time. This is a more formalized way to take advantage of unsold time, and gives the media station some flexibility in filling up its advertising schedule. You still might try some last minute negotiation for better rates if the station already has your commercial, in the can, from running previous advertising. Instead of renewing a run of station arrangement, let it lapse and call periodically for good rates for the next day or two, and you are likely to save even more money on your advertising.

The only disadvantage with last minute purchasing or run of station is that you will rarely get the best placement or time slots for your advertising. A TV ad that airs at 3am won't be seen by many viewers. Some of your savings in advertising costs may be offset by lower response rates to the ads.

Run of station television advertising is typically aired during the daytime or late at night, during non-prime-time periods. But your specific target market may in fact be daytime or late night viewers, so this may end up working to your advantage. Indeed, many direct response advertisers have been quite successful with late night advertising. This is likely due to the fact that many late night programs are reruns, and the viewer may not be quite so glued to the program. Because the viewer already knows the plot, he or she might be more willing to break away and make the telephone call to your 900 number.

The fact is, you can save considerable money by offering to purchase unsold space or air time at the very last minute, when the media company will be eager to get at least something. Don't be afraid to try this technique - it works!

Now I'm going to discuss no-cost advertising. How, besides media partnerships or per inquiry arrangements, can this be accomplished? The news release. The initial launch of your program is a newsworthy event. You may be able to get several media companies to publish your news release. Your program may feature a recurring newsworthy event, such as a contest. The winner's hometown newspaper will normally be happy to publish a news release about the lucky local person's good fortune.

For a news release to be accepted and published, there are several basic rules that must be followed:

1. It must be typed on clean white 8 1/2" X 11" paper (no letterhead).

2. It should be mailed first class to all logical mass media, including news directors at radio and television stations, city editors at daily newspapers, or to specialty editors at magazines or trade publications.

3. The name, address and telephone number of the contact or author should appear at the top left corner of the first page.

4. The news should be immediate and timely. Don't wait for several weeks after you launch your program to send out the news releases.

5. Double space the text and use wide margins so that the copy can be easily edited. One page is best, and two pages should be the maximum length.

6. Don't ramble. Keep it tight, accurate, and not too "pluggy."

7. Use a summary lead style (who, what, where, when, why) whenever possible. Use short, concise sentences with active verbs. Grammar and spelling must be perfect.

8. Spend 80% of your effort on the first paragraph, if not the first sentence, which should convey the meat of the message, and should be able to stand alone if the rest of the text were cut out.

9. Go from the most important to the least important material. Editors usually cut news releases from the bottom (end) up.

10. Whenever possible, mail the news release to a name, not just a title. Call first to find out who to send it to. Then follow-up with that person by telephone to see if he or she has any questions.

11. When appropriate, include a substantive quote.

Now let's put all of this together in a sample news release. The following news release was used quite successfully in promoting the first edition of this book. Notice that this news release does in fact plug the book, but doesn't use real hard-selling or flowery sales language. Editors recognize that any news release is a plug of some sort, but they don't want it to read like an advertisement.

Aegis Publishing Group
796 Aquidneck Avenue
Newport, R.I. 02842   NEWS RELEASE
                                                    October 21, 1992
CONTACT: Robert Mastin   For Immediate Release

HELP FOR 900 NUMBER ENTREPRENEURS

Newport, R.I. -- Anyone planning to launch a legitimate 900 number information service can now get straightforward help from a new book, titled *900 KNOW-HOW: How to Succeed With Your Own 900 Number Business*. Because the get-rich-quick hucksters have been perpetuating the myth of easy riches, the serious entrepreneur has had to navigate a "minefield of misinformation" about the industry, according to the author, Robert Mastin.

A 900 number excels as a convenient means for delivering information and exchanging payment. As a result, 900 numbers are emerging as an important element of the Information Age. The industry is steadily gaining respectability, no longer perceived as strictly dial-a-porn. From pork belly prices to medical advice to airline schedules, reputable companies and entrepreneurs are launching valuable 900 information programs to meet the needs of our information-hungry society. Quick, convenient access to timely or specialized information is no longer a luxury: it's absolutely essential in this hectic, fiercely competitive world. And the telephone is the quickest way to get access to very specific information.

"The future of the 900 industry will be with specialized information programs that meet specific information needs, offering superior convenience along with good perceived value," says Mastin. "Starting a 900 business is the easy part. The challenge is in satisfying a target market's most important information needs in a more responsive way."

Mastin's book offers nuts-and-bolts advice on launching a successful 900 number service, outlining the various types of 900 applications, marketing considerations, financial projections, the regulatory environment, and what pitfalls to avoid. According to syndicated careers columnist Joyce Lain Kennedy, "It was only a matter of time until somebody wrote a frank, no-hype book on launching a 900 pay-per-call business."

"I have been involved in the audiotex industry for over 5 years and *900 KNOW-HOW* is one of the best books that I have seen," says Bill Gundling, vice president of The Nine Call Corporation, Cambridge, Mass. "The information provided is accurate and concise. This book is a must for anyone contemplating getting into the business."

900 KNOW-HOW is a 174 page paperback. It's available directly from the publisher for $19.95 plus $3 P&H, or at many fine bookstores. The address for Aegis Publishing Group is 796R Aquidneck Avenue, Newport, R.I., 02842. The toll free number is 1-800-828-6961.

###

Editors' Note: Black & white photographs of the book are available by request. A 1700 word article about the 900 industry, titled "The Future of 900," is available on a no-cost, non-exclusive basis from the author. Please call the contact number above or use the enclosed reply card.

Notice how the first quotation introduces a newsworthy statement about the get-rich-quick attributes of the industry. This serves two purposes. First, the use of a quotation means that the editor doesn't have to necessarily agree with the statement. Second, it introduces a newsworthy idea, even if it is somewhat negative. Even a negative idea, as long as it is news and it doesn't hurt the perception of your company or service, will help to get your news release published. The more "newsy" the better, and your objective is to get the news release published. Otherwise, all your efforts will be wasted.

In a similar fashion, the quotations by industry professionals lend solid credibility to the news release. This allows the inclusion of very favorable comments without resorting to self-serving sales language.

And remember, a news release is much like editorial copy. It is much more believable than any advertisement can possibly hope to be, and much more likely to be read. The news release is a powerful, no-cost tool which should be used extensively at every possible opportunity. Indeed, you might even think about creating opportunities for sending out news releases on a regular basis.

I have sold thousands of books through the use of free publicity. Needless to say, I'm a firm believer in the power of the news release. Remember, there are tens of thousands of media companies that must regularly fill-up millions of pages of print. They all actively want to hear about interesting or newsworthy topics or events. The only reason they exist is to tell us about these things. All you have to do is to give them what they want and need. It really is that simple.

Although it takes more time and effort to get exposure with free publicity, as opposed to simply choosing the media and paying for the ad, the payoff can be quite handsome. Done properly, with the right news release, you could get lucky and generate the equivalent of tens of thousands of dollars in advertising -- for free!

To make your job easier, there are companies that specialize in distributing your news release to any number of media contacts as you wish. You simply provide this company with a news release and the selection criteria (i.e., for a business service, the business editors at major daily newspapers with circulations above 100,000; plus all business and trade magazines). This company will then print and send your release to its list of contacts, which is often up-dated daily, and which will usually include the name and title of the current cognizant editor.

The Publicity Handbook by David Yale lists several such companies that provide these services, and that's where I found out about the company I frequently use for mailing out news releases:

Bacon's Information, Inc.
332 S. Michigan Ave.
Chicago, IL 60604
800-621-0561

I don't bother anymore trying to keep an up-to-date list of media contacts because Bacon's can do a much better job of keeping current with all the changing names, addresses and titles.

Contests, Games & Sweepstakes

The possibility of winning a prize of value appeals to everyone, and adding a prize element to a 900 program, when appropriate, can multiply call counts significantly. Everyone knows that Publisher's Clearinghouse gives away millions of dollars a year in prizes. You have probably entered their sweepstakes at least once. This promotional technique obviously works very well for many companies, or they wouldn't be doing it with such predictable regularity.

The nature of the program will dictate whether or not a prize feature is appropriate. Telephone games and contests are obvious candidates. Product, service, or event promotions are another likely application. For example, Paramount sponsored a 900 sweepstakes in conjunction with a polling application in order for *Star Trek* fans to select their favorite episodes for an up-coming *Star Trek* television marathon featuring the ten most popular episodes. In return for calling to register their vote, Trekkies were given a chance for a walk-on part in Paramount's *Star Trek: The Next Generation.*

The entertainment industry in particular has embraced the use of 900 games, contests or sweepstakes in promoting its products and services. New Line Home Video, The Nashville Network, NBC, TBS,

MTV, Fox Broadcasting, HBO, and MCA/Universal are just some of the entertainment companies that have developed 900 telepromotions in order to generate interest in their products or services. Very often, the prizes being offered are tied into the product or service being promoted: concert tickets, videos, or promotional novelties.

The long distance carriers have established some fairly stringent guidelines in allowing 900 programs with contest features. See Appendix H for specific details. Expert legal assistance will be essential in properly executing any game, contest or sweepstakes. Every state has its own lottery laws, and these laws are constantly changing or being re-interpreted. In some cases, the laws are being applied more stringently to 900 promotions in particular. Needless to say, this is not an area to jump into without some expert legal help.

Promotion law is a specialized field, and it is unlikely that your local attorney will be equipped to help you set up your promotion. The Promotion Marketing Association of America (PMAA) is a valuable source of information for not only legal information, but also for all other aspects of running a successful promotion. See the Resource Guide for further information about the PMAA plus a listing of law firms active in promotion law. Appendix I will give you a general idea of what is involved, from a legal standpoint, in conducting a contest, game or sweepstakes.

Chapter 7
Choosing a
Service Bureau

Why do you need a service bureau? Sure, you can purchase and service your own call-handling and audiotex equipment. But even a simple 24 line system will cost thousands of dollars, and you need to be technically capable of programming, operating and troubleshooting the system. There will also be a substantial investment in installing the system, including the telephone lines and related equipment, such as a T-1, with the telephone company. As a start-up IP, these costs are probably prohibitive, and a service bureau can provide all the equipment and services you need for a very reasonable monthly and/or per-minute charge. Keep in mind that most *Fortune 500* companies use service bureaus, so why should you be any different?

What is a Service Bureau?

At the heart of any service bureau is an impressive array of computerized call-handling equipment, with the capability of processing hundreds, or even thousands, of incoming calls simultaneously. The larger service bureaus are capable of handling the huge call volumes resulting from TV promotions, with many well-recognized national clients. These service bureaus may have millions of dollars invested in state-of-the-art equipment and facilities, including back-up generators for uninterrupted service during power failures, and professional sound studios for voice recording. Call Interactive in Omaha, Nebraska and Home Shopping Network in Clearwater, Florida are the current leaders in volume capability, with 10,000 and 20,000 ports, respectively.

A good service bureau can be extremely helpful in designing and setting up your program. It has probably already dealt with just about every conceivable kind of interactive program imaginable, and will have excellent suggestions for your program - perhaps ideas you never even considered feasible. Its programmers are a very talented and creative bunch who typically enjoy new challenges.

Besides helping with your program design, some service bureaus can also help with other useful services:

1. Voice talent for professional quality recording of your program.

2. Marketing help. Some service bureaus have in-house advertising capabilities to help with media placement or planning advertising strategies.

3. Television or radio production facilities.

4. Live operators for simple messages or order taking.

5. Voice capture capabilities for order taking or contest entry, and transcription services as required.

6. Turn-key information or entertainment programs which are offered on a program sharing basis.

Of course, you may not require the services of a large service bureau if your program is targeted to a relatively small niche market. A smaller company may be able to offer you more personalized services. Another reason for not allowing call handling capabilities to be an overriding concern is the fact that the smaller service bureaus can enter into call allocation arrangements with the long distance carrier and another service bureau. For example, a smaller service bureau, with equipment capable of handling only 48 simultaneous calls, can contract with a larger service bureau to accept a predetermined percentage of the incoming calls for a specific period of time corresponding with a television promotional campaign. The long distance carrier is simply instructed to route this percentage of calls to the larger service bureau.

Another advantage to using a service bureau is the leverage it has with the long distance carriers. Because it generates so much revenue for AT&T, MCI or Sprint, the service bureau is in a strong negotiating position with its long distance carriers. This should come as no surprise. The biggest customers always get the best treatment. Working through a service bureau is often less expensive than dealing directly with the long distance carrier because it can pass along to the IP its savings from doing a volume business with the IXC.

Finally, the title "service bureau" doesn't always mean that the company possesses its own call-handling equipment. Some companies, usually program sponsors, call themselves service bureaus even when they own no equipment. Other companies simply serve as a middle-man between the IP and the service bureau. If they offer an attractive program sharing arrangement, with a lot of experience and marketing help, fine. But if you're launching a new program of your own, it makes little sense to use such a middle-man when you can deal directly with a full service bureau to start with.

Equipment Capabilities

You have already heard the terms "call handling" or "audiotext equipment." What does this really mean? The basic building block of any call handling system is the Voice Response Unit (VRU). This piece of equipment is somewhat larger than a VCR, and usually consists of 24 or 48 "Ports," which means it is capable of handling that number of telephone calls at any given time.

The main function of the VRU is to allow callers to communicate with computers without sitting in front of a terminal. The touch tone telephone keypad becomes the terminal, and communication with the computer is achieved from any remote telephone. Think about what this means to the computerphobe who is afraid of computers, or to the many thousands of households that haven't yet purchased computers (the vast majority). It means that these people can be given the same access to information that heretofore has been available only to highly computer-literate people with the access to on-line databases, and the expertise to find the information they seek. The IP, through an imaginatively designed interactive program, is making it possible for people to get information that would otherwise be unavailable to anyone without a computer and the ability to use it for data retrieval.

A large service bureau will have scores of VRUs that are tied into a powerful mainframe computer. It will also be capable of "dynamic allocation," which automatically routes incoming calls to other VRUs if the primary VRU becomes saturated with calls. This is how it handles the large call surges from a national television promotion.

A small service bureau, on the other hand, may have only one VRU and a desktop PC. A nice feature of the technology, however, is that any size service bureau can easily expand its volume capabilities by simply adding VRUs. It's a nice, neat modular technology.

900 Number Ownership

You may get some confusing and conflicting information regarding the ownership of a 900 telephone number. First of all, the only entity that comes close to "owning" a 900 number is Bellcore, and to a lesser extent, the long distance carrier. The IXCs are allocated the rights to a certain number of three digit NXX prefixes by Bellcore, the cooperative research branch of the Regional Bell Operating Companies (RBOCs). Any long distance carrier may apply to Bellcore for the rights to additional NXXs at any time. It should be noted that NXXs currently cannot be transferred from one long distance carrier to another, and once you have committed to a carrier and a specific 900 number, you are essentially married to that carrier unless you are willing to change your 900 number. There is some talk about making the numbers transferable from one carrier to another, but this may be years away. See Appendix J for a list of current NXX assignments.

Either the IP or the service bureau may contract with the long distance carrier for the use of a 900 number, becoming the "client of record" with the carrier. The client of record deals directly with the carrier, receiving monthly call summary reports and net call revenues directly from the carrier. This may sound like a real advantage for the IP. Not necessarily. It can be quite expensive for an IP to be the client of record, because there are no price breaks for doing a volume business with the carrier. A small IP, even with a couple of 900 programs, will pay full price for start-up fees and monthly charges. AT&T, for example, charges $1200 for a start-up fee, plus $500 per month for an individual client of record. The service bureau, on the other hand, will be amortizing this same cost over hundreds of telephone lines.

When a service bureau is the client of record, it will typically pass along its volume savings to the IP, allowing you to launch a program for significantly less money. The service bureau also has a lot more clout with the long distance carrier because it is a profitable, high-volume, long-term customer. It talks to its carriers every day, and has the leverage to get your program approved and launched very quickly.

As long as you're dealing with a reputable, financially sound service bureau, there is really little benefit for you to be the client of record. Besides being more expensive, your relationship with the service bureau is not quite as advantageous. When the IP is client of record, he is essentially leasing equipment and services from the service bureau. The service bureau is less a partner in profit, and might have less incentive to make sure the program is always functioning properly. The service bureau doesn't have quite the same vested interest in the viability of the program.

Not being responsible for the program content, the service bureau has no reason to defend the program with the carrier should a legal conformance problem arise. The client of record is responsible to the carrier for all aspects of program content, and a service bureau is simply in a better position to make sure the program doesn't violate any new rules or regulations that may pop up from time-to-time.

Now for the other side of the coin. Not being the client of record can be dangerous to your financial health. Notice that I qualified the previous statement, "As long as you're dealing with a <u>reputable, financially sound</u> service bureau, there is really little benefit for you to be the client of record." This statement needs to be expanded upon to some extent.

A smaller service bureau, lacking sufficient financial resources, can suffer very seriously if one of its major IP clients gets hit with a huge retroactive chargeback covering a period of several months. If the service bureau is the client of record with the long distance carrier, it will be responsible for covering the bill. A huge unanticipated expense such as this can completely dry up its cash flow, and guess who ends up holding the bag? The rest of the service bureau's client IPs, who have no control over the situation, and whose chargeback records might be impeccable. They could wait for months to receive their money from the service bureau, or worse, lose it all if the service bureau can never recover and goes out of business.

And I'm not just talking about a hypothetical possibility here. It has happened, and some of the service bureaus have been fairly large and well-known. Over the past couple of years dozens of service bureaus have gone under, pulling many IPs down with them. Had the IP been client of record, it would have been relatively simple to transfer the 900 number and program to another service bureau. And any funds due would come from the long distance carrier, paid directly to the IP, so there would be no interruption in the IP's incoming cash flow.

According to W. Brooks McCarty, an industry veteran and one of the founders of the National Association for Interactive Services (N.A.I.S.), "A service bureau that not only offers billing in the name of the IP, but encourages it, is not only protecting itself but its clients as well." It should be further noted, however, that the only major long distance carrier that will currently accept IPs as clients of record is AT&T. MCI generally contracts only with service bureaus or companies in whose name the trunk group is registered, but it will deal directly with IPs that own their own equipment on a case-by-case basis. Check with your service bureau for the current status of both major carriers.

An established, successful IP who can easily afford the higher monthly costs as client of record is generally well advised to deal directly with the long distance carrier. Clearly, the alternative is to make sure that the service bureau is financially sound. And many of them are quite sound. Some service bureaus offer either option, so you can save money by starting out with the service bureau as client of record and then change over if and when your program becomes successful. This would be the best of both worlds.

What to Look For in a Service Bureau

The specific capabilities and services to look for in a service bureau will be a function of your unique program needs. Some of the following features will be critically important to the success of your program, and others will be of little value. You will be the only one to judge the relative importance of these criteria:

1. Call volume capabilities. We have already discussed call allocation arrangements, which allow smaller service bureaus to handle higher call volume. Nevertheless, if you anticipate large call volume surges resulting from TV advertising, you might as well start with a service bureau that can handle the volume.

2. Long distance carriers. Because SPRINT has drastically reduced the scope of its 900 services, there are essentially only two major players left: AT&T and MCI. Some service bureaus use both, others offer only one. MCI is currently a little less expensive but AT&T is quicker in paying out money and has the lowest charge-back rates in the industry. It may boil down to what three digit prefix, or NXX, is available for spelling a distinctive word. The long distance carrier may also allocate certain NXXs to different service bureaus, so if these numbers are important, ask the prospective service bureau for

a list of NXXs available. See Appendix H for more information about the major long distance carriers and their current pricing.

3. Types of programs and clients. Does the service bureau currently serve programs such as yours? Having a lot of experience in a certain type of application, which is similar to yours, will mean a shorter learning curve for the service bureau, and fewer program glitches.

4. Call count access and verification. It is very useful, indeed, almost indispensable, to have 24-hour automated access to call counts. This is usually accomplished by calling an interactive program at the service bureau, often using a toll-tree 800 number, entering an exclusive access code and/or password, and then receiving recorded call count and/or call minute information for your program. A good system will feature a menu of selections so that call counts can be determined by the day or by the hour for the preceding week.

5. Written reports. In addition to telephone access to call counts, this information should be confirmed weekly and/or monthly with written reports. The written reports should summarize interactive menu selections by callers, average hold times, and time of day for calls. The monthly reports should include a copy of the long distance carrier report as a further independent verification of call count numbers. A service bureau is often able to customize the written reports to meet any specific needs or requirements.

It is extremely important to be able to independently verify call count information. A reputable service bureau recognizes this need, and provides this service without being asked. It is very easy for a dishonest service bureau to fudge the numbers when there is no way of checking their accuracy.

6. Rotary capabilities. It is now possible to offer interactive audiotex services to rotary callers by using speech recognition, a new technology with the capability of recognizing the caller's spoken word, eliminating the need to use the touch tone keypad. Advanced Telecom Services, a service bureau located in Wayne, PA, has pioneered a voice recognition system called "Voice Tone." The caller simply states the menu number selection, and the computer recognizes the instruction,

or responds with, "speak louder," or "I did not understand that," if the caller's enunciation was not clear.

Although rotary callers may not be the best target market for most 900 programs, there are always notable exceptions to every rule. According to AT&T, 38.5 percent of all households are still on rotary telephones, with the heaviest concentration in older urban areas. Table 7-1 demonstrates the percentage of rotary telephones in several selected cities, and shows rotary usage by age group.

ROTARY PENETRATION IN SELECTED CITIES

City	%	City	%	City	%
Syracuse, NY	50%	Raleigh-Durham, NC	29	Orlando, FL	22
Poughkeepsie, NY	50	Dallas, TX	29	Columbia, SC	22
Buffalo, NY	50	Baltimore, MD	29	Albuquerque, NM	21
Binghamton, NY	50	Tampa, FL	27	Portland, OR	20
Albany, NY	50	San Francisco, CA	27	Miami, FL	20
New York, NY	49	Atlanta, GA	27	Detroit, MI	20
Columbus, OH	44	Springfield, MA	27	Chicago, IL	20
Pittsburgh, PA	42	San Jose, CA	25	Birmingham, AL	20
Philadelphia, PA	42	Houston, TX	25	Tucson, AZ	18
Cleveland, OH	40	Boston, MA	25	Salt Lake City, UT	18
Louisville, KY	39	San Diego, CA	23	Colorado Springs, CO	16
Stockton, CA	37	New Orleans, LA	23	Seattle, WA	14
Sacramento, CA	37	Minneapolis, MN	23	Jacksonville, FL	14
San Antonio, TX	35	Los Angeles, CA	23	Denver, CO	14
Fresno, CA	34	Fort Worth, TX	23	Phoenix, AZ	11
Charlotte, NC	33	Washington, DC	23		
Omaha, NE	30				

* US National Average: 38.5%

ROTARY USAGE BY AGE GROUP

Age	%
Under 25	11.5%
25 - 29	9.0
30 - 34	13.5
35 - 39	16.3
40 - 44	13.4
45 - 49	20.7
50 - 54	24.7
55 - 59	21.4
60 - 64	28.9
Over 65	43.4

Source: AT&T Inbound Conference, Orlando, FL, April 1991

Table 7-1

As this data indicates, without rotary capabilities, you stand to lose a significant percentage of the potential market in many of the older urban areas of the northeast and midwest. In some cases touch tone service simply isn't available in these areas, so it is not necessarily a negative reflection on the progressiveness of the population. They may in fact be good prospective 900 callers. For example, touch tone service simply isn't currently available in West Hartford, CT unless you purchase premium services such as call waiting or call transfer.

Notice also that the under 35 age group, the overall target market for pay-per-call, averages over 11% in rotary usage. Combine these lost prospects with those in the older urban areas, and a very significant percentage of the market is unable to call an interactive program that does not offer rotary capabilities.

West Interactive, in Omaha, Nebraska, is another service bureau that has recently begun offering rotary capabilities with voice recognition technology. As this technology matures and becomes more reliable at a lower cost, it is likely that many service bureaus will follow suit by adding rotary recognition services in the near future.

7. Turn-key programs. As I stated earlier, some service bureaus offer their own 900 programs for program sharing arrangements. Many of these service bureaus typically started as IPs, and purchased their own call-handling equipment. Because they have unused call-handling capacity, they can offer these services to other IPs. Tapping into someone else's successful program can be a very economical way of starting in the 900 business. On the other hand, if you are launching a new program that would compete with a turn-key program by the same service bureau, you will be in the uncomfortable position of competing with a company that is providing you with very important services, and with ready access to information about your business and its level of success.

8. Prices. Service bureaus generally require a one-time start-up fee to get your program on-line. This charge will often include the long distance carrier one-time charge, account set-up, and a certain amount of programming services. In a competitive market, however,

this fee can be completely waived or kept very small. In any case, this fee should rarely exceed $1000, and is very often quite a bit less.

Of more importance for an ongoing successful program are the monthly service fees and per-minute charges. The monthly fees can range from zero to a few hundred dollars, depending upon call volume, programming, and voice storage needs for the program. Many service bureaus will waive the monthly fee if call volume exceeds a certain level. The per-minute charges can range from 5 to 15 cents per minute, with 10 cents being about the norm. Again, many service bureaus will adjust the per-minute charge downward as call volume increases.

When comparing prices, make sure you get all relevant costs that will be required for your specific program, and then compare them at several different call volumes. A service bureau with very low monthly charges but high per minute charges will look good at low call volumes, but may be quite expensive once you start achieving the higher volumes.

Also, check out prices for other services such as transcription, custom reports, or voice storage. The relative importance of these costs will obviously depend upon the nature of your program needs. Beware of unusually low prices. There may be hidden charges, or the service bureau may be grasping for business because it's on the verge of going under.

9. Power interruption protection. Does the service bureau have a back-up generator or a bank of batteries to assure uninterrupted service during a power failure? This may not seem to be very important until you have invested lots of money in a heavy television promotion, only to lose thousands of calls because a violent thunderstorm knocked out power to your service bureau while your best TV spots were airing nationwide.

10. Remote program updating. Chances are you will have some kind of recorded interactive program that must be updated frequently. You should be able to accomplish this by calling the service bureau on a dedicated "editing line," which allows you to update the program

using your touch tone telephone along with an interactive menu designed specifically for updating your program.

Choosing the Service Bureau

First of all, carefully outline all of your program needs. Do you need live operators? Professional voice talent? Are rotary callers a potential part of your target market? Do you require a lot of voice storage? Then, plan ahead and try to anticipate future needs. Will you add additional telephone lines to the program? Will you launch new programs? Will you eventually try your hand at television advertising?

Once you have a good handle on current and future program needs, plus all the relevant price information from several prospective service bureaus, you should be able to narrow down your choices to a few leading candidates. At this point it is imperative to ask for references, and then follow through and contact each one.

In the final analysis, the service bureau will be your partner in profit. Like any other partnership, there must be two-way trust and respect. Even the largest service bureau should recognize that you're just starting your program, and that it will take time for call counts to grow. It should be willing to help even the smallest IP in every way it can to assure success for the IP's new program. After all, the service bureau makes most of its money on the per-minute call revenue, so it's in its best interest to help you be as successful as possible.

See Appendix F for a comprehensive listing of service bureaus, arranged alphabetically by state. Although there are obvious benefits to working with a company that is located nearby, like seeing how your money is spent, keep in mind that geographic proximity is not critically important. The service bureau's capabilities, services, prices and reputation are much more important.

Chapter 8
Financial Projections

Now you have at least tentatively selected both a 900 program and a reputable service bureau. How do you know whether your program will be financially successful? Frankly, you really won't know for sure until after you have actually launched the program. Nevertheless, realistic financial projections will serve as a helpful road map on your journey to success. The heart of any business plan are the financial projections and the assumptions behind them. This is the final step before making the decision to launch your program. A realistic evaluation of the numbers may indicate that the program may not succeed as expected, allowing you to pull the plug before spending any more money. On the other hand, unrealistic, overly optimistic revenue expectations may result in losing a considerable investment with an unsuccessful program.

This part of the process is called "number crunching." Many people are afraid of numbers and avoid them like the plague. But virtually every successful businessman or entrepreneur is very good at number crunching. Cash is the lifeblood of any business. Only when it's coming in faster than it goes out does the business stay healthy.

Any new business must be prepared for a net outflow of cash for the first few months of operation, and if you don't budget enough for cash transfusions, you won't last long enough to eventually become successful. It's called undercapitalization, and many potentially successful companies have failed for lack of sufficient start-up capital.

Start-up Costs

You are now in a position to calculate all one-time start-up costs associated with launching your program. The following is a fairly comprehensive listing of typical start-up costs, but there may be other costs unique to your program or situation, so don't forget to include them as well:

1. Research. This includes purchasing this book, subscribing to trade publications, calling 900 numbers to see how potential competitors operate, travelling to visit a service bureau, or attending a pay-per-call trade show.

2. Service bureau start-up fee. We discussed this earlier, but make sure you haven't overlooked programming costs or voice talent charges.

3. Advertising development. This includes creative graphics work for print advertising copy or production costs for TV or radio commercials. Although classified as start-up costs, these costs will become recurring costs as ads are changed or new ads are tested.

4. Source information. There may be a one-time fee for access to the information or entertainment featured on your program, such as a licensing fee for a 900 telephone game.

5. Equipment. Depending upon the nature of your program, you may need to purchase a computer, a fax machine, or office furniture.

6. Legal and accounting. As a new business, you may wish to incorporate. You may want your attorney to review your contract with your service bureau. If you offer a contest feature, you will need expert legal help setting up the contest rules and procedures. You may want an accountant to set up your bookkeeping system.

After you have assigned realistic numbers to these categories, plus any others unique to your program, you will have a good estimate of how much it will cost to get your business off the ground. This figure will not include, however, the reserve capital you will need to cover any monthly operating deficits in the first few months of operation.

Recurring Monthly Costs

These are essentially fixed monthly expenses that are incurred regardless of the level of volume or revenue achieved. What makes or breaks a business is being able to regularly cover these fixed expenses with sufficient revenue. Needless to say, the monthly profit is the amount by which revenue exceeds these expenses:

1. Service bureau fee. As stated before, the service bureau will usually charge a minimum monthly fee unless a certain minimum call volume is exceeded.

2. Telephone. This will apply if you install a separate business line. Or, if working from home, you should keep track of long distance charges associated with your business.

3. Space. Office rent, if applicable, plus utilities.

4. Payroll. This includes not only salaries, but also payroll taxes, benefits, and any other costs associated with having employees.

5. Insurance. This will normally be limited to office contents, tenant betterments, or business interruption type coverages.

6. Office supplies. From staples to stationary, even the smallest home business can spend $100 or more a month on such supplies.

7. Interest. This applies if you took out a loan to finance the start-up of your business.

8. Program source information. Any applicable costs associated with getting your program information on a regular basis.

9. Miscellaneous. There are always numerous costs which don't fit nicely into any given category, or there may be unique cost elements associated with your program.

10. Advertising. Advertising is not really a fixed monthly cost. You could elect to spend nothing and quickly go out of business.

Nonetheless, you should establish a monthly advertising budget and stick to it. And this should be the largest expense category in your budget.

Variable Costs

Variable costs are tied to the volume of business activity. In a pay-per-call business, the variable costs are the per-minute charges that go to the long distance carrier and the service bureau. For example, using a simple $1 per minute call charge, the variable costs would be broken down as shown in table 8-1.

These variable costs will change for different long distance carriers and service bureaus. Furthermore, the variable costs will likely be reduced for higher call volumes, so your revenue projections should be based upon a realistic range of several levels of call volume.

VARIABLE COSTS		
	Per minute	
Gross revenue		$1.00
Less variable costs:		
IXC transport fee	0.30	
IXC billing & collection fee (10%)	0.10	
Service Bureau fee	0.10	
Total variable costs		(0.50)
Net revenue		$0.50

Table 8-1

The typical transport fee for long distance 900 services ranges from 28 to 32 cents per minute, but can go as high as 44 cents a minute (see Appendix H). It should be noted here, however, that LEC transport fees for regional 976 services are much lower, usually 10 cents or less per minute. A 976 pay-per-call program would obviously be more cost-effective for any kind of limited regional program application. The same variable cost models can be used as shown - simply substitute the appropriate LEC fees for the corresponding IXC fees.

A flat rate call charge for a program with a set call hold time would be calculated in a similar manner as the per-minute example in table 8-1, except that volumes would be based upon the number of calls, not the number of minutes. A program featuring a dual price structure, for example, $2 the first minute and then $1 each additional minute, would be treated as shown in table 8-2. Notice that the extra dollar earned for the first minute is subject only to the 10% billing and collection fee. In order to be able to properly project revenue, assumptions must be made concerning both number of calls and the average duration of each call.

VARIABLE COSTS - DUAL PRICE STRUCTURE		
	First minute	Each minute
Gross revenue	$1.00	$1.00

Less variable costs:
    IXC transport fee
    IXC billing & collection fee (10%)
    Service Bureau fee
        Total variable costs
	
	0.10
	
	(0.10)
		
		.30
		0.10
		0.10
		(0.50)

Net revenue	$0.90	$0.50

Table 8-2

For example, assuming the average hold time for each call is 5 minutes, monthly net call revenue would be calculated as shown in table 8-3. Notice that every minute earns 50 cents in net revenue, while every <u>first</u> minute earns an extra 90 cents.

DUAL PRICING REVENUE	
Number of calls	1000
Call minutes	5000
1st. minute revenue (1000 X $0.90)	$ 900
Per minute revenue (5000 X $0.50)	$2,500
Total net revenue	$3,400

Table 8-3

Projecting Revenue

Costs can be fairly accurately identified. Potential revenue, on the other hand, is much more difficult to pin down. Statistical information on response rates and call volumes for different kinds of 900 programs just isn't yet readily available, and probably never will be. The industry is still too new, and this kind of information is often jealously guarded by the IPs.

Nonetheless, you have to start somewhere. The key to projecting revenue is determining a realistic response rate to your advertising. If you have targeted 500,000 readers/viewers/listeners, how many of them are likely to call your program? One out of 100? More? A lot less?

If you're offering a specialized service that permits precise rifle shot marketing, the response rates will be higher than with a program targeted to a more general market. However, there are no ready formulas to help you predict what rate of response you might achieve, not until you launch your program and conduct some actual market testing. We'll talk more about this in the next chapter.

What kind of numbers should you begin with? Well, a 5% response rate, even for the most precise rifle shot marketing, would be wildly optimistic. A new program, in its early stages of market exposure, will probably pull less than 1% in overall response. To be conservative you should start with a number well under 1%.

Say you're advertising a specialized service in a well-targeted monthly magazine with a circulation of 500,000 readers. You decide that an initial response rate in the range of 0.25% to 0.75% would be realistic. By the way, response rates should be based upon circulation, not readership, and the response rate is applied to each issue in which your ad is published.

Let's further assume that your call charge is $1 per minute, and the average hold time is five minutes, which, using the previous variable cost example in table 8-1, results in a net revenue per call of $2.50 ($0.50 X 5 minutes). Also, lets assume that a decent size display ad costs $5000 per issue. Table 8-4 summarizes the projected revenue at response rates ranging from 0.25% to 0.75%.

REVENUE PROJECTIONS			
	Response rates		
	Low: 0.25%	Medium: 0.50%	High: 0.75%
Calls per month/issue (500 K circulation X response rate)	1,250	2,500	3,750
Total call minutes (calls X 5 min./call)	6,250	12,500	18,750
Net call revenue per month (# calls X $2.50)	$ 3,125	$ 6,250	$ 9,375
Cost of ad	($5,000)	($5,000)	($5,000)
Net revenue after ad cost	($1,875)	$1,250	$4,375

Table 8-4

The net call revenue must cover all of the recurring monthly costs, including the $5000 per month advertising budget.

Now let's make some further assumptions regarding your monthly expenses and variable costs. We'll assume that you're working from home, with very low overhead and no payroll costs. The total monthly expenses are summarized in table 8-5.

MONTHLY EXPENSES	
Service bureau fee	$ 300.00*
Advertising (budgeted)	5,000.00
Other/miscellaneous	700.00
Total monthly expenses	$6,000.00

* the service bureau fee is zero if a total of 7,500 call minutes are achieved per month, and if call volume exceeds 15,000 minutes per month, the service bureau per-minute charge is reduced from $0.10 to $0.07.

Table 8-5

Using these assumptions, the revenue projections will be somewhat different, as outlined in table 8-6, which takes into account different service bureau charges at various volume levels in arriving at the bottom line net income.

Table 8-6 demonstrates how both variable costs (the service bureau per-minute charge) and fixed monthly costs (the service bureau monthly charge for call volume less than 7500 minutes) will be different at various projected levels of anticipated call volume. For this reason, it is always a good idea to project call volumes at several levels within the expected range.

In this example, the lower response rate may be realistic for the first few months after the program is initially launched, and the higher rates would be achieved after the program benefits from longer media exposure and repeat calls from satisfied customers. Obviously, the initial capitalization costs must be sufficient to cover both start-up as well as any anticipated operating deficits for the first few months of operation. Further, once you start earning positive revenues, you must account for the time delay in receiving your first check from the service bureau, which will be a function of both the IXC and the service bureau collection and accounting policies. A delay of 30 to 60 days is not uncommon, and check with your service bureau for the exact timing of call revenue payments.

NET INCOME PROJECTIONS			
	Response rates		
	low: 0.25%	med: 0.50%	high: 0.75%
Calls per month	1,250	2,500	3,750
Total call minutes	6,250	12,500	18,750
Net revenue: a. $0.50/min.($0.10 SB fee) b. $0.53/min.($0.07 SB fee)	$3,125	$6,250	$9,938
Less monthly expenses: Service bureau Advertising Other	$ 300 $5,000 $ 700	-0- $5,000 $ 700	-0- $5,000 $ 700
Total expenses	($6,000)	($5,700)	($5,700)
Net income (loss)	($2,875)	$ 550	$4,238

Table 8-6

Before projecting revenue, you must first establish the charge for your program. And it had better be realistic. A charge of $5 per minute might work for live technical advice, but if your program is an interactive game, your revenue projections might look quite impressive, but in reality it's very likely nobody will call your program.

In Chapter 2 we saw numerous examples of 900 applications, along with the call charges in effect. There was a reason for including the charges. It was to give you a handle on what IPs are charging for different kinds of programs. Also, in researching your competitor's programs you will find out what they are charging. Your charges had better be in line with these numbers, or even lower, or you will be headed for real trouble.

Breakeven Analysis

A useful financial tool is calculating the revenue or volume that must be achieved in order to cover fixed costs, also known as breakeven analysis. At levels below this number, operating deficits result, and above this number, surplus or profit is earned.

Using the previous example, we know that the net call revenue per minute is $0.50, and that the fixed monthly expenses are $6000. The breakeven volume level is calculated as follows:

$$\$6000 / \$0.50 = 12,000 \text{ minutes}$$

This demonstrates that we must generate 12,000 call minutes per month in order to breakeven on expenses, and this translates to 2400 calls (12000 / 5 minutes per call) per month.

We can also work backwards to determine what advertising response rate we must achieve in order to breakeven:

$$2400 \text{ calls} / 500,000 \text{ circulation} = 0.48\%$$

Breakeven analysis gives us a concrete number that serves as a target or goal to exceed as quickly as possible. Financial success, or profit, is measured by the amount by which the breakeven point is exceeded.

For example, if a volume of 20,000 call minutes is achieved in a given month, the net profit for that month can be quickly computed:

$$20,000 - 12,000 = 8,000$$

$$8,000 \text{ X } \$0.50 = \$4,000$$

The 8000 minutes that exceed the breakeven point are pure gravy, and the full $0.50 per minute net call revenue is applied to each minute above the 12,000 breakeven point.

Knowing your breakeven point allows you to quickly compute your profit or loss, so you will know at a glance how well you did for the past month.

Please keep in mind that the preceding example should in no way imply that you will generate a similar response rate to your advertising. A response rate to carefully targeted direct mail marketing in the range of 1% to 3% is often considered quite good, and may be achieved only after extensive testing. And remember, direct mail is the most precisely focused rifle shot marketing available, allowing for a lengthy and compelling sales message. Be careful, therefore, about being too optimistic about anticipated response rates. Better to be prepared for the worst case scenario, only to be pleasantly surprised later by better results.

Larry Werner of CommVox (a service bureau) put it quite well: "I've never met a pessimistic entrepreneur. There isn't enough equipment capacity to handle all the projected call volume expected by optimistic entrepreneurs."

Chapter 9
Measurement
and Testing

Even though you have already conducted thorough market research and have selected some very promising media sources for your initial advertising, you can't stop here. Advertising is your largest expense category, and it will pay off handsomely to be able to spend your advertising budget as cost-effectively as possible.

As we saw in the last chapter, even small variations in the rate of response to an ad resulted in significant changes in the projected revenue. To get the biggest bang for your advertising buck, you have to be able to somehow measure the effectiveness of your advertising. What we're really looking for here is the lowest cost-per-response.

Advertising measurement and testing is an extremely important function for any business. Hundreds of books have been written about this subject. Many highly educated professional people are paid impressive salaries for their expertise in this field. It is a fascinating science unto itself. But it all boils down to finding out the lowest cost for generating a response or purchase.

Fortunately, the pay-per-call industry has a unique characteristic shared by few other businesses: direct, immediate response. When your 900 program ad hits the streets or the airwaves, most of your response will be immediate.

Coca Cola or General Motors do not benefit from such direct response, and they have to spend a lot of money on measurement information which is by nature quite subjective. Think about it, do you remember what specific advertising motivated you to purchase your last automobile? Well, the manufacturer doesn't really know either.

Testing ads of different sizes and types, in different media, and then measuring the results, will eventually result in finding out what works best for your program. Indeed, the process never ends. There are literally hundreds of ways you can vary any given ad, and it takes time to test every possible variation. The measurement and testing process in an ongoing effort for the life of any business.

How is effectiveness actually measured? Using the example from the last chapter, we were spending $5000 to generate a response, of say 0.5%, or 2500 calls, at an average net revenue per 5 minute call of $2.50. The total cost-per-response was $2 ($5000/2500 calls). Fortunately, the net revenue per call exceeded the cost per call. Now lets say we tested a different publication. The ad cost is $3000, and a total of 2000 calls are generated from the ad. The cost per response in this case is $1.50 ($3000/2000 calls). This is obviously a better investment than the first example. Although the total number of calls are lower, you must ask yourself whether it would be better to spend more of your advertising budget on larger ads in this publication while dropping the other publication altogether. Yes, both publications are actually making money, but one of them is making money more cost-effectively than the other.

This decision shouldn't be made too hastily, however. Doubling the size of the ad will not necessarily double the response. It may increase response only slightly, or it could triple response. You won't know for sure until you try it. Or, you may find that a smaller ad is even more cost-effective. A $1000 ad pulling 1000 calls costs only $1 per response. This would allow you to spread your advertising budget out into other media, leaving some left over for your ongoing testing efforts.

Another consideration is market saturation. Any specific publication has a relatively static group of subscribers or readers. After an initial rise in response rates, you may in fact experience a gradual drop-off after all of the likely callers have tried your program. This is particularly true for novelty programs such as games. If and when this happens, it might be advisable to switch to a similar type publication for a fresh group of likely callers.

If your program features valuable information with many repeat callers, continued advertising to those callers might not be very cost-effective because they are calling despite the ads. You might try stopping the ad for a couple of months to measure the drop-off in call volume.

Advertising Schedule

Accurate measurement is possible only when calls can be reasonably tied to specific advertising. It will be impossible to measure the effectiveness of any given ad if several are published nearly simultaneously in various publications or media. There are ways around this problem, however, which will be discussed later. Nonetheless, in the absence of a methodology for differentiating the response, the only way to properly measure results is to space the timing of the advertising such that the response from each ad can be determined before the next ad is published or aired.

Fortunately, each media type has unique characteristics relating to their typical time of response periods. For example, radio and TV are essentially immediate. As long as you know the station's schedule for airing your spots, you will be able to measure response on an hourly basis. Nearly all the response to your spot will occur during or shortly after the ad is aired.

A monthly magazine, on the other hand, will have the longest response period. It may lie around for several months before being discarded, resulting in calls months after the ad first appears.

Nevertheless, most of the call volume resulting from a magazine ad will occur during the first two weeks after the on sale date.

A weekly newspaper will be similar to a monthly magazine, except that most of the response will be experienced during the half-week after the on sale date instead of the first half-month.

Knowing these characteristics of different media types, you can in fact conduct advertising in various media fairly close together. For example, a TV spot which is run a week after a monthly print ad appears will hopefully result in a measurable spike in call volume just after the spot airs. By subtracting the average daily counts from the total for the day the TV spot aired, a reasonable estimate can be made for the TV response alone.

The actual advertising schedule can be a simple wall or desk calendar that notes the on sale or air dates for all advertising, plus the daily and/or hourly call counts. Tracking call counts by the hour will be necessary only if using TV or radio advertising.

Caution! Do not make any long-term commitments for advertising until you have completed at least some initial testing with that media company. You will be enticed with lower-cost ads for making a commitment to repeat advertising with any media company. You must resist this temptation until you are convinced, through actual testing and measurement, that the response rates justify allocating a significant portion of your advertising budget on a long-term basis.

Testing Strategies

We have talked about several different variables that may influence the response rate to your ad, and it will be instructive to summarize all the variables here:

1. The medium. Radio, TV, print, or novelty. Rifle shot or shotgun.

2. Ad size or length. Full page or quarter page, 60 second or 30 second.

3. Ad appearance or design. How well does it grab attention and induce people to read the ad.

4. Ad copy. Does the ad copy successfully induce the target audience to take action? Does it follow the AIDA principle (Chapter 6)?

5. Timing. Does the ad appear when your target market is most likely to call? Time of day will be important for radio or TV, whereas seasonal factors might effect response to magazine ads. The Christmas edition, for example, may be more carefully read because people have more leisure time during the holidays.

6. Price. The price of the information service will likely influence the response rate, so it may be prudent to test different price structures.

Start multiplying out the options for each of these variables and you can end up with hundreds of different combinations. It would take years to test all possible combinations if you had to rely on adequate time spacing alone for proper response measurement. Plus, a true test will take more than one repetition for each ad. How can you streamline the testing process in order to get measurable results more quickly?

First, you can use smaller local or regional media sources before launching a national advertising campaign. In order to measure response, you will simply need to know where the calls originate from. This can be accomplished two ways: Automatic Number Identification (ANI) or Online Call Detail Data (OCDD). Either way, you will know where each call originated, by area code, so you can test different ads in different regions at the same time.

ANI information is provided monthly by the IXC to the service bureau in the form of raw data, including the originating caller's telephone number, date and time of call, and call duration. A sophisticated service bureau will then collate the data in any way you require: by originating area code, hold time, or time of day. You receive a monthly report which tells you where your calls are coming from.

OCDD information is not as detailed as ANI, and is typically limited to summarizing call volumes from different telephone area codes or states. Nonetheless, OCDD information is more timely, available weekly instead of monthly, and it is typically less expensive to receive than ANI.

Depending upon how sophisticated you want to get with your response measurement, you may elect to receive both sources of information. Make sure your service bureau can provide this service and check out the costs involved.

Either ANI or OCDD permits you to advertise simultaneously in several geographic markets without losing track of which ads draw what response. Another possibility is the use of different telephone extension numbers displayed with each ad. The caller is simply instructed to press the appropriate number, and the monthly call report will break down the calls by extension number. Although less expensive, this option complicates the program and could be perceived in a negative light by the target market.

Unfortunately, testing different price structures for the program isn't quite so simple. Virtually all program preambles are required to include a statement giving the price of the call, and all associated advertising must obviously match this information. The only way, therefore, to test more than one price is to use separate 900 numbers that tie into separate programs with appropriate preamble price information. This results in additional costs associated with adding another 900 number plus any programming costs for using different preambles with the program.

Despite the additional expense, it could be well worth it to test different pricing. Although the net call revenue per minute will be lower, a lower priced service may result in a significant increase in call volume which more than compensates for the lower per-minute revenue. Also, having a second number in place allows you to experiment with other program changes, including the script, voice talent, format, or even adding a promotional incentive for calling.

Customer Database

The ability to know your customers, by name and address, could be quite valuable. They have already called your program once, and a follow-up direct mail piece could be a cost-effective means of generating additional calls from these people. Perhaps you could include a business card or Rolodex card for handy reference to your 900 service. As long as they have been satisfied customers, your previous customer base is by far the most likely group to call your program again and again. You have already spent a lot of money in advertising to find these people, and now you want to try and keep them.

How do you get the name and address of people who call your program? One way is to simply ask for it. Offer a prize or other promotional incentive, and include a menu slot in the program for the caller to leave his or her name and address.

Another way is by using the ANI data. With ANI you already have the telephone numbers, and now you need to match telephone numbers with names and addresses. There are data service companies that provide this kind of service. One such service, offered by The Times Journal Company, is called Telematch. This company offers computerized reverse matching of names and addresses to telephone numbers. In fact, it also offers "Telename," a reverse directory assistance 900 service which does the same thing. The number is 1-900-884-1212, and the charge is $1.50 the first minute, and 75 cents each additional minute. Simply give the operator the telephone number (including area code), and she will check the database of over 65 million residential listings for the corresponding name and address. Unlisted telephone numbers are not included in its database.

Telematch
6883 Commercial Dr.
Springfield, VA 22159
1-800-523-7346

Your in-house mailing list of self-generated leads could become one of your most effective marketing tools. Although unsolicited direct mail is probably not cost-effective for most 900 programs, direct mail follow-up to previous customers is a different ballgame. They have already called once, and it probably won't take much effort to get them to call again. Repeat business from satisfied customers is the most cost-effective way to build up call volume and revenue.

Chapter 10
The 900 Roundtable

The following industry experts have generously contributed their time and experience in addressing some of the most commonly asked questions by start-up IPs. The 900 industry is widely represented here, including IPs, service bureaus, telephone companies and supporting companies and organizations. The format is structured much like a live roundtable discussion, with the participants answering a series of topical questions. A lot of knowledge and experience is represented here, and you will be wise to pay careful attention to what these people have to say.

The Participants

Bob Bentz, Director of Marketing, Advanced Telecom Services, Inc., a service bureau with offices in suburban Philadelphia, London and Toronto. He also authored the other major book on the 900 industry, *Opportunity is Calling* (see Appendix C).

Ellie Ryan, Senior Manager, 900 Business Unit, MCI, a major long distance carrier second in size only to AT&T. Because participation in this roundtable was a collaborative effort of several people in the MCI 900 Business Unit, answers will be credited to MCI instead of any individual person.

Gene Chamson, founder and President, Intermedia Resources, Inc., an IP, consulting firm and reseller of 900 services, based in Oakland, California. Prior to launching Intermedia Resources, Gene worked as a planning engineer with AT&T; then served as the Product Development Manager for *California 900* at Pacific Bell; and capped his experience as the Manager of New Product Development for Automated Call Processing (ACP), a leading 900 IP and service bureau, where he helped develop interactive voice applications for clients such as *Fortune* Magazine, Reuters, Charles Schwab, *Consumer Reports, Sports Illustrated* and many other well-known companies.

Antoinette (Toni) Moore, President, Moore Telecommunication Consultants, San Diego, California. Toni has been training and consulting in the audiotex business since 1987. She authored *Dialing For Dollars* (Appendix C), publishes the monthly newsletter *900 NewsReport* (Appendix A), and is a frequent guest on radio and TV talk shows.

Henry Wener, President/CEO, RENEW Interactive Marketing Services, Inc., a service bureau based in Totowa, New Jersey. Henry has over 30 years of experience in direct response marketing and telemarketing, and has written articles published in *Telemarketing, Teleprofessional, PROMO, Direct,* and *TARGET Marketing.*

Carol Morse Ginsburg, editor and publisher of *Audiotex News,* the leading industry newsletter, entering its sixth year of publication. Carol is an industry veteran who has been featured on CNBC's *Steals & Deals* talking about the industry as well as numerous radio programs. Widely quoted in the media, she has been featured in such publications as *Small Business Opportunity Magazine, Audiotex Briefings, Advance Magazine, Cable & Broadcast, Newsday* and the *Los Angeles Times.* She is the U.S. editor for *World Telemedia,* the international pay-per-call/audiotex magazine.

Donald Young, President, New Tech Telemedia, based in Chicago. In business for 34 years, Don developed the second voice messaging system after VMX, Voice & Data Systems. Sold it to Canadians. Operated a service bureau since 1982. Started Information

Command which combined with Stargate Communications as New Tech telemedia in June, 1993. President Mid America Information Services Association (MISA), a 5-state organization serving as a forum for carriers, information providers, related services, and as a stimulus to doing business within the "fraternity" of telephone-related companies. On the national board of NAIS.

Peter J. Brennan, Director of Voice Information Services for the Phoenix Media/Communications Group, Publishers of the *Boston Phoenix, Providence Phoenix* and *Worcester Phoenix*. He is Director of Development for Tele-Publishing, Inc. of Boston, a leading voice information service bureau. Mr. Brennan is a past Chair of the Voice Information Services Division of the Information Industry Association, and is a frequent public speaker and published expert in the field of voice services, technology, legislation and applications. Mr. Brennan has offered testimony before both houses of the US Congress, various Attorneys General and Public Utility commissions, and has been published in *InfoText Magazine, Telemarketing Magazine* and *Information Times*.

Mike Urbanski, Product Marketing Manager, AT&T MultiQuest 900®. The AT&T Roundtable answers have been provided by the AT&T MultiQuest 900® Service Product Team. The six-person team contained a combined total of 83 years telephony experience, including account executive, sales manager, applications consultant, product & marketing managers and international network design. The team was led by Mike Urbanski, Product Marketing Manager, based in Bridgewater, NJ. AT&T is not only the largest long distance telephone company, but also the largest carrier of long distance 900 services.

The Roundtable

In one sentence, how would you define 900 pay-per-call services?

Toni Moore: A service that provides access to immediate

information, entertainment, and exchange of personal opinions on a pay-for-use basis.

Gene Chamson: 900 pay-per-call services are special phone numbers where the caller pays a fixed rate to hear information or receive a service provided by an independent sponsor, who sets the rate for the call and receives the proceeds after billing and collection by the telephone carrier.

Peter Brennan: 900 services provide a billing mechanism for a telephonic information transaction.

Mike Urbanski: A telecommunications service that allows a program sponsor to offer callers the opportunity to listen to recorded messages, speak with and/or ask questions of subject-matter-experts or to access computer data bases and is distinguished by the fact that the caller generally pays for the message.

When should a 900 number be considered the medium of choice, instead of, for example, a newsletter?

MCI: When it is interactive, or when it needs to be a real time transaction.

Toni Moore: 900 numbers should be considered when the perceived value of the program is enhanced by immediacy, real-time information, convenience and/or anonymity. Any or all of these may be a deciding factor, plus the convenience of billing that is not dependent upon possession of a credit card, or the IP's ability to accept credit card billing.

Henry Wener: When information is very timely or just a short piece of information is needed.

Gene Chamson: A 900 number should be considered the

medium of choice for delivering information that is timely, changes rapidly, is concise, and is not otherwise easily available from other sources. Often, newsletters and 900 numbers can work together, and shouldn't be viewed as substitutes. For example, many publishers of stock market newsletters have discovered that 900 numbers provide an effective way of getting out their latest buy/sell recommendations, but they don't take the place of the printed newsletter which can go into more depth, provide a larger volume of information, and present graphs and pictures. Usually a newsletter is a good way to promote a 900 number and vice versa.

Mike Urbanski: In selecting 900 Service as a medium of choice a company or individual goes through a series of minor decisions that can lead to the ultimate choice. Some twenty years ago, AT&T developed an acronym that helped clients through a similar decision process. The acronym is FUDVLAC.

F... FUNCTION: What is the purpose of the communication... to prospect, education, encourage participation?

U... URGENCY: Is the material time-sensitive? How will a delay in communications affect its importance? Is timing critical?

D... DISTRIBUTION: How many people need to receive your message? In how many locations?

V...VOLUME: How long is the message? With what frequency will you repeat it?

L... LANGUAGE: Is your message one that is best spoken, or does it require supporting documentation? Is your audience bi-lingual/multi-lingual?

A... ACCURACY: All forms of communications must be accurate, however, this process requires you to predict how your message will be received, its retention needs and what you want the audience to do.

C... COST: When, after evaluating the other components of this acronym, you must match the requirements with your expectations. You might have to go back and reevaluate your needs, or maybe just a fine-tuning is in order.

Selecting 900 Service over alternative mediums requires as much planning, analysis and attention as you would give to any other major communications channel.

Once the medium has been determined, other factors come into play. RELIABILITY, INNOVATION AND ONGOING CONSULTATION must be available and should be part of the decision in selecting your 900 Service carrier.

What types of services have been successful in the past, and why?

Toni Moore: Personal services such as date-lines and psychic lines proved to be very lucrative, however the market is experiencing an oversaturation in these areas. There are many IPs now vying for the same market share. The curiosity factor that created a percentage of the calls has also lessened.

Henry Wener: Comedy, soap operas, horoscopes, sport news because they were a novelty.

Gene Chamson: I believe the types of services which have been successful have had one or more of the following characteristics: 1) They take advantage of the convenience and timeliness of providing a service by phone. Examples would include sports and lottery results, sports picks, and stock market recommendations. 2) They have a well known sponsor, whose name and reputation gives credibility and appeal to the service. Examples would include *Wall Street Journal's* Journal Phone, Jeane Dixon's horoscopes, *Consumer Reports'* Car Pricing Service - each of these services has been successful while "generic" versions of similar services have come and gone. 3) They take advantage of a sponsor's ability to advertise a service inexpensively in their own media. For example, newspapers, magazines and cable TV stations have been successful with 900 numbers like stock quotes and sports scores which never would have survived in they had to pay regular advertising rates to promote them. And 4) They appeal to people's basic needs in an impulsive way, providing an "instant fix." In this category I would include sex lines, date lines, chat lines, horoscopes, psychics, games and jokes. The truth is people are often lonely, bored, or depressed, and these 900 numbers provide some short-term relief.

Mike Urbanski: Successful applications have included simple information dissemination, i.e., product or corporate announcements, "help services" and consumer information lines. More recently, 900 Services have been successfully deployed by the computer hardware/software industry to offer a different level of technical support services to vintage equipment owners, and out-of-warranty software users. Some also use 900 numbers for the introduction of lower-priced products.

Well funded, high quality, value-added entertainment applications provided by broadcasters and consumer goods companies have also had success using 900 Service. For example, using the AT&T Vari-A-Bill℠ feature, funding-raising applications can give the caller a quick and easy way to support charities and select a donation level.

What kinds of services will be successful in the future, and why?

Carol Morse Ginsburg: Entertainment has a place and always will. The public is accustomed to paying for entertainment, be it movies or miniature golf. Consumers want information, and they want it fast. Applications, business or otherwise, can utilize that concept and have it work for them.

When people look for help, they want it immediately. So lines that provide aid for your computer, your finances, your kid's problems, and legal, medical and marital predicaments lines will have their place. Look for the advent of the home fax to play a part in the future of 900. Let's face it, some information is better suited to the printed page than audiotex.

Bob Bentz: Joint ventures with niche media sources will remain successful. Voice personals continue to grow in public acceptance and will continue to be good producers. Sports handicapping is a solid investment because it permits a high priced call, interactive fax-on-demand has tremendous potential that will be fully realized when the fax machine becomes as common in homes as the VCR.

Toni Moore: The services that will prosper and survive into the next decade will be those that offer timely, and valuable services, such as: consultation; technical assistance, access to current and detailed data-bases, and possibly order-entry capabilities. It is my opinion that once the industry has stabilized, and the public sees the true value, fulfillment of approved products will be billable via phone bills.

Henry Wener: Timely information about how to use a product. Advice services about cars, energy, software, etc.

Gene Chamson: Mass market 900 services will become the domain of large firms, media companies, and well known brand sponsors. The future of 900 services for the entrepreneur who doesn't have access to any of these is in specialized or niche market applications. For example, I expect we'll see more live professional advice services where the caller can get expert advice in a variety of specialized areas on demand. I also think we'll see more use of 900 numbers with targeted media like newsletters and cable TV. And as the technology for retrieving information by fax becomes more widespread, I think there will be a flock of new applications combining fax-on-demand with 900 numbers.

Donald Young: In the future of 900 will most likely trend to consumer services unless the newly-discovered "business-only" 900 exchanges take off. Most businesses block 900, and the probability of consumers using the 900 line for any but important information, or that for which they are reimbursed in coupons, has a low likelihood of surviving. Until the FCC mandates disconnects for those who do not pay their 900 bill, the industry will spend too much time and money concerning itself with this critical no-pay issue. Legal, medical, therapeutic, financial services should rise in popularity with this home group.

Mike Urbanski: Opportunities for 900 Numbers in the future are dependent upon consumers' demand for expedience and non-traditional service options. Programs could involve fax-back document requests to support time sensitive information, as well as technical applications. In addition, on-line software exchange and updates, access to electronic bulletin boards, and other computer based applications are natural partners with pay-per-transaction services. The acceptance of the AT&T Business to Business Exchange (900-555) will see an increase in business usage as more and more telecommunications managers program their companies PBXs to allow calls to specific 900-555 numbers without fear that employees can call non-business programs.

Gazing harder into the crystal ball, there may be opportunities in the area of product or catalog fulfillment with payment via a single or multiple 900 call(s). Pay-per-view television may look to offer alternate billing methods through 900 calling for access to movies, educational programs, and special events.

What, if any, has been the common element found in most successful 900 applications?

Carol Morse Ginsburg: A line is considered successful when it is a money maker. There are three elements that most successful lines have in common.

One - they fulfill a need or a want. Will people call your number? Yes, if it fulfills a need. Does anyone want the information you are providing? Is the information you are providing easily obtained - free or at a low cost - from other sources? Of course, there is competition; but the question is - do you have a different spin than the competition does? Do you know how to reach that market?

Two - they generate repeat callers. Advertising is expensive;

therefore repeat callers are the backbone of a successful program.

Three - they give value - real and perceived. Callers who when they hang up feel they have gotten good value are the callers who will keep the number and call back another day.

Bob Bentz: A media partnership joint venture almost guarantees success.

Toni Moore: The common element is offering the callers the promised value, and ensuring the advertisements give a clear picture of what the caller will receive. There are some 900 lines that are financially successful for short periods of time due to their appeal to a gullible public, however these are short-lived, and the public will eventually become more aware of such "scams" and the free giveaways that entice callers to call a 900 number to register their prize.

Peter Brennan: The most successful services are those that combine the following ingredients in a variety of proportions: (a) time critical information - ie., the latest sports result or business report - and (b) value to the caller - ie., novelty, convenience, content of specific interest. Furthermore, services have succeeded when they have capitalized on a buyer's impulse and when they have been enhanced by the imprimatur of a recognizable provider of content in other forms - ie., newspapers, TV stations, etc.

Mike Urbanski: The common element found in all successful corporate 900 service applications has been the ability to integrate the new channel into the total business plan. Pay-per-call service is receiving support, at the highest levels in our client corporations, equal to that of other channels in the business or marketing mix, such as telemarketing, advertising, and direct mail. Consistent with successful applications, whether the Information Provider is a corporation or an individual, is the element of "commitment."

Commitment to the idea, by itself, isn't enough! The belief that you are providing value for a fair price to your audience and the dedication to that value/price relationship is vital to its success.

When IPs elect to use 900 Service, they must decide they are in it "for the long haul." Quick "get-rich-quick" schemes and immediate high volume programs are not the reality.

What has been the major cause of failure for most new 900 programs?

Carol Morse Ginsburg: Not selecting the right service bureau. After deciding to go into the 900 business, probably the most important decision an IP will make is the selection of a service bureau. The service bureau is the link to the long distance carrier. The right one will hold your hand, and hopefully, send you checks. They are responsible for the record keeping, programming and servicing of the equipment. Additionally, they can help plan your budget, give advice about advertising and marketing, and advise on program viability and design. IPs need to spend time on checking out the service bureau.

Not knowing where or how to advertise and not having sufficient funds to do so is another major cause of failure, as are unrealistic expectations about the industry. A caller once complained he had paid $54 for advertising and hadn't gotten any calls.

Bob Bentz: Unrealistic expectations through inflated call count projections.

MCI: No demand for the service and high caller credits.

Toni Moore: The major cause of failure is lack of idea analysis, or feasibility, and under capitalization of a marketing plan. Many novice IPs are buying into the idea that they can advertise a simplistic line for $200 per month and make a profit. This is highly unlikely.

Henry Wener: Narrow audience appeal and not enough advertising money to reach and determine the best market segments.

Gene Chamsom: In my experience, most new 900 programs fail for one or more of the following reasons: 1) They have a poor idea. 2) They aren't marketed well. 3) The sponsor is underfunded and doesn't have enough money to do the job right. Unfortunately, usually it's a combination of all three. As far as having a good idea goes, most 900 entrepreneurs never ask themselves these three questions:

Who would use this service, and how large is this potential market?

How valuable would this service be to people, and what would they be willing to pay for it?

What are the alternatives or substitutes for this service, and what advantages and disadvantages would the 900 service have over them?

Objective, informed answers to these questions would save many entrepreneurs a lot of time and money in creating a service with a flawed idea. My favorite example of this is the "garage sale line," an idea for a 900 service that would provide a listing of garage sales. This seemed like a good idea to its originators until they recognized that newspapers already do a very good job of providing this information for free. What's more, you can carry around a newspaper as you drive through a neighborhood, but you'd have to copy down all the information you hear on a 900 number in order for it to be useful.

Even with a good idea, if it isn't well marketed, no one will find out about it. Many 900 entrepreneurs don't know much about marketing or advertising, and they don't have the good sense to hire a professional. Even worse, many don't have enough money to do much advertising anyway! The typical 900 entrepreneur spends a wad of time and money developing their program, and then has hardly any money left to do advertising.

There's this widespread myth that with a 900 number all you have to do is place one ad and then the money will keep coming in, with profits available to reinvest in more ads which will bring in more money, etc. The reality is that most 900 numbers don't make money in their first few months, and you should have enough money to keep going for at least three months.

I recall one client who spent $5000 and 4 months setting up his

900 number. He placed one small ad in a national daily for $400 and then sat back expecting to become rich overnight. The next day when his ad appeared, he received five calls for a total of $34 in gross revenue. He was so discouraged that he immediately pulled the plug on his number. It's too bad, because he had a good idea and a good program, and with a little persistence, and some better advertising, he might have had a successful service.

Donald Young: Major cause of failure for 900 programs: undercapitalization and lack of understanding of advertising.

Mike Urbanski: Lack of planning! Many IPs put in a line and wait for good things to happen. Without a business plan, things will happen, but not all of them good. Inadequate (or non-existent) planning results in poorly financed programs, improper target market identification and usually an offer that doesn't match the needs or wants of the intended audience.

Where are the opportunities, if any, for the entrepreneurial start-up IP with a limited budget?

Bob Bentz: I recommend that such IPs approach niche magazines and offer to operate a 900 service reporting on the subject of the magazine. The IP does all the daily updating; the magazine provides the advertising space. The two parties split the profits evenly.

Toni Moore: The highest potential for a feasible idea on a low budget is to joint venture with an existing business that already advertises. Most IPs don't go that route because they lack the know-how to JV.

Henry Wener: None

Gene Chamson: Rather than setting up a new 900 number, find an arrangement where you can help advertise an existing and successful 900 number. You'll spend your money on advertising and get a share of the call proceeds. These types of arrangements are becoming more common as entrepreneurs with successful numbers but limited funds offer investors a predictable and easy way to make money. By sharing the proceeds of a 900 line, you get to have your cake and eat it too: you make money from a proven service on your own 900 line, but you avoid the costs and responsibilities of setting it up and running it yourself.

Donald Young: There are few if any opportunities for an IP without an adequate budget in 900 to survive. The only possible approach is to test market a number in a small area which provides modest advertising rates, then graduate to larger markets as the payoff comes along, this will take months, and the IP will probably lose interest and money.

Peter Brennan: The wining entrepreneurs will be those that are able to add value to raw content - by dint of a particular access methodology or spin on content of some other "hook." I would advise any entrepreneur on a shoestring not to waste time and money unless he/she can afford to effectively market the service.

Mike Urbanski: Small start-up IPs should work with a service bureau or with some other turn-key provider. Additionally, AT&T offers a switched access service called "Express 900 Service" that terminates on an existing business line, eliminating the need for extra equipment. The service was created especially for low volume and test market applications.

It should be mentioned that the price of the 900 Service is not the limiting factor in the cost equation, but rather an advertising budget that will be able to drive back and sustain sufficient call volumes.

Where is 900 headed in the next decade?

Bob Bentz: 900 will continue to grow at a moderate pace, but not at the break-neck speed it grew in the early 90's. Its reputation will improve dramatically as more legitimate programs proliferate. International premium rate services will explode as Europe, Asia, and South American increase their interest in American sports and entertainment.

Toni Moore: There are applications for data-base access, Fax-on-Demand, and with the future of interactive television, a possible marriage of some of those services. Few people will seek simple, recorded information. Many businesses, small and large, will see the value of offering their customers access, 24 hours a day, to a lot of information. The benefits will be fewer manhours, and better customer service.

Gene Chamson: I think 900 services are just a first step in the area of premium billing services to be offered by the phone companies. In the next ten years you'll see other third party billing options, where an IP will be able to bill for a service on the telephone company bill without having to use a 900 number to deliver it. I think you'll also see some standardization of laws and regulations governing pay-per-call services, similar to what happened in the credit card industry when it first started. Both these developments will restore some legitimacy and credibility to the pay-per-call business, as well as lowering the cost. And as a result, I think you'll see a whole new birth of applications from large and small businesses for relatively small volume pay-per-call services.

Donald Young: 900 is another optional vehicle for enabling response from callers. Until the companies stop blocking and the FCC mandates payment, it will grow at a reduced rate.

Peter Brennan: 900 as we know it may disappear but the precedents set will control on-line, pay-per-view and a variety of new spontaneous, transaction-based industries.

Mike Urbanski: Even taking into account AT&T's experience in the 900 business, our industry must be thought of as pay-per-transaction rather than pay-per-call.

The key word is "pay" in the short term, we all need to recognize this is as much a billing business as it is a communications business.

As we look toward the future, technology will remain a critical issue. In 7 to 10 years, consumers will have personal communications devices that combine the functions of telephones, televisions, computers and more. Video dial tone will be a reality.

The way consumers and businesses acquire information, goods and services may change dramatically, but their fundamental needs will remain the same. To meet that future successfully, the pay-per-transaction industry must understand and take advantage of this powerful technology.

However, pure growth through mass adoption of 900 usage will be directly tied to the correction of the historic "image" problems. Public perception, although gradually, is inexorably improving, consumers must identify value, integrity and service with every single 900 number as well as with the industry as a whole. We all must work hard, everyday, to create a future where both consumers and businesses alike view 900 numbers a an integral part of their daily lives.

What should a prospective IP do to learn more about the business?

Carol Morse Ginsburg: After reading this book and attending my seminars and subscribing to my newsletter, IPs should consider attending industry conferences and talking to as many service bureaus and other IPs as possible. Sending away to the various TelCos for their packages helps, and visiting their local service bureaus can be a good source of information.

MCI: Read trade magazines and this book. Join NAIS (National Association for Interactive Services).

Bob Bentz: Read this book and *Opportunity is Calling* written by me (see Appendix C).

Henry Wener: Get all the information offered by the carriers. Read *900 KNOW-HOW* three times. Find a friendly service bureau or pay a few hundred dollars for consultation.

Gene Chamson: Read a book like this one from someone who isn't trying to sell you something. Call several service bureaus and discuss your application with them. Ask lots of questions. Many of the larger bureaus will send you information packets with much useful information. Get hold of a copy of *Voice Processing* magazine. Go to the library and do a search for articles about 900 numbers. You'll find many, and learn a lot from reading them. But whatever you do, please avoid "free" seminars or anything sold through a late night infomercial. These people will give you biased information because they're trying to sell you something. If you're new to the industry, you're vulnerable to be misled by these fast talkers and slick salesmen. Another good source of information is the *Audiotex Directory* which is an excellent directory of industry resources. Finally, contact a consultant. This will cost you some money, but it can save you a lot more in the long run. Of course, I recommend that you call me first. For a telephone consultation, call me directly at 1-900-446-6075, ext. 800 ($2.95/minute).

Donald Young: Nascent IPs should read voraciously every publication they can find that serves the field that reaches the audience they are attempting to reach. They should also analyze cable shows and commercials from the standpoint of content, and the types of commercials. They should familiarize themselves with the editorial and program content, and the type of advertisers and the advertising rates so they can understand the scope of what they have to do to become a success. Without an understanding of the media the program does not stand a chance.

Peter Brennan: A prospective IP would do well to read the trades, attend trade shows and ask questions. He/she should explore all carrier and service bureau options. And he/she should understand that this business is like most other retail businesses - it requires hard work, and daily attention. Ours is not an ivory tower industry.

Should a prospective IP attend any of the trade shows, and if so, which one?

Bob Bentz: The *Infotext* show was always the highlight of the industry. It has now combined with the "Voice" Show, but no longer reports exclusively on the audiotext industry so its effectiveness remains in question. For international opportunities, World Telemedia is a must.

Toni Moore: I don't feel the novice will gain much more than info-overload by attending most of the audio-text trade shows. For less than $100 they would have access to better information via books, magazines, etc.

Henry Wener: No

Gene Chamson: Trade shows are great if you work for a big company that is paying for it, or if you have money to burn. If you're a start up entrepreneur with limited capital, I think your money is better spent elsewhere. One exception: trade shows are a unique opportunity to network with key players in the industry. If this is important to what you are doing, for example, if you are searching for a high powered sponsor or media partner for your unique program, then a trade show is a good place to go.

Peter Brennan: It is difficult to say - so much uncertainty in the market now. In the past Infotext has been meaningful - but if it concentrates on the technical aspects the content side might be left behind. The Information Industry Association (IIA) and the National

Association for Interactive Services (NAIS) also run good programs. *Audiotex News* does a good job at acquainting the beginner. Stay away from shows which seem to guarantee that you'll be a millionaire in the next twenty minutes.

What are the most common mistakes made by start-up IPs?

Carol Morse Ginsburg: Insufficient information about the industry. Buying their lines too soon. Not having a good business plan or at the least a budget and a plan that includes a step-by-step progression into the business. With the last, not the first step, being buying their lines.

Not understanding the billing and collection issues. Not understanding the elements of advertising and marketing a line. Not understanding that there is a time lag in getting paid.

Thinking of this as a get rich scheme that needs little information, little expertise and little money. A sure recipe for disaster - 900 is like every other business; you need to know what you are doing.

Not having a broad perspective on the industry and not keeping up with the quick changes and understanding how these changes impacts what's going on. It's astonishing how little individual entrepreneurs know about the industry as a whole and even more astonishing is their lack of interest in finding out. Yet changes and trends impact them in a very real way.

MCI: Not enough market research to prove that the program is in demand.

Bob Bentz: When most IPs consider starting a 900 service, they ask their friends and business associates if they would call such a service. This is not acceptable marketing research because most people tend to associate with others like them who will respond in the affirmative. Be sure to poll consumers not in your immediate circle. This will prevent you from having unrealistic expectations.

Also, many IPs simply don't know when to throw in the towel.

900 is direct response advertising that gives immediate feedback. Know when to quit and go on to your next idea.

Finally, almost all IPs have unrealistic expectations in terms of call counts. Your first goal should be to break even, not get rich.

Toni Moore: Failure to: Verify the feasibility of their idea. Failure to target their market. Failure to create an advertising plan based on facts. Lack of enough knowledge of the industry to know what questions to ask when looking for a service bureau. Lack of training.

Henry Wener: Do not have at least $3,000 a month for 4 months advertising. Pay too high a per-minute fee to a service bureau, such as over 20 cents. Get rate information from the carriers.

Gene Chamson: In addition to the mistakes I mentioned before, I'd like to mention three others which are frequently made, and yet easy to avoid:

The first is failure to do any market research. This tends to be an "idea" business, and entrepreneurs fall in love with their ideas. Everyone wants to get rich quick, and no on wants to waste any time doing tedious market research. But if you're going to spend a chunk of your time and money, you'd be wise to get answers to some basic questions before you start. You'll be surprised how easy this can be. For example, if you're thinking of starting an Asian Personals service in your city, you'll probably want to get answers to questions like: How many Asians live in this area? How many of them are single? Are there existing media that directly target this group where you can advertise your service? Are there any competing 900 services? What about Asian dating services? How many are there? How long have they been around? etc. You can answer these questions in a day or two using public information. By doing a little market research in the beginning you can avoid spending your resources on a bad idea, maybe change a bad idea into a good one, or have more confidence that your idea is a winner.

The second mistake is related to the first, and that is the failure to do market testing. Again, 900 entrepreneurs fall in love with their services, and they don't see any reason not to tell the whole world about them as soon as they can. I've see many IPs spend the bulk of their advertising budget the day after their 900 number is turned on. This is a bad idea for several reasons: First, there are almost always bugs (unanticipated problems?) in the way your program works when it's new. This is just Murphy's Law. Better to be totally confident that everything's OK before you turn up the gas on the your advertising. Like the saying goes, "You never get a second chance to make a first impression," and even a small error in a pay-per-call service can turn a caller away forever, or even worse, drive them to call the phone company and ask for a refund! But perhaps even more important, you don't want to spend a lot on advertising in the beginning because despite what you might think, you don't know if your service is a winner, or if your ads will work.

Test marketing is especially important in the 900 business because you can easily measure results, and quickly change things that aren't working. Better to run a few ads that don't work than a whole lot of them. Be methodical: run an ad, measure the response, tweak some things, see if results get better, learn from trial and error. Do this on a small scale until you come up with a formula that works, meaning your advertising produces a respectable profit. Then you're ready to reproduce that formula on a large scale.

Peter Brennan: The three most common mistakes are the lack of enough capital to advertise, over-estimating the appeal of your service in the marketplace and being taken in by the 900 number shysters.

What characteristics are shared by the most successful IPs in this business?

Carol Morse Ginsburg: A thorough understanding of the business, careful attention to what is happening on a month-by-month basis. Tenacity in analyzing call counts and what media is working for them. Sufficient capital and knowing where and how to spend it. A willingness to put the time in when needed.

The most successful treat this as a regular business, subscribing to industry publications, joining industry associations, keeping up on with happening. Letting their congressmen and state legislators know they are interested in how they vote.

Using an ad agency who knows the 900 business; or taking the time to place their advertisements properly, writing the best ads they can, tracking other ads.

Testing ads and spending time in the library reading and researching niche publications, checking ads there.

Bob Bentz: Knowledge of advertising to generate the first call to the service and consistent and informative updating to keep those calls coming.

Toni Moore: The successful IPs look on this opportunity as a business, not a get-rich quick scheme, or a hobby. They do their homework, they seek professional advice and take it, and they persevere by creating a plan and sticking to it.

Henry Wener: Program tailored to a niche group working with a publication that services that group. Have a good supply of advertising money and ads to test.

Gene Chamson: Because 900 numbers are an advertising driven business, I believe the most consistently successful IPs have been companies already in the media business (newspapers, magazines, cable TV) who have access to virtually free advertising through unsold space or time. Also more likely to be successful are companies who are marketing-savvy and are experts in direct response advertising, or who have enough money and good sense to hire such expertise.

Peter Brennan: Attention to detail, but more importantly, a commitment to build a business and an industry for the long haul.

When should an IP be the client of record with the long distance carrier?

Bob Bentz: Only when the service bureau's financial stability is in question. And if the bureau is not stable, you shouldn't be there in the first place!

Toni Moore: Once an IP is successful enough to have 2 or more profitable 900 lines, he/she should consider taking on client of record status. This isn't always necessary, however many IPs would feel more comfortable getting the check first, and in having easier access to changing to another service bureau.

Henry Wener: When they have a program with over 50,000 minutes a month.

Gene Chamson: IPs with large start-up budgets, many numbers, or ongoing programs with significant call volumes should consider becoming the client of record for their number(s). In return for paying more up front and more per month, the IP is assured of getting paid, and usually getting paid quicker. Think of the extra cost as an insurance policy. If you're not making much money yet, it's probably not worth spending more to protect it. Also consider becoming the client of record if your relationship with your service bureau is deteriorating, or if they have a lot of questionable 900 programs running, since uncollectibles from these programs could quickly and suddenly drive a service bureau out of business.

Donald Young: The only time an IP should become the client of record is when they have determined the success of their program in advance of its debut and are willing to take what would have been good advertising dollars and put them into the ownership deposit required to become a client of record. Otherwise, a simple letter of understanding with the service bureau will enable them at an appropriate time to become the client of record if they wish. Protection would seem to be the only advantage for the IP to relate directly with the carrier.

Peter Brennan: An IP should insist on being the client of record only when they have enough traffic to negotiate a more favorable rate from the carrier. Most reputable service bureaus will allow a client to take a number with them, provided their account is in good standing - and IPs should look for that in their contact. This is often a false issue that trips a lot of people up. Transmission is a commodity.

When should an IP purchase his or her own voice processing equipment and bypass the service bureau?

Bob Bentz: If you needed something printed, would you buy a printing press? Leave voice processing to the professionals and hire a service bureau.

Toni Moore: The first consideration would be the cost of the equipment, programming and maintenance (plus expandability). All of this should be covered by existing profits, and not on hoped for profits. It's important to realize that there are no guarantees of longevity of any program, so take into consideration, what you would need to do with said equipment if you no longer kept your program active.

Peter Brennan: An IP should bypass a service bureau when they are generating enough traffic to use equipment most efficiently, or when the nature of the program is so unique that dedicated equipment is absolutely the only way to go. Last year's "state-of-the-art" is next year's doorstop.

What is the price range for purchasing a complete in-house audiotext/voice processing system, say, from a fairly simple 2 port interactive system to a sophisticated 200 port system?

Bob Bentz: The minimal system I would be comfortable with costs $30,000. That cost, however, is only the beginning. You'll need at least four engineers to supply 24 hour, 7 days per week coverage of the equipment.

Toni Moore: $6,000.00 to $100,000.00 plus

Henry Wener: $3,000.00 to $175,000.00

Peter Brennan: $5,000 to $100,000. But the processing equipment is only part of the puzzle. There are many other components to provisioning service: local loop, switching equipment, channel banks, call diverters, back-up power etc.

What are the most important capabilities to look for in a service bureau, and why?

Bob Bentz: The most important capability is its ability to pay you what you deserve. Many bureaus are not financially stable. Second, be sure that the "service" in a service bureau is emphasized. Too many bureaus are currently overloaded with accounts and under-staffed. Finally, be sure that the service bureau has an effective way to process rotary calls or you will be blocking out 38.5% of your potential market.

Toni Moore: It's important that your service bureau can provide: Detailed menu driven programs, voice capture, call counts, personal program access to enable the IP to re-record messages, possibly fax on demand capabilities, approval process, flow chart and script assistance. Timely and detailed report, PLUS automatically including a copy of the phone company billing with the statement to the IP.

Henry Wener: Marketing assistance, not just an in-house agency.

Donald Young: Capabilities in a service bureau should include an ability to relate to the IP in areas of need, i.e., advertising, packaging, pricing. Dependability and reliability as derived from other clients of some longevity. The carrier recommendation may or may not be enough to assuage concerns among the beginning IP who may have heard stories of how people were burned. Success stories that can be checked are useful.

24-hour service available through calling the company which forwards to a pager after hours or a pager direct that activates an immediate response are requisites for the responsible bureau. On staff counselling or related professionals for advertising media and copy for IPs.

Peter Brennan: The single most important capability to look for in a service bureau is honesty, because they assume a fiduciary responsibility to the IP. Beyond that commitment to client service, capacity, and the capability for internal programming may be important considerations depending on the nature of the program. The bureau's relationship with the carrier(s) should also be considered.

What are the least important capabilities of a service bureau, and why?

Bob Bentz: Too many IPs worry about simultaneous call capacity. If your primary advertising is print, most service bureaus will have plenty of capacity. Only if the advertising is television which yields large call bursts does simultaneous call capacity become important.

Toni Moore: If a service is required by the IP, then it becomes important enough to be considered by the service bureau. In other words, there are no un-important capabilities.

Henry Wener: Call capacity. Most clients have no idea of how traffic is generated and processed.

Donald Young: Least important are the lengthy descriptions of the equipment and staff. The business is really one on one, and the IP deals usually with one or two people at most.

Peter Brennan: The site of physical location is usually not very important unless it impacts cost.

How have the services and functions of service bureaus evolved over the years, and where are they headed in the future?

Bob Bentz: Good service bureaus have become partners with IPs, not simply vendors of services. They are being relied on more for consulting and advice. Service bureaus now realize that their success is dependent on the success of its IPs.

Toni Moore: Service bureaus have evolved from merely equipment providers to pro-active service providers. In order to stay competitive in the legitimate information services market, they will need to hone their marketing skills, enhance their equipment with state-of-the-art capabilities, and seek sound business applications for audiotext services.

Henry Wener: Voice recognition and digitizing of voice messages for transcription.

Peter Brennan: Generally, the bureaus have become more consultative - less willing or able to simply provide a service to client specs without altering them based in the bureau's experience. Therefore, experience is an important criteria when shopping for a bureau. The winner is the program provider and, of course the user.

How many service bureaus have gone out of business in the last few years, and what was the main reason?

Bob Bentz: I suspect over half have gone out of business in the last few years. Many disappeared with the demise of adult entertainment. Many went bankrupt when Telesphere went out of business. Others bought a lot of equipment before having enough customers. Finally, smaller bureaus could not compete on price when AT&T began giving large discounts to the larger bureaus.

Toni Moore: I'm unaware of the actual number, however I would say the main reasons for failure are: undercapitalization, and poor marketing.

Henry Wener: At least half of all the bureaus that started. Chargebacks and low call volume.

Peter Brennan: I don't know how many - but many have. Undercapitalization, lack of a broad product line, the demise of adult services, technological advances - all of which have contributed to a consolidation in the industry - have been main reasons.

How many service bureaus will be around 5 years from now, and how will they be different?

Bob Bentz: There is definitely consolidation going on in the service bureau industry. Successful bureaus will need to become more involved with 800 programs and international opportunities.

Henry Wener: 250, be more marketing oriented.

Peter Brennan: I don't know - it depends on what happens with the convergence of other media - tv and on-line, etc. - and what if any role service bureaus will play in the new environment. It also depends on what role the baby bells are allowed to play in this mix.

What are some of the best markets, or demographic and psychographic characteristics, for 900 services, and why?

Bob Bentz: To date, the best callers to 900 services have been at opposite ends of the educational spectrum. Those without high school degrees and those with Master's degrees or above. Minorities, especially African-Americans and Hispanics are good callers.

Toni Moore: The 900 programs that succeed in the future will be those offering legitimate self-help, technical assistance, and detailed data-base access. The target markets for these lines will be the middle to upper income professionals, including the growing ranks of the self-employed, and home based businesses.

Henry Wener: Lower, middle income, 25 to 45 years of age. Not the smartest people.

Donald Young: Business-related services stand an excellent opportunity to succeed if the originators can pinpoint media required to reach that segment most interested in the service. Lower ad costs, greater probability of payment of bills.

Peter Brennan: Traditionally, younger people on the lower end of the socio-economic spectrum have been the most lucrative market, but that may be because of the products being offered. People outside that traditional market have demonstrated a willingness to use the services, if they are the right services.

Is any particular advertising medium, such as TV, significantly better than others for a broad range of 900 applications, and why?

Bob Bentz: I like magazines the best because of their ability to effectively target a specific market and because of their longer shelf life than newspapers. TV is very effective but also frustrating because 900 is often relegated to late night and there are no consistent advertising content standards.

Toni Moore: I feel television and magazine advertising are the best mediums. TV has a high impact, and can be targeted to specific time slot programming. Magazine advertising is less expensive and has longevity per insertion. Magazines are also a more targeted medium.

Gene Chamson: The best advertising medium for a 900 application is the one that targets the most potential users at the lowest cost per exposure. That said, my preference is almost always print (newspapers, magazines). I think it's easier to target an ad to the right audience using print, and there's some permanence to the ad, so a caller doesn't have to remember the phone number. With radio or TV, you typically have 30 or 60 seconds to get the person to call. The trouble with radio is that most people listening to it are either waking up, going to sleep, driving somewhere, or doing something; they're not near their home phones ready to make a 900 call. TV is better, especially late night TV, because the viewer is usually bored or lonely, sitting by their home phone, and your commercial can given them something more exciting to do than the silly program they're watching. Psychic lines and fantasy lines do well on late night TV. The trouble with TV is it's expensive, and so I wouldn't recommend it for anyone with a budget of under $10,000. If you're doing TV, make sure your service bureau has enough lines to handle the spike in call volume that hopefully comes during your ad. Ask for a report that shows how many lines you used vs. how many were available. My favorite way to advertise is classified and in-column display ads because I can target where they go, and I can test the ad and refine it without spending that much, and then run the same ad in many places. Also, it's easier to muscle in on the competition with these ads. Just find out where your competition is advertising, then place your ad so that it's bigger, comes first, or makes your service seem better than the rest.

Peter Brennan: I favor print because it allows the use of a printed menu and unlike television, it rarely creates a surge which the telephone network cannot handle. Ultimately, it depends on the program.

In the absence of having a media partner, what should be the minimum monthly advertising budget for a national 900 program?

Toni Moore: Assuming minimum means one's best shot at reaching the target market through a national publication(s), I would have to say $5,000.00 to advertise in one or two national publications.

Bob Bentz: For standard programs, I would recommend at least $5,000 per month. For niche programs, it could be less.

Peter Brennan: It depends on the program and the marketing objectives. Sometimes the program is purely a direct response mechanism - then you need to advertise for every call. Other programs - for example a medical information service - call for the generation of top-of-mind awareness, which is a different marketing task and would require a different approach.

Is it possible to grow a 900 information business slowly, starting with a fairly modest budget, and using imaginative, low-cost marketing strategies?

Bob Bentz: Yes, but you'd better not make too many mistakes early or you may be out of the business before you find the winning formula.

Toni Moore: This is a difficult question. There are so many variables. I'd venture to say yes it's possible, but riskier. This is often where the novice needs a feasibility study.

Gene Chamson: Yes. The more unique your 900 service, the more you can (and should) take advantage of low-cost promotion using publicity. I recall some years ago, the Potato Board of America sponsored a 900 number giving out potato recipes. I thought it was a sure loser, but then they got written up in *USA Today,* and their lines were humming for weeks. If you're doing a "me-too" service like a date line or joke line, don't bother with press releases, unless you can come up with a unique angle. But there are other low cost advertising strategies you can use. For example, if you can find media partners who are willing to advertise your service for a share of the profits, you'll eliminate your advertising risk and gain greater exposure. There are many books about "guerrilla marketing" that can give you other good ideas.

Peter Brennan: It is certainly possible, but not at all easy (How modest is modest?).

Under what circumstances, if any, would a 900 information business be a good choice for a home-based or part-time entrepreneur?

Carol Morse Ginsburg: This is an excellent home-based business, and over the years I've spoken to many retirees, as well as parents, who are running 900 businesses from their homes while raising their families.

Bob Bentz: If the entrepreneur has a media partner, has specialized information not readily available anywhere else, or has experience in advertising.

Toni Moore: If that person had a source of valuable information, such as his/her own database, or expertise in a specific field. In such cases, 900 numbers may be a good way to create additional revenue. It would be assumed that the entrepreneur had a marketing plan!

Henry Wener: When they use a pre-packaged proven program like psychics or adult.

Gene Chamson: Starting a new 900 service can be a time consuming, expensive, and ultimately risky endeavor. But there are some proven ways that a 900 number can work for a home office or part-time entrepreneur. First, if you're already in some form of advice or information business, you can use a 900 number as a tool in your business. Prepare a recorded message with some type of specialized information related to your field. For example, one of our clients, a small business consultant, has a line with a recorded message that gives 12 tips on how to increase your business without spending money on advertising. The 900 number establishes his credibility as an expert, promotes his consulting business, and earns money 24 hours a day! Or use a 900 number to offer telephone consultations and let the telephone company do your billing and collection. We recently set up a service called The Professional Network, which lets professionals share a 900 number for live consultations through the use of extensions. This way the cost of the 900 number is affordable, and practical for low call volumes.

If a 900 number doesn't make sense as part of your primary occupation, you can still make money with one by tapping into someone else's successful service. Find an arrangement where you can help advertise an existing and successful 900 number. You'll spend your money on advertising and get a share (typically 50%) of the call proceeds. This way, you'll have a reliable way to make some extra cash that won't require a major investment of time or money. As an example, our firm uses advertising partners for some of our date lines. It's a great deal for us because we have people promoting our lines in all different parts of the county. And it's great for them because for only a few hundred dollars, they have a business they can run in their spare time that requires no special skills and can earn a good return. It helps if you know something about advertising, but even if you don't, we supply sample ads that you can run in your local newspaper.

Donald Young: The majority of individuals who bring programs to our service bureau - upwards of 95% - are presently employed. They see this business as a possible add-on to their existing income. Only if they have retired or have a chunk of cash "in between assignments" do they vary from that profile. The business of 900 is perceived as one they would LIKE to grow into full time. But rather than risk everything, they stick their foot in the water. Without adequate risk capital the foot will be bitten off by the alligator of undercapitalization.

Peter Brennan: The key to a successful service is a source of information to sell. If that information can be generated by an entrepreneur at home, fine.

What new legislation or restrictions do you see on the horizon?

Bob Bentz: Hopefully, we have seen the end of the legislation. It has gone from non-existent to obtrusive in less than three years. Campaigning against 900 is currently politically correct and many politicians have made a name for themselves by vigorously attacking the 900 industry.

Toni Moore: I believe the bulk of the significant restrictions will be in place by the time this is published. There may be more stringent rulings in the future regarding "sweepstake" direct mail pieces. However, what I am hoping will happen due to the newest regulations, is that callers will be more responsible for their 900 calls, and the local Telcos less likely to offer immediate, no questions asked adjustments.

Peter Brennan: The legislation that will have the most substantial effect on the 900 industry going forward will be state consumer legislation - which the federal law does not preempt - and the federal legislation and regulation of parallel industries: telephone and television.

The Roundtable participants were asked to add their own question and answer or to comment on any topic of their choice:

Toni Moore: Q: What would you consider to be the most negative aspect of the 900 industry now?

A: I feel the multitude of resellers that are offering "cheap" lines to an ignorant public is degrading the business to a get-rich-quick scheme. There may need to be some truth in advertising regulations required, or a concerted effort by those of us in the industry to educate the public.

Gene Chamson: Q: How can a new IP protect their idea?

A: You really can't, so it's better to assume your idea will be copied, and prepare yourself to deal with the competition. In the long run, it's how you execute the idea, and not the idea itself, that will determine your success.

Over the years, I've talked to hundreds of prospective IPs. They'll say, "I've got the greatest idea for a 900 number and I need you to help me set it up." When I ask them what their idea is, they usually say something like, "Oh, I can't tell you yet. It's a secret, and I don't want anyone to steal my idea." That's when I know that their idea isn't really great. A good idea can be easily copied and improved upon. A great idea preempts the competition. Here's an example: a recorded horoscope on a 900 number is a good idea. But once the idea is out, there'll be lots of competitors with similar services eating into your business. But a recorded horoscope from Jeane Dixon, America's best known astrologer, now that's a great idea! Because every competitor that enters the market just reinforces your position as the premiere horoscope service. And indeed, while hundreds of horoscope lines have come and gone, Jeane Dixon is still around after a decade.

So when you come up with that next great idea for a 900 number, don't think about how you can keep others from stealing or copying it. Think about what you're going to do that will make your service better than all those who will copy it when it turns out to be a success.

Donald Young: The 900 business attracts idealists who have a dream of success and money without the necessary underpinning of understanding about the business. Most typical is the individual (and sometimes a company) that produces a 5-10 minute voice program that intends to "educate" a caller.

The best thing that can be done for these aspirants is to counsel them on either reducing the text to 90 seconds, tops, or converting to fax delivery if this information is required to understand whatever the theme. There is a tolerance level among callers that seldom exceeds 90 seconds on a listen-only basis. The ability to follow a complicated set of instructions (they all sound complicated after 90 seconds) is limited to a very small, select group.

A bureau is serving its own interests only -- a short-term business-building philosophy -- by taking the startup money and first month deposit. Usually the same minds that conceived that program will advertise in a very limited fashion with incorrect media. The bureau should offer advertising services either through staff counselling, or through related professionals with whom the IP may deal directly, totally unrelated to the cash flow of the bureau.

A successful advertising program will benefit the IP and hence ultimately the bureau through longevity of relationship.

Peter Brennan: It is difficult to address this industry as a whole. When people tell me we are in the 900 industry it is like a restaurant saying they're in the credit card industry. It is just a payment mechanism - one of many. Therefore be careful what conclusions are drawn from anecdotal experience, and remember that in more ways than not ours is like other businesses which require constant attention and commitment.

Chapter 11
Parting Thoughts

What types of programs have been successful in the 900 industry? Your review of current media advertising will give you some indication. Lots of repeat advertising for any generic type of 900 program is a good indication that this kind of program has been successful. Personal classified or dating lines are very successful, and you will find them advertised in just about every alternative weekly newspaper, as well as in quite a few mainstream newspapers.

Adult programs still appear to be quite popular, although most of the steamy, indecent programs have migrated over to 800 lines. The more tame "romance" or "chat" programs, however, can still be found on 900 numbers, usually with third party billing.

Horoscope, Tarot Card, and Psychic type lines are doing well. Sports lines can be successful, particularly specialized programs that deal in information which is not readily available elsewhere, like the Penn State *Blue White Hotline* or the National Lacrosse Association's 900 line.

Except for the sports lines, what do these programs have in common? Well, they appeal to lonely people or to people trying to improve their social lives or conditions. This is a common thread that is worth remembering. However, although these types of programs are successful, the playing field is getting somewhat crowded, and the market may soon become saturated with too many of these programs. Or you may be in direct competition with a big media company that owns the best media vehicle for reaching the target audience, a company that will likely not want to feature your advertising for a similar program that would compete with its own. You might have to invent a better mousetrap that still appeals to the basic human motivations that drive these successful 900 programs. And remember, these types of programs would be targeted to large homogeneous markets that are expensive to reach with your advertising.

Folio magazine's 1-900-PROFIT survey			
Magazine	**Service**	**Cost**	**Success Rate**
Newsweek	"Voice your comments" to the editor.	$1.95 1st min. 95¢ ea. addl.	5
Ladies' Home Journal	Monthly poll asking readers' opinions on various issues	75¢/call	7-10
New Woman	Horoscope forecast	95¢/min.	NC
Mirabella	Weekly horoscope	95¢/min.	8
Harper's Bazaar	Astrological Hotline	$1.50/min.	10
Elle	Weekly numerology line	$1.25/min.	10
Sassy	Music hotline	95¢/min.	9
Spin	Sample music release	95¢/min.	NC
New York	Respond to personal ad	$1.50/min.	8
Playboy	Talk to a Playmate Vote for Playmate of the Year	$3/min. $1/call	7+ 7+
Penthouse	Talk to a Penthouse Pet Penthouse Dateline Talk to Two Girls	$5/1st, $3/addl. $5/1st, $3/addl. $5/min.	10 10 10
Source: *Folio* Magazine, 2/15/93 issue			NC: Declined comment

Table 11-1

The February 15, 1993 issue of *Folio,* a trade magazine for magazine publishers, presented some interesting results from a survey of some of its subscribers who offer 900 number services. The participating magazines offer a variety of 900 services to their readers, and they were asked to rate their success on a scale of 1 to 10 based on reader response and profitability. The results, displayed in table 11-1, seem to indicate that these 900 programs are doing quite well for the most part. It is safe to assume that many more media companies will add 900 information or entertainment programs to their mix of services. After all, 900 services dovetail nicely with a publisher's or a broadcaster's primary function anyway: delivering information. Such pay-per-call services allow the media company to better serve its customers in a manner that is complimentary to its main function, while at the same time earning a new source of revenue.

Link Resources has projected the revenue breakdown for several general 900 application categories out through 1996, as displayed in table 11-2. It is readily apparent that entertainment applications are by far the most prevalent kinds of programs, comprising a substantial majority. Included within this classification are the classified personals lines, which account for most of the revenue.

Applications Breakdown (Revenues in millions of dollars)										
Application	1987	1988	1989	1990	1991	1992	1993	1994	1995	1996
Entertainment	$12	$61	$130	$410	$344	$308	$340	$366	$394	$450
Prod./Event promo.	0	10	31	99	83	74	82	88	95	109
Polling	0	5	12	38	31	36	44	52	56	64
Live	7	23	45	144	120	108	119	128	138	157
Information	0	0	1	3	3	2	3	3	3	3
Other/Adult	16	54	105	332	278	242	263	278	289	342
Source: Link Resources										

Table 11-2

It's pretty obvious where all the action is in 900, but this doesn't mean you should become a lemming and follow the crowd - specially if they are heading for a cliff! The fact that there are numerous 900 sports programs doesn't mean that they are all profitable - it simply means that there are lots of sports programs. Many of these programs may in fact be quite short-lived. The market could be over saturated with such programs, and fierce competition for a limited pool of potential callers may result in a high percentage of failures.

Targeting a Market

Another approach, which hasn't yet been tried to a very large extent, is to identify a precise target market first, before coming up with a specific 900 application. You will remember that we addressed this approach back in Chapter 5, and that the best opportunities for a start-up IP with a limited budget will be in specialized niche markets. According to Bob Bentz, Director of Marketing at Advanced Telecom Services, "Most people start with the idea, and then look for the right advertising medium. My recommendation is to look to the medium first, and then design the application to fit that medium."

Remember, advertising drives this business and represents the largest ongoing expense. It makes sense to seek out a precise target market which is capable of being reached with rifle shot advertising, and then design a 900 application which will appeal to this market, hopefully resulting in many repeat callers. This will keep advertising expenses at a very cost-effective level, resulting in the lowest cost-per-response possible.

How do you find such a target market? Back in Chapter 5 several reference publications were listed -- most of which can be found in decent size libraries -- that list thousands of periodicals and organizations that serve specific, well-defined markets. Think about collectors of all stripes, sports enthusiasts, professional or business associations, hobbyists, or any organization with a special interest. Consider minority groups or foreign language applications. Any specialized grouping of people or businesses will generally be served by a specific magazine, periodical, or mailing list, so they will be easy to reach. They also have specialized information needs that can possibly be delivered through a successful 900 program.

Many start-up entrepreneurs overlook business-to-business services when evaluating their market options. Businesses will spend money on valuable information that helps get the job done in a cost-effective way. A 900 number can be much more economical than other alternatives, such as on-line computer databases that would be accessible via a PC and a modem, along with the pertinent software and monthly subscription fees. A 900 number allows the business user to get only that specific information she needs right when she needs it, without the hassle and expense of on-line services.

Up to now, however, many businesses have blocked all access to 900 numbers to prevent employees from running up the phone bill with unauthorized calls to horoscope lines or Dial-an-Insult. AT&T has recognized this problem, and has done something to open up the market to the business use of 900 information services. AT&T launched a new Business Exchange with a dedicated prefix (900 NXX) of 555, which can be selectively unblocked by businesses wishing to have access to business related information services. The standards are quite stringent to get the 555 prefix, and only irreproachable programs providing valuable business related services are accepted.

Once you target your market and the media that serves it, think about a profitable partnership with that media. Why pay for all the advertising yourself when you can get it for free? Structure a win-win relationship with the host media and launch a successful 900 program with minimal financial risk. Media partnerships are really the name of the game in this business, because it's awfully expensive to undertake all advertising costs by yourself.

Most of the experts in this industry will tell you that, for a nationally marketed program with wide market appeal, you will need to budget five to ten thousand dollars a month for marketing a 900 program, and that a positive cash flow might take 6 or 9 months to achieve. For a start-up entrepreneur, these numbers are a little scary! This is why media partnerships are so attractive, if not absolutely essential, for ambitious national-scope programs targeted to large homogeneous markets.

Turn-Key Programs and Program Sponsoring

An alternative way to reduce your risk in entering this industry is to share a canned program with an experienced program sponsor. Chances are pretty good that the program sponsor is only offering fairly successful programs, or they wouldn't still be operational. The program sponsor should be able to give you extremely valuable advice about what marketing works best for its programs, so you can avoid the expense of ineffective market testing. You won't be throwing your hard-earned money down a rathole with advertising that generates about as much enthusiasm as a frontal lobotomy.

Many program sponsors offer standard ad copy or even canned TV commercials that you can use. This can save big bucks in creative and production costs. Even if you are not spectacularly successful, the financial risk is low. And if nothing else, you will get your feet wet and quickly learn the 900 business.

How about becoming a program sponsor yourself? After all, this is an effective way to spread out advertising costs among several people. Instead of trying to go it alone, get several other partners to share in the marketing of your program. This obviously won't work with a very precise target market served by only one specialized periodical. Everyone would be competing with each other for ad space, selling the exact same product or service. But with a more general 900 application, this may be the only way to keep your advertising costs down to a manageable level. This approach works quite well for numerous sponsors of turn-key programs, and there is no reason that it can't also work for you.

Target a specific company, or group of companies, and design a compatible 900 application that can be joint ventured or licensed. Get a well-established, financially sound company to underwrite all the costs for program execution, including marketing. Design an entertainment program that can be syndicated nationally to daily or weekly newspapers.

Get More Help

What is the common thread that pervades this discussion up to this point? Advertising costs. Success in this business is not possible unless advertising costs are shared, cut to the bone, or optimally cost-effective. I've said it before and it bears repeating. This business is very easy to get into. Maybe way too easy. But it is not necessarily easy to succeed. Not if you don't have a good handle on how to get lots of people to call your program without spending a fortune on ineffective advertising.

Get as much advice as you can from the experts before launching a program. Seek them out at the next pay-per-call trade show and pick their brains clean. Contact advertising agencies and consultants who specialize in the 900 industry. Talk to people at prospective service bureaus. They have worked with all kinds of programs and their advice is free. Ask lots of questions and listen very carefully to their answers. However, don't pay too much attention to anyone who claims you will get rich quickly in this business. Or anyone who is wildly enthusiastic about all of your 900 application ideas, no matter how flakey they might be.

Chapter 6, Marketing and Market Research, is one of the longest chapters in this book, but it really only touches on the subject of marketing. If you're planning to go it alone, without the help of advertising professionals, you need to collect more books on this subject. And there are literally hundreds of books about advertising, from direct mail to print to television. Check them out from the library or purchase them for ongoing reference. Find books that specialize in the media you will be using for your program, and become an expert in advertising. The easy part is learning the 900 business and launching a program. The hard part is learning the advertising - what works and what doesn't work. Avoid too much hands-on education - it can become a pretty expensive lesson! Prepare yourself as thoroughly as possible before you start marketing your program. This is the only way to succeed in this business.

Pay very close attention to the advice from the industry veterans in *The 900 Roundtable* and those you seek out yourself. These people know what it takes to succeed in the 900 business. They are working with a lot of successful programs, and they have also seen many programs fail.

Yes, it is possible to succeed in the 900 business. Heed the advice in this book and your chances will be quite good. I'm not trying to scare you away from this business. On the contrary, I'm trying to offer solid guidance so you can maximize your chances for success.

The future of the 900 industry is quite exciting. The public's perception is gradually but inexorably improving. Electronically literate young adults are becoming an ever increasing force in the marketplace. There are plenty of novel 900 applications that have yet to be attempted. Pay-per-call will always be an ideal home based business for a start-up entrepreneur with a good workable idea, and the drive to make it succeed.

Unfortunately, just when the 900 industry began exploding the recession hit, which has adversely affected the profitability of many 900 programs. Now we're beginning to pull out of the recession, and consumers are becoming more willing to part with their money - perhaps spending some of it on your 900 information service.

The advantages to operating a successful 900 business are quite impressive. Even unique. In what other business can you earn money 24 hours a day, even while out on the golf course or while vacationing in Hawaii?

There's no reason you can't be a successful 900 IP. Equipped with the right knowledge, and a realistic business plan, you will be able to succeed in this business. Good luck!

Appendix A
Magazines & Newsletters

InfoText. Published monthly by Advanstar Communications, P.O. Box 6016, Duluth, MN 55806
Telephone: 800-346-0085 x-447
Annual subscription: $24.00 (see *Voice Processing* below)

This used to be an autonomous magazine, recognized as the major trade publication for the pay-per-call and audiotex industries. This is no longer a separate magazine, having merged with (as a special section) *Voice Processing Magazine* (see below), probably a result of both publications being recently purchased by Advanstar Communications, and the fact that both subject areas are closely related. Nonetheless, I have listed the magazine separately because of the many references to it -- primarily when it was a separate publication, up until late 1993 -- in this book.

InfoText contains current topical information relating to all facets of the audiotex industry, including new applications, legal up-dates, marketing information, and many newsworthy articles. This remains one of the best sources for information in the industry.

Voice Processing Magazine. Published monthly by Advanstar Communications, P.O. Box 6016, Duluth, MN 55806
Telephone: 800-346-0085 x-477

Annual subscription: $24.00

This magazine covers voice information products, services, applications and technologies. The tag line for the magazine, "The source of application for computer-telephone integration and voice automation," describes the editorial content, which leans toward the technical and equipment side of the industry, and encompasses the entire voice processing industry, not just pay-per-call. This is the major trade magazine for both the audiotex and the voice processing industries.

Audiotex News. Published monthly by Audiotex News, Inc, 2362 Hampstead Turnpike, Second Floor, East Meadow, NY 11554
Telephone: 516-735-3398
Annual subscription: $249.00

This is the leading newsletter for the audiotex industry, published by Carol Morse Ginsburg, in a format which allows it to respond quickly to fast-breaking information and news about the audiotex industry. It does not accept advertising, and its stated purpose is "to give the audiotex industry access to the information it needs quickly, accurately, efficiently and to select and generate that information free from the influence of advertising." This newsletter is now the only periodical devoted exclusively to audiotex and pay-per-call, and is essential for the serious IP in keeping up-to-date about the industry.

Telemedia News and Views. Published monthly by OPUS Research, INC., 345 Chenery St., San Francisco, CA 94131
Telephone: 800-428-OPUS
Annual Subscription: $450

This newsletter was launched in May 1993 as the successor to *Audiotex Now* and *800/900 Review,* both of which were published by Strategic Telemedia, which has apparently decided to withdraw from the newsletter business. Nonetheless, OPUS Research is closely allied with Strategic Telemedia, and this newsletter is a vehicle for publishing some of Strategic Telemedia's research results. This newsletter is a good source for in-depth analysis and behind-the-scenes coverage of telemedia markets and trends, including new developments in the evolution of the Information Superhighway envisioned by President Clinton. An important source of timely information and intelligence for the serious players in this industry.

900 NewsReport. Published monthly by Moore Telecommunications, 6046 Cornerstone Ct., West, #126, San Diego, CA 92121
Telephone: 619-587-8126
Subscription: $35.00

Published by Toni Moore, a respected industry consultant and author of *Dialing For Dollars,* this newsletter offers helpful nuts-and-bolts advice aimed at the start-up IP, at an affordable price.

Teleconnect Magazine. Published monthly by Telecom Library, Inc., 12 West 21st St., New York, NY 10010
Telephone: 215-355-2886 (subscriptions)
        800-LIBRARY (publications & catalog)
Subscription: $15.00

This is the major trade magazine covering the overall telecommunications industry. According to its tag line, it is "the independent guide to choosing, using and installing telecommunications equipment and services." This magazine will keep you up-to-date on all facets of the telecom industry, of which audiotex is only a small part.

The Telecom Library also publishes *Call Center* magazine and several telecommunications books that may be of interest to you. Call or write for its catalog.

World Telemedia & Voice International. Both published by Triton Telecom Publishing, Ltd., 41-47 Kings Terrace, London NW1 0JR, United Kingdom
Telephone: 011 44 71 911 6002

These magazines are the international versions of *Infotext* and *Voice Processing*, respectively. Pay-per-call has already gone international, and these resources will help you keep on top of what's going on globally, primarily in Europe and Asia.

Appendix B
Trade Shows & Seminars

VOICE Spring/Fall

Advanstar Expositions, a Division of Advanstar Communications, Inc., P.O. Box 42382, Houston, TX 77242

Telephone: 713-974-6637   Fax: 713-974-6272

This trade show has become the major event for the voice processing/audiotext industry, replacing the *InfoText* sponsored exposition that was held each January in Las Vegas, back when *InfoText* was a separate trade magazine for the audiotext/pay-per-call industry. The same way that *InfoText* has become a section within *Voice Processing Magazine,* there is an independent event, called *InfoText 'XX* (the year), held concurrently with the larger Voice Spring annual event, which is always held on the west coast during the spring. Because of the merger, this trade show (Voice Spring) has a much broader focus, encompassing voice processing & automation, computer-telephone integration, and interactive information technologies, as well as audiotex and voice information applications.

Voice Fall, which is held annually on the east coast, does not include the *InfoText 'XX* event as a concurrent trade show, and therefore holds less interest for information providers or anyone interested solely in audiotex applications. The Voice component of this trade show, like its sponsoring magazine, *Voice Processing,* is oriented primarily towards the equipment/technical side of the industry.

If you can't afford the time or money to attend a trade show, purchasing the cassette tapes (seminar recordings) of the latest one is a good substitute. For more information call Advanstar Communications at 800-598-6008 or 216-243-8100.

Audiotext Forum

R.j. Gordon & Company, Inc., 9200 Sunset Blvd., Suite 515, Los Angeles, CA 90069

Telephone: 310-278-8080   Fax: 310-274-8686

With the demise of *InfoText's* annual conference in Las Vegas dedicated to the audiotext/pay-per-call industry, R.j. Gordon & Company has decided to fill in the gap with an event that specifically targets the information providers in this industry. Although the adult/entertainment side of the industry is heavily represented, this conference will be quite helpful for IPs offering any kind of information services. Like its *InfoText* predecessor, this event is held annually in January in Las Vegas.

The Voice/Fax Integration
& Enhanced Fax Processing Conference.

Advanstar Expositions, a Division of Advanstar Communications, Inc., P.O. Box 42382, Houston, TX 77242

Telephone: 713-974-6637   Fax: 713-974-6272

As the name implies, this conference is focused on Fax technologies and applications. This is an annual event, usually held in October on the east coast.

Voice Asia/Europe.

Advanstar Expositions, a Division of Advanstar Communications, Inc., P.O. Box 42382, Houston, TX 77242

Telephone: 713-974-6637   Fax: 713-974-6272

Advanstar Communications has gone international, with conferences held in London and Hong Kong. See Voice Spring/Fall for a description of these events, which are quite similar.

World Telemedia Asia & Voice International Asia. Triton Telecom Publishing, Ltd., 41-47 Kings Terrace, London NW1 0JR, United Kingdom
Telephone: 011 +44 71 911 6002 Fax: 011 +44 71 911 6020

The pacific rim countries hold half the world's population, in economies that are growing fast. This Hong Kong exposition is for IPs who want to investigate Asia as a viable market. This is a two-track event, with World Telemedia covering audiotex and information services while Voice International covers the equipment side of the business.

900 Business Seminars. Conducted by Carol Morse Ginsburg, editor & publisher of *Audiotex News*, 2362 Hempstead Tpke., 2nd Floor, East Meadow, NY 11554
Telephone: 516-735-3398

These seminars are ideal for the start-up IP who wants a first-hand education by an experienced industry veteran. These seminars are offered regularly throughout the year in Hampstead, NY and Washington, DC. Call or write for the current schedule. If you cannot find the time to attend a seminar, cassette audio tapes of the full seminar are available for $49.95.

Appendix C
Books & Directories

Money-Making 900 Numbers:
How Entrepreneurs Use the Telephone to Sell Information
By Carol Morse Ginsburg and Robert Mastin
Published by Aegis Publishing Group, 796 Aquidneck Ave., Newport, RI 02842-7202
Telephone: 800-828-6961
Price: $19.95

This book consists of nearly 400 profiles of 900-number programs in 12 different categories: Customer Service & Helping Consumers; Government & Non-Profit Organizations; Professional Services & Advice; Investment, Finance & Business Information; Sports; Environmental Information; Lifestyle, Travel & Leisure; Education, Careers & Self-Improvement; Entertainment; Product & Business Promotion & Marketing; Fundraising & Charity; and News, Politics & Opinions.

This book answers the question: What programs are out there, which have been successful and which have failed? The profiles are from one paragraph to several pages in length. An excellent overview of the industry, demonstrating what elements make a successful 900-number program. This book will spark your imagination, giving you the ideas, the inspiration, the insider's perspective and the know-how to launch your own 900-number service.

The Power of 900
By Rick Parkhill, published by Advanstar Communications, 7500 Old Oak Blvd., Cleveland, OH 44130
Telephone: 800-598-6008
Price: $45.00

This is the original book about the 900 industry. Great section on the history and evolution of the pay-per-call business. The original edition was published in 1991 and has become somewhat dated, but a new edition may be published, so ask about its status.

Opportunity is Calling:
How to Start Your Own Successful 900 Number
By Bob Bentz. Published by ATS Publishing, 996 Old Eagle School Rd., Suite 1105, Wayne, PA 19087
Telephone: 610-688-6000
Price: $29.95

Written by Bob Bentz, the director of marketing at Advanced Telecom Services, and a contributor to the 900 Roundtable in Chapter 10, this book is quite valuable for serious IPs in this business. In helping establish some 3,000 pay-per-call programs, Bob has probably seen every conceivable 900 application or idea, from the totally unworkable pie-in-the-sky scheme to the highly imaginative and well-conceived success story.

Marketing Your 900 Number: A User-Friendly Guide
By the editors of *Audiotex News,* 2362 Hempstead Tpke., 2nd Floor, East Meadow, NY 11554
Telephone: 516-735-3398
Price: $39.95

This is a one-of-a-kind reference guide packed with specific know-how and advice for marketing a 900 number. It covers all marketing options from getting free publicity with press releases to writing powerful ad copy to using infomercials. Also covers direct mail, media partners, TV advertising, radio and print advertising.

The Directory of "900" Service Bureaus: How to Select One
By *Audiotext News* (see above)
Price: 19.95

Arranged alphabetically by state, this directory provides the address, phone number and contact person for more than 160 service bureaus. Also included are 20 important questions (selection criteria) to ask a service bureau, and a complete discussion about the pros and cons of working with a service bureau as opposed to working directly with the long distance carrier. What makes this directory unique is that it is updated monthly in order to keep current.

Print Media Placement
By *Audiotex News* (see above).
Price: $49.95

Arranged alphabetically by state, this resource contains newspaper advertising rates, circulation, addresses, telephone numbers and restrictions (if any) for accepting 900 number advertising. Featured are more than 200 newspapers in 49 states, including dailies, weeklies and nationals.

The 900 Source
Published by Mike Landers, 910 15th St., Suite 920, Denver, CO 80202
Telephone: 303-861-5503
Price: $79.00

This is the 1992 edition of a comprehensive directory and reference guide for the 900 industry. Although somewhat dated, it contains seven chapters and six appendices packed with very useful information, totalling over 200 pages. The chapters titled "The Elements of Pay-per-call," "Service Bureaus" and "Marketing, Advertising and Media Placement" are particularly valuable for budding infoprenueurs.

Operating a "900" Number For Profit
- Entrepreneur Business Guide No. 1359

Published by Entrepreneur Group, 2392 Morse Avenue, Irvine, CA 92714

Telephone: 714-261-2325

Price: $69.95

Published by the same company that publishes *Entrepreneur Magazine*, this is one of the latest in a long series of helpful business guides designed for the start-up entrepreneur. This comprehensive 200 page guide describes not only the specifics of starting a 900 business, but also the numerous considerations common to launching any new business venture. This guide will be particularly helpful for anyone who has never started a new business.

The Voice Response Reference Manual & Buyer's Guide

By Marc Robins

Published by Robins Press, 2675 Henry Hudson Pkwy., West, Suite 6J, Riverdale, NY 10463

Price: $85.00

Telephone: 800-238-7130

This reference book is a complete resource for interactive voice technology, vendors and systems. It provides up-to-date information necessary for purchasing or building a voice response system. Included are comprehensive equipment vendor profiles and surveys on over 50 vendors and 60 systems. Hardware/software specifications, configurations & pricing, host computer interfaces, user management features, and selection/implementation advice are all included.

The 1992 Telemedia Almanac

By Advanstar Communications, 7500 Old Oak Blvd., Cleveland, OH 44130

Telephone: 800-598-6008

Price: $45

This 255 page manual is packed with useful information including 800/900 history, a service bureau directory, regulatory issues, industry forecasts, a 900 media buying guide and voice processing equipment vendors. At this time it's unknown whether or not this publication will be updated, but it's still useful as is.

InfoText Service Bureau Review
By Advanstar Communications (see above).
Price:$19.95

This is a comprehensive listing of 800/900 service bureaus, summarizing for each company what services are offered, types of clients served, areas of specialization, year established, geographic areas served, and which long distance carriers are available.

InfoText Telemedia Applications Showcase
By Advanstar Communications (see above).
Price: $19.95

This manual describes pay-per-call applications for advertisers, employers, businesses, entertainers, fund-raisers and others. Profiles over 750 programs covering 25 application categories, including hundreds of information sponsors from dozens of industries.

DIALING FOR DOLLARS: A Guide to the 900 Business
By Antoinette Moore. Published by Moore Telecommunications Consultants, 6046 Cornerstone Court West, Suite 126, San Diego, CA 92121
Telephone: 619-587-8126
Price: $29.95

Written by telecommunications consultant Toni Moore, this is a good introductory book about the 900/976 pay-per-call business, offering immediately useful nuts-and-bolts information for the start-up information provider. The step-by-step Activation Guide is both unique and helpful, and this book reflects the author's considerable experience in this business.

The 900# Directory
Published by Pay Per Call Ventures, 209 A Street, N.E., Washington, DC 20002
Telephone: 202-547-6595
Price: $129.00

This directory is a complete listing of over 700 newspapers that will accept 900 advertising, saving the advertiser considerable time in tracking down the right media for placing advertising.

Newton's Telecom Dictionary
By Harry Newton, published by the Telecom Library, Inc., 12 West 21st St., New York, NY 10010
Telephone: 800-LIBRARY
Price: $24.95

This massive 1,120 page volume was written by Harry Newton, the publisher of *Teleconnect, Call Center* and *Imaging* magazines, in an easy-to-read non-technical style. This is an everyday working dictionary for anyone involved in telecommunications. The user-friendly prose reads more like a good tutorial than a technical dictionary, and you'll never be confused again with the arcane language of the telecommunications industry.

The 900 Guide
By Madeline Bodin, published by the Telecom Library, Inc. (see above).
Price: $11.95

This helpful 96 page booklet offers sound advice from several experts in the 900 industry; including Brad Magill, Direct Response Broadcasting Network, Philadelphia, PA; Keith Dawson, associate editor of *Call Center* magazine; Deborah Vohasek, a voice response service bureau marketing expert; Gary Maier, president of Dianatel, a maker of PC boards; and Madeline Bodin, editor of *Call Center* magazine, to name only a few.

The McGraw-Hill TELECOMMUNICATIONS FACTBOOK

By Joseph A. Pecar, Roger J. O'Conner and David A. Garbin
Published by McGraw-Hill, Monterey Ave., Blue Ridge Summit, PA 17294
Telephone: 800-262-4729
Price: $29.95

This is a good guide for learning just about everything you will ever need to know about the overall telecommunications industry: Definitions, terminology, networks, LEC/IXC operations, analog vs. digital signals, transmission systems, circuit switching systems, premises distribution systems, and much more.

Service Access Codes 800/900 NXX Assignments (800/900 List)

Published quarterly by Bell Communication Research (Bellcore), and available by calling its Document Hotline:
Telephone: 800-521-2673
Price: $40.00 (subject to change)

This is a compilation of all NXXs assigned within the Service Access Codes (SACs) 800 and 900 by the North American Numbering Plan Administrator. For each of the NXXs assigned, the name of the company to which it is assigned and the telephone number of a contact in that company are given. NXX availability changes regularly, and this publication will give you the latest assignments.

Infopreneurs: Turning Data Into Dollars

By H. Skip Weitzen, published by John Wiley & Sons, 605 Third Avenue, New York, NY 10158-0012
Price: $14.95

This book shows you how to make money selling information. Covers how to consolidate and communicate information; generate new information products and services; use volatile information profitably; price your computer services; and the use of the telephone and credit cards for instant payment.

PC-Based Voice Processing

By Bob Edgar, published by The Telecom Library, Inc., 12 West 21st St., New York, NY 10010

Telephone: 800-LIBRARY

Price: $29.95

This is the first book written exclusively about voice processing, aimed at the developer of a PC-based voice processing system. For programmers and value added resellers (VARs) in this growing industry.

Appendix D
Trade Associations

The National Association for Interactive Services (NAIS). 1250 Connecticut Avenue, N.W., Suite 600, Washington, DC 20036-2603
Telephone: 202-833-2545
Membership dues: Starting at $250

NAIS is a trade association representing the interests of the evolving interactive media industry. In its formative years, the NAIS primarily represented the business interests of the pay-per-call industry, including 900, 976 and 800. Today, the NAIS has broadened its focus to include a variety of other interactive, emerging industries.

The NAIS advocates the business and public policy interests of a wide variety of companies, including computer, consumer electronics, publishing, telephone, television and other multimedia companies. NAIS members include cable television companies, long distance carriers, RBOCs, audiotex companies, information providers, service bureaus, local exchange carriers, and a variety of others.

The NAIS offers business development opportunities to its members through networking and cross-industry education. A sponsor of various conferences, executive "teleforums," and member publications, the NAIS provides a carefully screened stream of updated information to its members about the rapidly evolving interactive media industry.

Other important functions of the NAIS are to advocate industry perspectives, to develop and enforce national industry standards through self-regulation, and to serve as a clearinghouse for industry information and education. Of particular value are the NAIS's efforts in promoting a positive image for the industry and in lobbying with regulatory and legislative authorities with regard to proposed regulations and laws concerning the industry.

Any serious IP planning to stay in the 900 industry for the long haul should join NAIS. This organization represents all the leading businesses in the industry, and the networking opportunities with these business leaders is alone worth the membership fee.

Information Industry Association (IIA). 555 New Jersey Avenue, N.W., Suite 800, Washington, DC 20001
Telephone: 202-639-8262
Membership fee: Starting at $500

IIA's Voice Information Services Division brings together equipment vendors, service bureaus, telecommunications companies, information providers, marketing organizations, consultants, and other businesses involved in the voice information field. Membership benefits are targeted to the larger players in the industry, and membership would be inappropriate for the start-up IP.

An established IP, on the other hand, should seriously consider joining this organization. IIA has been particularly active in pay-per-call consumer education, and has established Standards of Practice for voice information services.

Promotion Marketing Association of America, Inc. (PMAA). 322 Eighth Avenue, Suite 1201, New York, NY 10001
Telephone: 212-206-1100

PMAA is a trade organization specializing in the use of promotion marketing - games, contests, and sweepstakes - as a means for enhancing sales or consumer awareness. Its membership list reads like a "who's who" of major national companies, and also includes many service/supplier members who can help execute all facets of a successful promotion.

Of particular value are the associations' legal information services, including regular legal bulletins which track all relevant state and federal legislation. Also available to members is Frank Dierson's very comprehensive book, *Promotion Marketing Law*, the most thorough reference source available on the subject.

PMAA sponsors two annual trade conferences. The Promotion Law/Marketing Conference is held each Fall, and the UPDATE National Conference, the premier promotion marketing event in the industry, is held each Spring.

Appendix E
Alternative Newspapers

Alternative newspapers, which are predominantly weeklies, have been a good print medium for 900 program advertising. Besides the fact that most of these newspapers are quite liberal about the kinds of advertising they will accept, including all types of 900 programs, alternative newspapers are read by an audience that is quite receptive to 900 programs: Young, well-educated, progressive people who are always among the first to embrace a new fad or concept, and who like to be on the cutting edge of new trends and technology. Known in marketing parlance as "early adapters," these people generally lead the way to changes in fashions and lifestyles.

The following list of newspapers is from the Association of Alternative Newsweeklies (AAN) membership directory. The AAN will coordinate group discount advertising and insertions for advertisers who wish to place ads in multiple publications:

> The Association of Alternative Newsweeklies (AAN)
> 1201 East Jefferson, Suite 260
> Phoenix, AZ 85034
> Telephone: 602-229-8487   Fax: 602-253-5871

Athens News
14 N. Court Street
Athens, OH 45701
Telephone: 614-594-8219
Circ: 17,500

Austin Chronicle
P.O. Box 49066
Austin, TX 78765
Telephone: 512-454-5766
Circ: 80,000

Baltimore City Paper
812 Park Ave.
Baltimore, MD 21201
Telephone: 410-523-2300
Circ: 88,000

Bloomington Voice
2620 N. Walnut St., Ste. 1500
Bloomington, IN 47404
Telephone: 812-331-0963
Circ: 12,000

Boston Phoenix
126 Brookline Avenue
Boston, MA 02215
Telephone: 617-536-5390
Circ: 128,000

Casco Bay Weekly
551 A Congress St.
Portland, ME 04101
Telephone: 207-775-6601
Circ: 30,000

Chicago Reader
P.O. Box 11101
Chicago, IL 60611
Telephone: 312-828-0350
Circ: 135,000

Chico News & Review
353 E. Second Street
Chico, CA 95928
Telephone: 916-894-2300
Circ: 45,000

City Newspaper
250 N. Goodman Street
Rochester, NY 14607
Telephone: 716-244-3329
Circ: 25,000

City Pages
401 N. Third Street, #550
Minneapolis, MN 55401
Telephone: 612-375-1015
Circ: 100,000

Cleveland Free Times
11610 Euclid Avenue, Ste. 100A
Cleveland, OH 44106
Telephone: 216-229-1600
Circ: 31,000

Coast Weekly
668 Williams Ave.
Seaside, CA 93955
Telephone: 408-394-5656
Circ: 42,000

Columbus Alive!
689 N. High St.
Columbus, OH 43215
Telephone: 614-221-2449
Circ: 43,500

Creative Loafing
750 Willoughby Way, NE
Atlanta, GA 30312
Telephone: 404-688-5623
Circ: 148,000

Creative Loafing
402 Reo St., Ste. 218
Tampa, FL 33609
Telephone: 813-286-1600
Circ: 70,000

Creative Loafing
1620 South Blvd., Ste. A3
Charlotte, NC 28203
Telephone: 704-375-2121
Circ: 40,000

Dallas Observer
P.O. Box 190289
Dallas, TX 75219
Telephone: 214-637-2072
Circ: 92,000

Eastsideweek
123 Lake St., South B-1
Kirkland, WA 98033
Telephone: 206-827-5550
Circ: 31,000

East Bay Express
P.O. Box 3198
Berkeley, CA 94703
Telephone: 510-540-7400
Circ: 67,000

Easy Reader
832 Hermosa Avenue
Hermosa Beach, CA 90254
Telephone: 310-372-4611
Circ: 70,000

EveryBody's News
22 West Seventh St., 7th Fl.
Cincinnati, OH 45202
Telephone: 513-651-2606
Circ: 25,000

Fairfield/Westchester Weekly
180 Post Road East
Westport, CT 06880
Telephone: 203-226-4242
Circ: 65,000

Folio Weekly
9456 Phillips Hwy., Ste. 11
Jacksonville, FL 32256
Telephone: 904-260-9770
Circ: 31,000

Gambit
4141 Bienville
New Orleans, LA 70119
Telephone: 504-486-5900
Circ: 37,000

Green Line
P.O. Box 144
Asheville, NC 28802
Telephone: 704-251-1333
Circ: 22,000

Hartford Advocate
30 Arbor St.
Hartford, CT 06106
Telephone: 203-232-4501
Circ: 60,000

Highpoint
1133 Euclid Ave.
Atlanta, GA 30307
Telephone: 404-524-5601
Circ: 14,000

Honolulu Weekly
1200 College Walk, Ste. 212
Honolulu, HI 96817
Telephone: 808-528-1475
Circ: 28,000

Houston Press
2000 West Loop South, #1900
Houston, TX 77027
Telephone: 713-624-1400
Circ: 80,000

Illinois Times
P.O. Box 3524
Springfield, IL 62708
Telephone: 217-753-2226
Circ: 30,000

In Pittsburgh
2100 Wharton St., Ste. 300
Pittsburgh, PA 15203
Telephone: 412-488-1212
Circ: 52,000

Independent Weekly
P.O. Box 2690
Durham, NC 27705
Telephone: 919-286-1972
Circ: 50,000

Isthmus
101 King Street
Madison, WI 53703
Telephone: 608-251-5627
Circ: 58,000

Ithaca Times
P.O. Box 27
Ithaca, NY 14851
Telephone: 607-277-7000
Circ: 20,230

L.A. Weekly
2140 Hyperion Avenue
Los Angeles, CA 90027
Telephone: 213-667-2620
Circ: 170,000

Los Angeles Reader
5550 Wilshire Blvd. #301
Los Angeles, CA 90036
Telephone: 213-965-7430
Circ: 90,000

Maine Times
The Great Bowdoin Hall, 1 Maine St.
Topsham, ME 04086
Telephone: 207-729-0126
Circ: 20,000

Memphis Flyer
460 Tennessee St.
Memphis, TN 38103
Telephone: 901-521-9000
Circ: 45,000

Metro
550 S. First Street
San Jose, CA 95113
Telephone: 408-298-8000
Circ: 80,000

Metro Pulse
602 S. Gay St., Level M
Knoxville, TN 37902
Telephone: 615-522-5399
Circ: 30,000

Metro Times
743 Beaubien
Detroit, MI 48226
Telephone: 313-961-4060
Circ: 100,000

Metroland Magazine
4 Central Ave.
Albany, NY 12210
Telephone: 518-463-2500
Circ: 31,000

Miami New Times
330 N. Biscayne Blvd., Ste. 1000
Miami, FL 33132
Telephone: 305-372-0004
Circ: 90,000

Monday Magazine
1609 Blanshard Street
Victoria, BC V8W 2J5
Telephone: 604-382-6188
Circ: 40,000

Montreal Mirror
400 McGill Street, Suite 200
Montreal, Quebec H2Y 2G1
Telephone: 514-393-1010
Circ: 80,000

Nashville Scene
301 Broadway
Nashville, TN 37201-2005
Telephone: 615-244-7989
Circ: 50,000

New City
770 N. Hallstead, Ste. 208
Chicago, IL 60622
Telephone: 312-243-8786
Circ: 50,000

New Haven Advocate
1 Long Wharf Dr.
New Haven, CT 06511
Telephone: 203-789-8786
Circ: 50,000

New Times
1509 Westport Rd.
Kansas City, MO 64111
Telephone: 816-753-7880
Circ: 35,000

New Times
197 Santa Rosa St.
San Luis Obispo, CA 93405
Telephone: 805-546-8208
Circ: 38,000

New York Press
295 Lafayette Street, 9th. Floor
New York, NY 10012
Telephone: 212-941-1130
Circ: 85,000

Now
150 Danforth Avenue
Toronto, Ont. M4K 1N1
Telephone: 416-461-0871
Circ: 95,000

NUVO
811 E. Westfield Blvd.
Indianapolis, IN 46220
Telephone: 317-254-2400
Circ: 40,000

Oklahoma Gazette
1200 N. Shartel
Oklahoma City, OK 73103
Telephone: 405-235-0798
Circ: 35,000

Pacific Sun
21 Corte Madera Avenue
Mill Valley, CA 94941
Telephone: 415-383-4500
Circ: 33,000

Palo Alto Weekly
703 High Street
Palo Alto, CA 94301
Telephone: 415-326-8210
Circ: 49,000

The Paper
540 Menocino Ave.
Santa Rosa, CA 95401
Telephone: 707-527-1200
Circ: 18,000

Philadelphia City Paper
206 S. 13th. Street
Philadelphia, PA 19107
Telephone: 215-735-8444
Circ: 67,000

Phoenix New Times
1201 E. Jefferson
Phoenix. AZ 85034
Telephone: 602-271-0040
Circ: 140,000

The Providence Phoenix
131 Washington Street, #301-311,
Providence, RI 02903
Telephone: 401-273-6397
Circ: 60,000

Pitch
3701 Summit
Kansas City, MO 64111
Telephone: 816-561-6061
Circ: 43,000

Private Eye
68 W. 400 South
Salt Lake City, UT 84101
Telephone: 801-575-7003
Circ: 30,000

Random Lengths
1014 S. Pacific Ave.
San Pedro, CA 90731
Telephone: 310-519-1442
Circ: 30,000

Riverfront Times
1221 Locust Street #900
St. Louis, MO 63103
Telephone: 314-231-6666
Circ: 100,000

Appendix E

S.F. Weekly
9 Kimberly Ct.
Oakland, CA 94611
Telephone: 415-541-0700
Circ: 80,000

Sacramento News & Review
2210 21st Street
Sacramento, CA 95818
Telephone: 916-737-1234
Circ: 70,000

San Antonio Current
2566 Boardwalk
San Antonio, TX 78217
Telephone: 210-828-7660
Circ: 32,000

San Diego Reader
1703 India St.
San Diego, CA 92101
Telephone: 619-235-3000
Circ: 134,000

San Francisco Bay Guardian
520 Hampshire Street
San Francisco, CA 94110
Telephone: 415-255-3100
Circ: 135,000

Santa Barbara Independent
1221 State Street, #200
Santa Barbara, CA 93101
Telephone: 805-965-5205
Circ: 40,000

Santa Fe Reporter
P.O. Box 2306
Santa Fe, NM 87504
Telephone: 505-988-5541
Circ: 23,500

Seattle Weekly
1008 Western, Ste. 300
Seattle, WA 98104
Telephone: 206-623-0500
Circ: 37,000

Shepherd Express
1123 North Water Street
Milwaukee, WI 53202
Telephone: 414-276-2222
Circ: 50,000

Springfield Advocate
1127 Main Street
Springfield, MA 01103
Telephone: 413-781-1900
Circ: 38,000

Suttertown News
1731 L Street
Sacramento, CA 95814
Telephone: 916-448-9881
Circ: 31,500

Syracuse New Times
1415 W. Genesee Street
Syracuse, NY 13204
Telephone: 315-422-7011
Circ: 46,000

Texas Observer
307 W. 7th St.
Austin, TX 78701
Telephone: 512-477-0746
Circ: 8,600

Times of Acadiana
P.O. Box 3528
Lafayette, La 70502
Telephone: 318-237-3560
Circ: 32,500

Tucson Weekly
201 W. Cushing
Tucson, AZ 85701
Telephone: 602-792-3630
Circ: 35,000

Twin Cities Reader
5500 Wayzata Blvd., Ste. 800
Minneapolis, MN 55416
Telephone: 612-591-2500
Circ: 110,000

Valley Advocate
87 School St.
Hatfield, MA 01038
Telephone: 413-247-9301
Circ: 27,000

Vermont Times
P.O. Box 940
Shelbourne, VT 05482
Telephone: 802-985-2400
Circ: 38,000

The Village Voice
36 Cooper Square
New York, NY 10003-7118
Telephone: 212-475-3300
Circ: 200,000

Washington City Paper
2390 Champlain Street, NW
Washington, DC 20009
Telephone: 202-332-2100
Circ: 90,200

Welcomat
1701 Walnut St.
Philadelphia, PA 19103
Telephone: 215-563-7400
Circ: 73,000

Westword
1621 18th Street, #150
Denver, CO 80202
Telephone: 303-296-7744
Circ: 110,000

Willamette Week
2 NW Second Avenue
Portland, OR 97209
Telephone: 503-243-2122
Circ: 65,000

Worcester Magazine
172 Shrewsbury St.
Worcester, MA 01604
Telephone: 508-755-8004
Circ: 40,000

Appendix F
Service Bureaus

This list of service bureaus was compiled in the fall of 1993, and was accurate at that time. Nonetheless, some of these companies may no longer be in business, or they may no longer serve 900 number information providers.

At the time this list was prepared most of the service bureaus listed were contacted, and it was verified whether each offered 900 number services and would work with start-up information providers. I do not endorse any particular company in this list, and the fact that any given company is included in the list does not imply that this company is recommended in any way. You should follow prudent business practices in checking out any company you plan to do business with, including asking for and speaking with references. See Chapter 7 for guidance on how to select a service bureau.

See Appendix A, Magazines & Newsletters, for publications that offer service bureau listings that are kept more up-to-date than a book such as this can be. I invite service bureaus to contact me to make any necessary corrections or changes to this list for future editions of this book.

Alabama

Information Management Consultants (IMC)
Tim Michael, President
208 Adams St.
Mobile, AL 36603
205-434-6409 / 800-627-4IMC

Info Touch
Tim Brown, Vice President, Sales
3000 Zelda Rd. Suite F
Montgomery, AL 36106
205-244-9868

Arizona

National Tel-Tec
Stewart Mazure, President
P.O. Box 4457
Scottsdale, AZ 85261
602-274-6444

California

Accelerated Voice
Ted Glenwright, President
25 Stillman St., Suite 200
San Francisco, CA 94107
415-543-2773

Alert Communications Co.
David Kissel, Sales Manager
5515 York Blvd.
Los Angeles, CA 90042
213-254-7171

Almarc
Ronald A. Resnick, President
8921 DeSoto, Suite 200
Conoga Park, CA 91306
818-773-2080

American Telecom/Dialtronix
Customer Service Department
4225 Executive Square, 12th Fl.
La Jolla, CA 92037
800-510-5500

Audiotext Facilities Management, Inc.
Charles Ryan, President
P.O. Box 82109
San Diego, CA 92138-2109
619-287-8292

Automated Call Processing
Marcy McCann, Manager, Business
Development
244 Jackson St., Suite 200
San Francisco, CA 94111
415-989-2200

Bellatrix International
David Kahn, President
4055 Wilshire Blvd. Suite 415
Los Angeles, CA 90010
213-736-5600

Intermedia Resources
Gene Chamson, President
6114 LaSalle Avenue, #230
Oakland, CA 94611
510-339-1792

Creative Call Management
Bob Kushner, President
316 W. 2nd St., Suite 1110
Los Angeles, CA 90012
213-687-0990

The Creative Services Group
Andy Batkin, President
2200 Pacific Coast Hwy., Suite 103
Hermosa Beach, CA 90254
310-798-0433

DataDial International
Gordon Clements,
650 Kenwyn Rd.
Oakland, CA 94610
510-601-0101

E-Fax Communications, Inc.
(FAX Service Only)
William Perell, Vice President, Marketing
1611 Telegraph Ave., Suite 555
Oakland, CA 94612
510-836-6000

Gigaphone, Inc.
Nancy R. Conger, President
1525 Aviation Blvd., Suite A188
Redondo Beach, CA 90278
310-374-4313

Integrated Data Concepts
Warren Jason, President
P.O. Box 93428
Los Angeles, CA 90093
213-469-3380
800-367-4432

Interactive Strategies, Inc.
J. Edward Hastings, Executive V.P.
31194 La Baya Dr., Suite 100
Westlake Village, CA 91362
818-879-9992

Interactive TeleMedia Services Corp.
Vance McDonald, Director of Sales
14651 Ventura Blvd.
Los Angeles, CA 91403
800-441-4486

Intertel Systems
Jeff Allen
P.O. Box 4384
Berkeley, CA 94704
510-649-0404

LO/AD Communications
Kris Flynn, Managing Director, Sales &
Marketing
200 South Los Robles Ave., Suite 250
Pasadena, CA 91101
800-255-5623

LCN
Robert Lorsch, President
8383 Wilshire Blvd., #1010
Beverly Hills, CA 90211
213-651-0500

MCE TeleCommunications
Michaelle Ashlock, Account Executive
17911 Sky Park Circle, Suite D
Irvine, CA 92714
714-476-8007

Network Telephone Services, Inc.
Gary Passon, President
6233 Variel Ave.
Woodland Hills, CA 91367
818-992-4300

New Media Telecommunications, Inc.
Thomas Doolin, Sales Manager
4225 Executive Square, Suite 1500
La Jolla, CA 92037
619-558-3333

SimTel Communications
Jim Simpson, President
31220 LaBaya Dr., Suite 254
Westlake Village, CA 91362
818-706-1921

Speech Solutions
Tim Marentic, CEO
139 Townsend St., Suite 301
San Francisco, CA 94107
415-243-8300

Strauss Communications, Inc.
Lance Strauss, President
P.O. Box 223542
Carmel, CA 93922
408-625-0700

Tel-Ad
Michael Newton,
7760 E. Doheny Court
Anaheim Hills, CA 92808
714-281-1206

The Telephone Connection
Marc O'Krent, President
2554 Lincoln Blvd., Suite 137
Marina del Rey, CA 90291
310-827-8787

Teleserve, Inc.
Sales Department
47000 Warm Springs Blvd., #460
Fremont, CA 94539
408-727-7764

TeleTel, Inc.
Horace Zhang
100 Wilshire Blvd., Suite 420
Santa Monica, CA 90401
310-458-6333

US Audiotex, Inc.
Sarah Harvey, Vice President
18 Crow Canyon Ct., Suite 300
San Ramon, CA 94583
510-838-7996

Colorado

Cook Communications Corp.
Jim Moreland, Director of Sales
602 Park Point Dr.
Genesee Ctr. 1 , Suite 120
Denver, CO 80401
800-FON-CALL/303-526-7400

IdealDial
Michael Couglin, Vice President
910 15th St., Suite 900
Denver, CO 80202
800-582-3425

Interactive Information Systems
Paul Kulas, Vice President
910 15th St., Suite 751
Denver, CO 80202
303-595-0888

Tela, Inc.
Ted M. Larson, President
910 15th St., Suite 1068
Denver, CO 80202
303-893-5150

Connecticut

Facsimile Marketing, Inc./GrayFire
Jeremy Grayzel, President
3 Landmark Square, Suite 403
Stamford, CT 06901
203-323-4400

Delaware

American TelNet, Inc.
William Rivell, Vice President, Sales
1701 Augustine Cut-Off, Suite 40
Wilmington, DE 19803
302-651-9400

District of Columbia

Telecompute Corp.
Warren Miller, President
1275 K St., NW, Suite G-9
Washington, DC 20005
202-789-1111
800-872-8648

Florida

Alternative Communications &
Technologies, Inc.
Barbara Johnson
12807 W. Hillsborough Ave., Suite J
Tampa, FL 33635
813-854-1755

Audiotext Services, Inc.
Roderic van Beuzekom, President
P.O. Box 2449
Orlando, FL 32802
407-426-8355

National Call Center, Inc.
Chris Soechtiz, Account Executive
P.O. Box 9090
Clearwater, FL 34618-9090
813-572-8585 Ext. 7000

ONE 800/900, Inc.
Robert Fernekes, Sales Department
200 Laura St. 12th Floor
Jacksonville, FL 32202
904-355-9000

Phoneworks
Kathy Montgomery
146 Second St. N., Suite 201
St. Petersburg, FL 33701
813-823-7144

Georgia

The Intermedia Group
Steven West
2980 Cobb Pkwy., Bl. 192, Suite 500
Atlanta, GA 30339
404-368-2838

Message Technologies, Inc.
Mark Abramson, President
2849 Paces Ferry Rd., #600
Atlanta, GA 30339
800-868-3684

Overlook Communications International
Jan Hart
2839 Paces Ferry Rd., Suite 500
Atlanta, GA 30339
404-432-6800

Tamona Enterprises, Inc. (Sports
Information Only)
Pati Johnston
8215 Roswell Rd., Bldg. 900
Atlanta, GA 30350
800-356-4466
404-604-3500

Technology Solutions International
(Business to Business Only for 900)
Joe Rosenthal, President
1400 Lake Hern Dr. NE, Suite 170
Atlanta, GA 30319
404-843-5890

Illinois

Ameritech Audiotex Services, Inc.
Jeff Thadie, Director, Sales & Marketing
300 South Riverside Plaza
Chicago, IL 60606
312-906-3130

ConServlt
Robert Morgan, Vice President, Sales
4205 Grove Ave.
Gurnee, IL 60031
708-249-5560

Document Retrieval Services
Ronald Duskey, President
644 W. Pratt Ave. North
Schaumburg, IL 60193
708-924-7464

DynamicFax, Inc.
James L. Hughes, Vice President, Sales
2470 Eastrock Dr.
Rockford, IL 61108
815-398-9009

Information Command, Inc.
Donald Young, President
444 North Wells
Chicago, IL 60610
312-245-1111
800-282-6541

MarketFax Chicago
Jack Smith, President
539 W. Wise Rd.
Schaumburg, IL 60193
800-666-5543

Northwest Nevada Telco
Michael Dawson, Director of Sales
1324 Evers Ave.
Westchester, IL 60154-3413
800-279-0909

Kansas

Brite Voice Systems, Inc.
Communication Services Division
Stan Brannan
7309 E. 21st. St. North
Wichita, KS 67206
800-SEE-BRITE(sales)
316-652-6500

Info Access, Inc.
Terry Hughes, Sales Director
4550 West 109th St.
Overland Park, KS 66211
800-453-1453

Maryland

A+ Communications
Ed Gurman, Director of Marketing
6610 Tributary St.
Baltimore, MD 21224
800-535-1187

Comm Vox, Inc.
Ed Erikson, Director of Marketing
7200 Wisconsin Ave., Suite 410
Bethesda, MD 20814
800-551-2552

National Phone Link
Scott Kleinknecht, President
6900 Virginia Manor, Suite 110
Beltsville, MD 20705
301-419-0365

TeleService USA
Barry Cockley, Executive Vice President
19723 Leitersburg Pike
Hagerstown, MD 21742
301-797-2323

Telesonic
E. Escobar, Sales Representative
120 Admiral Cochrane Dr.
Annapolis Science Center
Annapolis, MD 21401
410-841-6920

Massachusetts

Facsimile Services, Inc.
Edward Olkkola, President
573 Washington St.
South Easton, MA 02375
508-230-2000

Inpho, Inc.
Steve Kropper, President
225 Fifth St.
Cambridge, MA 02142
617-868-7050

Mass Communication
Stephen R. Picardo, President
432 Columbia St., Suite B-9
Cambridge, MA 02141
617-577-7285

Mercury Telemedia, Inc.
Jeanne Fox
42 Woodwar Ave.
Gloucester, MA 01903
800-999-2FAX

The Nine Call Corp.
Bill Gundling, Vice President
432 Columbia St., Unit 28A
Cambridge, MA 02141
617-494-9225

Tele-Publishing, Inc.
Paul Twitchell, Director of Marketing
126 Brookline Ave.
Boston, MA 02215
617-536-2340 / 800-874-2340

Michigan

Amrigon
Michelle Gustavus, Account Rep.
2750 South Woodward
Bloomfield Hills, MI 48304
313-332-2300

Dobbs Enterprises, Ltd.
John C. Dobbs, President
855 Forest St.
Birmingham, MI 48009
313-540-2149

World Data Delivery Systems
Matt Kennedy, Telcom Director
20542 Harper Ave.
Harper Woods, MI 48225
800-554-9337

Minnesota

Micro Voice Applications, Inc.
Michael A. James
5775 Wayzata Blvd.
Minneapolis, MN 55416
800-553-0003

Talk, Inc.
Patrick Dolan, Vice President
3415 University Ave., SE
Minneapolis, MN 55414
612-642-4559/612-642-4558

Nebraska

Call Interactive
Deanna L. DeSmet, Director of Marketing
2301 North 117th Ave.
Omaha, NE 68164
800-428-2400

SITEL Corp.
Kevin Blair, Vice President, Advertising
5601 N. 103rd St.
Omaha, NE 68134
402-498-6876
402-498-6810
800-445-6600

Wessan Interactive Network
Karen Westerfield, President
3033 North 93rd St.
Omaha, NE 68134
800-468-7800

West Interactive Corp.
David VanDerveer, Executive VP, Sales &
Marketing
9223 Bedford Ave.
Omaha, NE 68134
800-841-9000

Nevada

Arch Communications
Steve Carne
3700 S. Las Vegas Blvd., #1000
Las Vegas, NV 89109
702-597-1829

Audio Communications, Inc.
John Bostaph, Account Executive
3140 Polaris Ave., Suite 19
Las Vegas, NV 89102
800-527-5353

B.F.D. Productions
Bruce F. Dyer, President
1210 S. Martin Luther King
Las Vegas, NV 89102
702-387-3200
800-444-4BFD

Technology Support Corporation
Ben Greenspan, President
PO Box 6494
Incline Village, NV 89450
702-832-7358

New Jersey

Evergreen Systems, Inc.
Michael Osborn
PO Box 1400
Marlton, NJ 08053
609-985-8100

The Fax People, Inc.
Michael Rogers, President
34 Maple St., Suite 3
Summit, NJ 07901
800-FAX-NET1
908-277-2122

The Interactive Telephone Company
Abby Knowlton, Sales Director
Court Plaza North, 2nd Floor
25 Main St.
Hackensack, NJ 07601
201-342-1000

Most Telecom, Inc.
Ron Patetta, Vice President Sales
18 Condit Rd.
Mountain Lakes, NJ 07046
210-335-2255

RENEW Interactive Marketing Services,
Inc.
Henry Wener, President
41 Vreeland Ave.
Totowa, NJ 07512-1100
201-890-0889

Voice Communications, Inc.
Frank Giarratano, Director of Telecommunications
350 Main Rd.
Montville, NJ 07045
201-299-1200

New York

Automated Fax & Voice Solutions
Ken Gavranovic
90 Merrick Ave.
East Meadow, NY 11554
516-674-4600
516-794-1100

Fax Information Network of America, Inc.
Ralph Potente, President
20 Max Ave.
Hicksville, NY 11801
516-942-8000

Integrated Communications Ltd.
Jonathan Breger, Vice President
885 Third Ave., Suite 330
New York, NY 10022
212-230-2222

Phone Programs, Inc.
Lisa Ingraham,
40 Elmont Rd.
Elmont, NY 11003
516-775-5410

TRX Corp.
Gary Glicker
160 East 56th St.
New York, NY 10022
212-644-0370

Tele-Disc Services
Loni Barocas, VP, Audiotex Services
33 Great Neck Rd.
Great Neck, NY 11021
516-466-0404

VOCALL Communications Corp.
Laura Pettinato
70 East 55th St., Heron Tower
New York, NY 10022
212-754-2525

Ohio

900 America, Ltd.
Larry D. Lomaz, CEO
1 Cascade Plaza, Suite 1940
Akron, OH 44308
216-379-9900

ITI Marketing Services
Kirk VonDerhaar
531 North Wayne Ave.
Cincinnati, OH 45215
513-563-8666/800-562-5000

Scherers Communications, Inc.
MaryKay Dawson
575 Scherers Ct.
Worthington, OH 43085
614-847-6161

Oklahoma

900 Call Association
Thomas Hoshall, President
3608 NW 58th St.
Oklahoma City, OK 73112
405-947-5627

VoiceXpress, Inc.
Kevin Murray, Vice President
15 West 6th St., Suite 1310
Tulsa, OK 74119
918-583-8080

Voice FX Corp.
Chris Gongol, Vice President, Marketing
1100 E. Hector St., 4th Floor
Conshohocken, PA 19428
215-941-1000

Pennsylvania

Accu-Weather, Inc.
Sheldon Levine, Director of Sales
619 W. College Ave.
State College, PA 16801
814-237-0309

Advanced Telecom Services, Inc.
Bob Bentz, Director of Marketing
996 Old Eagle School Rd.
Wayne, PA 19087
215-964-9146

Automated Voice Production, Inc.
Gary Baron
295 Buck Rd., Suite 207
Holland, PA 18966
215-953-8568

Sports Network
Ken Zajac
701 Masons Mill Business Park
Huntington Valley, PA 19006
215-947-2400

General Fax, Inc.
Christopher Stephano, President
Front & Ford Sts., Suite A103
Bridgeport, PA 19405
215-277-1722

Inter#Net, Inc.
Barry Krueger, Director of Sales
1001 East Entry Dr., Suite 110
Pittsburgh, PA 15216
412-571-3350

South Carolina

Info-Tel
Chris Brunson, Senior Account Executive
217 Lucas St., Suite E
Mt. Pleasant, SC 29464
800-388-3528

Texas

Celebration Computer Systems
James F. Wiseheart, President
9207 Country Creek, Suite 140
Houston, TX 77036
713-625-4000

CommNet, Inc.
Dave Knapp, President
1206 Avenue R, Suite D
Lubbock, TX 79401
806-747-3025

Fax Access Xchange, Inc. (FAX, Inc.)
Jerry Bachmann, Vice President, Sales
4851 Keller Springs Rd.
Dallas, TX 75248-5928
214-931-5800

Modern Moral Innovations (MMI)
Jay Dietz, President
4019 Adonis
Houston, TX 77373
713-350-4664

NeoData
Kevin McKinnon, Marketing Manager
100 Crescent Ct., Suite 650
Dallas, TX 75201
214-871-5588

Teleservice Resources
Nanci Carroll, Sales Manager
4201 Cambridge Rd.
Ft. Worth, TX 76155
800-325-2580

Voicetext Interactive
Paul Cohen, National Marketing Director
702 Colorado St., Suite 125
Austin, TX 78701
512-404-2300

WTS Bureau Systems, Inc.
George Lyons
2170 Lone Star Dr.
Dallas, TX 75212
214-920-1900

Utah

Teleshare
Shane Heath, Director of Operations
227 North University Ave., Suite 103
Provo, UT 84601
801-377-0600

Virginia

Phone Base Systems, Inc.
Phil Gross, Senior Vice President
8620 Westwood Center Dr.
Vienna, VA 22182
703-893-8600

Ultra Communications
Paul Dalton, President
4330 M Evergreen Lane
Annandale, VA 22003-3211
703-642-3100

Washington

Bureau One, Inc.
Chris Schott, Director of New Accounts
921 14th St.
Longview, WA 98632
206-636-2000

Canada

Corporate Telemarketing, Inc.
David Filwood, President
12 Water St., Suite 401
Vancouver, BC V6B 1A5
604-685-6144

Fax Canada
Alana Samuels, President
980 Alness St., Unit 13
North York, Ontario M3J 2S2
416-650-9314

Interactive Telephone Marketing (ITEM)
Otti Lockhard
822 Richmond St. W., Suite 200
Toronto, Ontario M6J 1C9
416-363-5000

Messagebank of Calgary
Maury Wasserman, President
222 58th Ave. SW, #212
Calgary, Alberta T2H 2S3
403-531-4000

Appendix F

Phoneworks Canada
Dan Melymuk
181 Carlaw Ave., Suite 310
Toronto, Ontario M4M 2S1
416-778-7877

PRIMA Telmatic Inc.
Jack L'Africain
14 Commerce Pl., Suite 510
Nuns' Island, Quebec H3E 1P5
514-768-7676

Voice Courrier
Gordon Black, Sales Manager
1300 Bay St., Suite 200
Toronto, Ontario M5R 3K8
416-921-0033

Interactive Entertainment Group
Darian Brooks, President
26 Parkwood Ave.
Toronto, Ontario M4V 2X1
800-567-8965

Telepath Telecommunications
Warren Eugene, President
26 Parkwood Ave.
Toronto, Ontario M4V 2X1
800-567-8965

Appendix G
Federal Laws & Regulations

In order to get the proper perspective regarding the laws and regulations that currently govern the 900 pay-per-call industry, it will be instructive to follow some of the legislative history behind the enactment of the Federal law, which forms the basis and the authority for the resulting Federal regulations promulgated by the FCC and the FTC. To refresh the memory of those of you who are a bit rusty on the legislative process, agencies such as the FCC and the FTC create and enforce regulations in response to legislation passed by Congress. The logical place to start, therefore, will be with the Federal law passed by Congress, followed by the resulting FCC and FTC regulations.

Federal 900 Law

The actual text of the Telephone Disclosure and Dispute Resolution Act (TDDRA), the current federal law governing the pay-per-call industry, is too voluminous to reproduce in full here. Instead, reprinted here by permission is an excellent discussion of TDDRA that appeared in Volume 17:359, 1993 of the Seton Hall Legislative

Journal, written by Thaddeus J. Burns, Esq. and William W. Burrington, Executive Director and General Counsel for the National Association for Interactive Services (N.A.I.S.). For the purpose of clarity and brevity, footnotes and references that were included in the original article have been omitted in this reprint:

The Telephone Disclosure and Dispute Resolution Act

A. Legislative History

Largely in response to complaints from consumers, both the United States Senate and the House of Representatives held hearings and passed similar pieces of legislation designed to prevent fraud by companies offering pay-per-call services via 900 telephone numbers. On October 29, 1991, the U.S. Senate passed by voice vote S. 1579, the "900 Services Consumer Protection Act of 1991." The companion House bill, H.R. 3490, the "Telephone Disclosure and Dispute Resolution Act," passed the House of Representatives on February 25, 1992, by a vote of 381-31.

After the House passed H.R. 3490, it inserted the language of its bill into S. 1579, the Senate-passed bill. Minor differences between the two bills were resolved in an informal, staff level conference before the final legislation was passed by unanimous consent as H.R. 6191 by both the House and Senate in early October, 1992, just days before the 102nd Congress adjourned. While the Bush Administration did not threaten to veto the legislation, it opposed the legislation arguing that pay-per-call legislation is unnecessary since Federal agencies, such as the FCC, have already taken many of the same steps through regulations. The Telephone Disclosure and Dispute Resolution Act (Federal 900 law) was signed into law by President Bush on October 28, 1992.

B. Legislative Findings

In broad terms, the intent of the new Federal 900 law is to: (1) establish uniform standards for the pay-per-call industry at the Federal level; (2) ensure that consumers who call 900 services receive adequate information before they decide to utilize a pay-per-call service; and (3) give the FCC, the FTC, and States the authority necessary to protect the pay-per-call consumer. The new Federal 900 law specifically recognizes the interstate nature of the pay-per-call industry, and it is, therefore, especially concerned with the need to provide uniform nationwide consumer protection standards in order to avoid the development of a cumbersome and complicated patchwork of individual State regulations governing the pay-per-call industry.

The Federal 900 law requires both the FCC and the FTC to conduct rulemakings and promulgate regulations governing preambles, advertisements, collect call-backs, 800 numbers, and billing dispute procedures. The law requires both agencies to promulgate their rules by late July of 1993.

The law as enacted consists of four titles: Title 1 addresses the required FCC rulemaking, including the regulation of common carriers offering pay-per-call services and billing and collection practices. Title II outlines the required FTC rulemakings regarding advertising preambles and actions by states. Title III sets forth the requirements for the FTC rulemaking pertaining to the correction of billing errors with respect to telephone-billed purchases. Title IV outlines miscellaneous provisions governing non-pay-per-call issues.

C. Title I   Common Carrier Obligations, Consumer Rights, and the FCC Rulemaking

Title I of the law amends the Communication Act of 1934 by adding a new section 228 governing the regulation of common carriers offering pay-per-call services. For purposes of this new section, the term "pay-per-call service" is defined as any service in which a person provides:

(A)(i) audio information or audio entertainment produced or packaged by such person; (ii) access to simultaneous voice conversation services; or (iii) any service, including the provision of a product, the charges for which are assessed on the basis of completion of the call;

(B) for which the caller pays a per-call or per-time-interval charge that is greater than or in addition to, the charge for transmission of the call; and

(C)   which is assessed through use of a 900 telephone number or other prefix or area code [as] designated by the [FCC]....

The definition specially does not include: (1) directory services provided by common carriers or local exchange carriers or their affiliate; (2) tariffed services; or (3) services for which customers are charged only after entering into a presubscription agreement or "comparable arrangement." The congressional definition of pay-per-call services varies from the one adopted by the FCC 900 Rules in December, 1991.

The new law requires the FCC to promulgate regulations within 270 days after the date of enactment of the new section 228 of the Communications Act of 1934.   It further directs the FCC to establish several specific rules governing the conduct and obligations of common carriers - both interexchange carriers and local exchange carriers.

First, the FCC's final rules must ensure that common carriers, either by contract or tariff, require information providers (IPs) to comply with the Federal 900 law.   Second, the FCC must require that common carriers provide, on request, to Federal and State agencies as well as other interested persons specific information, including: (1) the telephone numbers for each pay-per-call service it carries; (2) a description of the type of each service, including the total cost or cost per minute of the service (and any other fees); (3) the IP's name, business address and telephone number; and (4) any other information the FCC requires. The FCC must also require that a common carrier terminate the IP's service if the carrier "knows or reasonably should know" that the pay-per-call service is not provided in compliance with the regulations promulgated by the FTC as required by Titles II and III of the law. In essence, the new 900 law places a burden upon common carriers to police IPs and ensure compliance with the FTC regulations to be promulgated. This new requirement will place a significant legal burden upon common carriers and will undoubtedly lead to even greater scrutiny by the carriers when deciding whether or not to accept pay-per-call programs and services placed by IPs.

The new FCC regulations required by the Federal 900 law also must prohibit a common carrier from disconnecting or interrupting a telephone subscriber's basic local and long distance telephone service due to the subscriber's nonpayment of pay-per-call charges. This requirement is similar to the current FCC 900 rules. In addition, the FCC rules must require local exchange carriers to offer, where technically feasible, blocking to all or certain specific prefixes or area codes used by pay-per-call services. Blocking must be offered at no charge to all telephone subscribers for 60 days after the FCC rules become effective, and to any new subscriber for a 60 day period after their new telephone number is placed in service. After this one-time free blocking service is offered, local exchange carriers will be allowed to charge a reasonable fee for blocking. Finally, in addition to the blocking requirements outlined above, local exchange carriers will be required by the FCC rules to offer subscribers, where technically and economically feasible, the option of presubscribing to or blocking only specific pay-per-call services for a one-time "reasonable" charge.

The law also requires the FCC to promulgate rules governing the use of 800 telephone numbers. The FCC is required to prohibit the use of any 800 telephone number , or numbers "advertised or widely understood to be toll free" in a manner which results in the calling party being charged for completing the call or being connected to a pay-per-call service. For example, a person who calls an 800 number, or some other number generally viewed as free, cannot be automatically connected to a 900 or pay-per-call service via a call to the toll free number. The FCC rules will not apply when the caller has a "preexisting agreement" to be charged for the service, or if the caller provides a "credit or charge number during the call" to the information provider. This requirement is problematic since the law does not define what constitutes a "preexisting agreement." For example, an individual could presubscribe to a pay-per-call service by entering into an agreement with the IP prior to using the service. This individual could access the pay-per-call service by calling a toll free 800 number. It is unclear what would constitute an "agreement" - whether the caller would have to request a presubscription arrangement in writing or whether this could be accomplished over the telephone. Finally the FCC is required to strictly prohibit the practice of calling a 800 number only to be automatically called back collect by the provider of pay-per-call services. Precisely how the FCC and the FTC formulate rules governing 800 and other toll free services will have a dramatic impact upon the future use and development of innovative 800 services.

Under the new law, Congress has directed the FCC to establish rules governing common carrier billing and collection for pay-per-call services. Under the required FCC rules, any local exchange carrier that offers billing and collection services to an IP must ensure that a caller is not billed for: (1) pay-per-call services that the local exchange carrier "knows or reasonably should know" violates the 900 law, or (2) under other circumstances that the FCC finds abusive. Common carriers must also establish a local or toll free telephone number to allow subscribers to get information and have their questions answered concerning pay-per-call services, including the name and address of any pay-per-call services offered through the common carrier by an IP. In addition, within 60 days from the effective date of the FCC's new regulations, the common carrier, either directly or through the local exchange carrier, must provide telephone subscribers with a disclosure statement outlining the rights and responsibilities of the subscriber with respect to the use and payment for pay-per-call charges be segregated on the subscriber's telephone bill from regular local and long distance charges, and must specify the date, time, and duration of the call, as well as the type of service called and the charge for the call. The FCC is also required to develop procedures consistent with Titles II and III of the 900 law to ensure that common carriers and "other parties providing billing and collection services" for pay-per-call services provide refunds to subscribers that have been billed for services deemed to have violated the 900 law or the Federal laws.

While the new law and resulting FCC regulations will place a number of new regulatory burdens upon common carriers, the law specifically limits common carrier liability. Common carriers will face civil or criminal liability under the new law only if the carrier "knew or reasonably should have known" that a particular pay-per-call service was provided in violation of the 900 or other Federal law. And, subject to a "good faith" test, a common carrier cannot be sued for terminating a pay-per-call service in order to comply with the 900 law.

The 900 law does not preempt Federal, State, and local election, consumer protection, or gambling laws. Furthermore, states are free to enact "additional and complimentary oversight" so long as these rules govern intrastate services and do not significantly impede the enforcement of Federal law. The new 900 law will also not affect the current dial-a-porn law and regulations previously enacted by Congress and the FCC. In addition, the law directs the FCC within one year from October 28, 1992, to submit to Congress recommendations concerning the extension of the new FCC rules to persons that provide, for a per-call charge, electronic data services that are not traditional pay-per-call services. Finally, with the respect to the FCC's rules, the 900 law does not prevent any State from adopting additional laws and regulations, "so long as [they] govern intrastate services and do not significantly impede the enforcement of this section [of the 900 law] or other Federal statutes.

   D. Title II - The FTC Rulemaking Regulating Unfair and Deceptive Pay-Per-Call Practices

   The FTC is the Federal agency primarily responsible for overseeing advertising practices. Until the new Federal 900 law was enacted, the FTC acted on a case-by-case basis against pay-per-call programs that it considered deceptive or misleading. Title II of the new 900 law requires the FTC to promulgate specific rules to prohibit unfair and deceptive pay-per-call advertisements. These new rules apply to IPs that advertise pay-per-call services. Like the FCC, the FTC has 270 days from the October 28, 1992 enactment of the 900 law in which to complete its rulemaking.
   The FTC rules must require that the person offering advertised pay-per-call services "clearly and conspicuously" disclose the cost to use the telephone number, including the total cost or the cost per minute, and any other fees. The 900 law does not define the term "clearly and conspicuously." For any service advertisement which offers a prize, award, service, or product at no cost or at a reduced cost, the FTC rules must require that the IP "clearly and conspicuously" disclose the odds of being able to win or receive the service or product. Unless the IP offers a "bona fide educational service," the FTC will prohibit all advertisements directed at children under twelve years of age. It is not clear form the new law just how the FTC will define what constitutes a "bona fide educational service." All pay-per-call advertising directed primarily to those individuals under the age of 18 must "clearly and conspicuously" state that the caller must have parental or legal guardian consent prior to using the service.
   Other FTC advertising requirements must include a prohibition against the use of advertising which emits an electronic beep tone to automatically dial a pay-per-call service. This requirement is aimed primarily at children. In addition, pay-per-call advertisements appearing in the print media and on television must "clearly and conspicuously" disclose the cost of the call (total cost or cost per minute) whenever the 900 number appears. In television advertisements, the cost disclosure must be displayed on the screen for the same duration as the 900 number. These same disclosure requirements apply to any telephonic solicitations for pay-per-call services. Finally, the new FTC 900 rules must prohibit the advertising of any 800 number, or any other telephone number widely understood to be free, from which callers are automatically connected to an access number for a pay-per-call service.
   The 900 law also requires the FTC to develop rules which establish certain service standards applicable to IPs. Each pay-per-call service provider will be required to include an introductory disclosure message (preamble) that: (1) describes the service; (2) specifies the total cost or cost per minute, and other fees of the call; (3) informs the caller that charges begin at the end

of the preamble; (4) informs the caller that parental consent is required for children; and (5) states that the service is not authorized, endorsed or approved by any Federal agency, if the program provides information on any Federal program.

Additionally, the FTC must require that IPs allow the caller to hang up after the preamble without incurring a charge. Similar to the FTC's advertising requirements, IPs will not be permitted to direct pay-per-call services to children under the age of 12, unless it is a "bona fide educational service." The IP will be required to stop charging the caller immediately upon disconnection of the call. Also, the IP must temporarily disable any bypass mechanism which allows frequent callers to avoid listening to the required preamble after the institution of any price increase. The FTC is required to prohibit IPs from providing pay-per-call services through any 800 number or other number advertised or widely understood to be toll free.

With respect to billing statements, the FTC must require that IPs ensure that such statements separately display pay-per-call charges, and list the type of service, the date, time, and duration of the call, as well as the cost of the call. Under the law, IPs will be liable for refunds to consumers for pay-per-call services that have been found to violate the 900 law or the FTC's new rules.

The FTC's rules applicable to IPs may include certain exemptions. The FTC may exempt from its rules calls by frequent callers or regular subscribers using a bypass mechanism and pay-per-call services provided at nominal charges. The 900 law does not define the term "nominal charges." This definition will be delineated in the FTC's new rules. Currently, the FCC 900 rules exempt from FCC preamble requirements those services with a flat-rate charge of $2.00 or less. It is uncertain whether or not the FTC will define "nominal charges" to be a figure which is greater than the current FCC standard.

Congress has also directed the FTC to consider requiring pay-per-call services to automatically disconnect a call after one full cycle of the program. The FTC must also require IPs to include a beep tone or other signal during live interactive group programs to alert callers to the passage of time. The transgression of FTC rules prescribed by Title II of the Federal 900 law will be treated as a violation of unfair or deceptive acts or practices under section 5 of the Federal Trade Commission Act.

Finally, section 202 of the Federal 900 law provides that state officials will be permitted to bring a civil action under the 900 law against IPs in the appropriate U.S. District Court. States may seek an injunction against further practices, obtain damages on behalf of their residents, or obtain other relief that the court deems appropriate.

E. Title III - The FTC's Billing and Collection Rules

The third title of the new 900 law directs the FTC to undertake a rulemaking to establish procedures for the correction of billing errors relating to telephone-billed purchases. The FTC must adopt rules substantially similar to those found in the Truth in Lending and Fair Credit Billing Acts. For purposes of this title, the 900 law defines "telephone billed purchase" as "any purchase that is completed solely as a consequence of the completion of the call or a subsequent dialing, touch tone entry, or comparable action of the caller." The term does not include: (1) a purchase made pursuant to a preexisting agreement; or (2) local or interexchange telephone service. Among other things, the 900 law directs the FTC to consider the procedures that subscribers must follow in order to correct alleged billing errors, as well as the method by which common carriers and third party billing entities must respond to such requests. The FTC must also consider (1) limitations on collection action; (2) the regulation of credit reports on billing disputes; and (3) notification to the purchaser of a credit to their account.

Conclusion

Since Congressional enactment and subsequent approval by the Second Circuit of the reverse blocking provision applicable to indecent pay-per-call services, as well as the promulgation of the three-tired FCC regulations, it appears that the First Amendment dimensions of pay-per-call regulation have been resolved. Providers of indecent pay-per-call services will be subject both to reverse blocking and the credit card/access code/scrambling restrictions. The new Federal 900 law will in no way affect the dial-a-porn legal framework fashioned over the last decade by Congress, the FCC and the courts.

The new 900 law and the resulting FCC and FTC rules, in concert with the FCC's enforcement of the indecency provisions of section 223, will provide the much needed legal and regulatory framework to protect consumers of pay-per-call services from the industry's bad actors while ensuring the pay-per-call industry, as a whole, continued opportunities for growth and innovation.

The Federal 900 law and the new regulations required to be enacted under the law will complete the development of a Federal legal and regulatory framework to guide the future of the pay-per-call industry. However, the precise language of the 900 rules promulgated by the FCC and the FTC, as well as how the new rules and the 900 law will be applied and interpreted will impact significantly the industry's future. Several critical issues remain to be decided by both the FCC and the FTC. First, the FTC's definition of "bona fide educational services" must be crafted carefully as it applies to pay-per-call services offered to children under 12. Second, the potential exists for the development of inconsistent preamble requirements between the FTC and the FCC. The FCC already has promulgated such requirements. The new 900 law also directs the FTC to develop its own preamble requirements. Given the FTC's important new role in the regulation and oversight of the pay-per-call industry, it is vital that the FCC and the FTC coordinate their respective rulemakings in order to avoid unintended duplication and confusion in the new 900 rules. Finally, the Title III billing and collection procedures developed by the FTC must be crafted carefully to ensure that they achieve their intended purpose - to protect both consumers and providers of pay-per-call services - without becoming overly burdensome to implement and administer.

The most important impact of the new Federal 900 legal and regulatory scheme will be its effect on State initiatives to regulate the industry. The Congress is correct in its finding that uniformity of Federal and State law is the most effective way of balancing the competing interests of consumer protection and industry growth. Indeed, while pay-per-call providers and consumers await the outcome of the FCC and FTC rulemakings, several states are already moving to pass laws which go well beyond the existing Federal laws to regulate the pay-per-call industry. For example, currently, the states of Alaska and South Carolina have proposed legislation and regulations that would drastically curtail public access to pay-per-call services, and California enacted a sweeping pay-per-call law which goes into effect on January 1, 1993. A rising tide of state legislation will result in a patchwork of inconsistent standards that will halt the continued growth and development of innovative and value-added pay-per-call services. Finally, the new Federal 900 law will hopefully achieve the objective of imposing the uniformity necessary for continued growth of the industry, while at the same time preserving the law that has evolved over nearly a decade to advance the compelling interest of protecting minors from the small segment of the industry that provides indecent adult pay-per-call services.

Federal Communications Commission (FCC) Regulations

Surprisingly enough, the FCC regulations that resulted from passage of the Federal law (TDDRA) are not so lengthy and cumbersome that they cannot be reproduced in full here. The following is a verbatim transcription from Title 47 of the Code of Federal Regulations, Part 64, Sections 64.1501 through 64.1515, which are the complete FCC regulations governing pay-per-call services:

Section 64.1501 Definitions

For the purposes of this subpart, the following definitions shall apply:
(a) Pay-per call service means any service
    (1) In which any person provides or purports to provide
        (A)   Audio information or audio entertainment produced or packaged by such person;
        (B) Access to simultaneous voice conversation services; or
        (C) Any service, including the provision of a product, the charges for which are assessed on the basis of the completion of the call;
    (2) For which the caller pays a per-call or per-time-interval charge that is greater than, or in addition to, the charge for transmission of the call; and
    (3) Which is accessed through use of a 900 telephone number.
(b) Such term does not include directory services provided by a common carrier or its affiliate or by a local exchange carrier or its affiliate, or any service the charge for which is tariffed, or any service for which users are assessed charges only after entering into a presubscription or comparable arrangement with the provider of such service.
(b)(1) Presubscription or comparable arrangement means a contractual agreement in which
    (i) The service provider clearly and conspicuously discloses to the consumer all material terms and conditions associated with the use of the service, including the service provider's name and address, a business telephone number which the consumer may use to obtain additional information or to register a complaint, and the rates for the service;
    (ii) The service provider agrees to notify the consumer of any future rate changes;
    (iii) The consumer agrees to utilize the service on the terms and conditions disclosed by the service provider; and
    (iv) The service provider requires the use of an identification number or other means to prevent unauthorized access to the service by nonsubscribers.
    (2)   Disclosure of a credit or charge card number, along with authorization to bill that number, made during the course of a call to an information service shall constitute a presubscription or comparable arrangement if the credit or charge card is subject to the dispute resolution procedures of the Truth in Lending Act and Fair Credit Billing Ace, as amended, 15 U.S.C. Section 1601 et seq. No other action taken by the consumer during the course of a call to an information service, for which charges are assessed, can be construed as creating a presubscription or comparable arrangement.

64.1502 Limitations on the Provision of Pay-Per-Call Services

Any common carrier assigning a telephone number to a provider of interstate pay-per-call service shall require, by contract or tariff, that such provider comply with the provisions of this subpart and of titles II and III of the Telephone Disclosure and Dispute Resolution Act (Pub. L. No. 102-556)

(TDDRA) and the regulations prescribed by the Federal Trade Commission pursuant to those titles.

64.1503 Termination of Pay-Per-Call Programs.

Any common carrier assigning a telephone number to a provider of interstate pay-per-call service shall specify by contract or tariff that pay-per-call programs not in compliance with Section 64.1502 shall be terminated following written notice to the information provider. The information provider shall be afforded a period of no less than seven and no more than 14 days during which a program may be brought into compliance. Programs not in compliance at the expiration of such period shall be terminated immediately.

64.1504 Restrictions on the Use of 800 Numbers.

Common carriers shall prohibit, by tariff or contract, the use of any telephone number beginning with an 800 service access code, or any other telephone number advertised or widely understood to be toll free, in a manner that would result in
(a) The calling party or the subscriber to the originating line being assessed, by virtue of completing the call, a charge for the call;
(b) The calling party being connected to a pay-per-call service;
(c) The calling party being charged for information conveyed during the call unless the calling party has a presubscription or comparable arrangement; or
(d) The calling party being called back collect for the provision of audio or data information services, simultaneous voice conversation services, or products.

64.1505 Restrictions on Collect Telephone Calls.

(a) No common carrier shall provide interstate transmission or billing and collection services to an entity offering any service within the scope of 64.1501 (a)(1) that is billed to a subscriber on a collect basis at a per-call or per-time-interval charge that is greater than or in addition to, the charge for transmission of the call.
(b) No common carrier shall provide interstate transmission services for any collect information services billed to a subscriber at a tariffed rate unless the called party has taken affirmative action clearly indicating that it accepts the charges for the collect service.

64.1506 Number Designation.

Any interstate service described in 64.1501 (a)(1) - (2) shall be offered only through telephone numbers beginning with a 900 service access code.

64.1507 Prohibition on Disconnection or Interruption of Service for Failure to Remit Pay-Per-Call or Similar Service Charges.

No common carrier shall disconnect or interrupt in any manner, or order the disconnection or interruption of, a telephone subscriber's local exchange or long distance telephone service as a result of that subscriber's failure to pay
(a) Charges for interstate pay-per-call service,
(b) Charges for interstate information services provided pursuant to a presubscription or comparable arrangement or
(c) Charges, which have been disputed by the subscriber, for interstate tariffed collect information services.

64.1508 Blocking Access to 900 Service

(a) Local exchange carriers must offer to their subscribers, where technically feasible, an option to block access to services offered on the 900 service access code. Blocking is to be offered at no charge, on a one-time basis, to
(1) All telephone subscribers during the period from November 1, 1993 through December 31, 1993; and
(2) Any subscriber who subscribes to a new telephone number for a period of 60 days after the new number is effective.
(b) For blocking requests not within the one-time option or outside the time frames specified in paragraph (a) of this section, and for unblocking requests, local exchange carriers may charge a reasonable one-time fee. Requests by subscribers to remove 900 services blocking must be in writing.
(c) The terms and conditions under which subscribers may obtain 900 services blocking are to be included in tariffs filed with this Commission.

64.1509 Disclosure and Dissemination of Pay-Per-Call Information.

(a) Any common carrier assigning a telephone number to a provider of interstate pay-per-call services shall make readily available, at no charge, to Federal and State agencies and all other interested persons:
(1) A list of the telephone numbers for each of the pay-per-call services it carries;
(2) A short description of each such service;
(3) A statement of the total cost or the cost per minute and any other fees for each such service; and
(4) A statement of the pay-per-call service provider's name, business address, and business telephone number.
(b) Any common carrier assigning a telephone number to a provider of interstate pay-per-call services and offering billing and collection services to such provider shall
(1) Establish a local or toll-free telephone number to answer questions and provide information on subscribers' rights and obligations with regard

to their use of pay-per-call services and to provide to callers the name and mailing address of any provider of pay-per-call services offered by that carrier; and

(2) Provide to all its telephone subscribers, either directly or through contract with any local exchange carrier providing billing and collection services to that carrier, a disclosure statement setting forth all rights and obligations of the subscriber and the carrier with respect to the use and payment of pay-per-call services. Such statement must include the prohibition against disconnection of basic communications services for failure to pay-per-call charges established by 64.1507, the right of a subscriber to obtain blocking in accordance with 64.1508, the right of a subscriber not to be billed for pay-per-call services not offered in compliance with federal laws and regulations established by 64.1510 (a) (iv), and the possibility that a subscriber's access to 900 services may be involuntarily blocked pursuant to 64.1512 for failure to pay legitimate pay-per-call charges. Disclosure statements must be forwarded to:

(i) All telephone subscribers no later 60 days after these regulations take effect;

(ii) All new telephone subscribers no later than 60 days after service is established;

(iii) All telephone subscribers requesting service at a new location no later than 60 days after service is established; and

(iv) Thereafter, to all subscribers at least once per calendar year, at intervals of not less than 6 months nor more than 18 months.

64.1510 Billing and Collection of Pay-Per-Call and Similar Service Charges.

(a) Any common carrier assigning a telephone number to a provider of interstate pay-per-call services and offering billing and collection services to such provider shall:

(1) Ensure that a subscriber is not billed for interstate pay-per-call services that such carrier knows or reasonably should know were provided in violation of the regulations set forth in this subpart of prescribed by the Federal Trade Commission pursuant to titles II or III of the TDDRA or any other federal law;

(2) In any billing to telephone subscribers that includes charges for any interstate pay-per-call service

(i) Include a statement indicating that:

(A) Such charges are for non-communications services;

(B) Neither local nor long distances services can be disconnected for non-payment although an information provider may employ private entities to seek to collect such charges;

(C) 900 number blocking is available upon request; and

(D) Access to pay-per-call services may be involuntarily blocked for failure to pay legitimate charges;

(ii) Display any charges for pay-per-call services in a part of the bill that is identified as not being related to local and long distance telephone charges;

(iii) Specify, for each pay-per-call charge made, the type of service, the amount of the charge, and the date, time and, for calls billed on a time-sensitive basis, the duration of the call; and

(iv) Identify the local or toll-free number established in accordance with 64.1509 (b)(1).

(b) Any common carrier offering billing and collection services to an entity providing interstate information services pursuant to a presubscription or comparable arrangement, or for interstate tariffed collect information services, shall, to the extent possible, display the billing information in the manner described in paragraphs (a) (2) (i) - (ii) of this section.

64.1511 Forgiveness of Charges and Refunds.

(a) Any carrier assigning a telephone number to a provider of interstate pay-per-call services or providing transmission for interstate tariffed collect information services or interstate information services offered under a presubscription or comparable arrangement, and providing billing and collection services for such services, shall establish procedures for the handling of subscriber complaints regarding charges for those services. A billing carrier is afforded discretion to set standards for determining when a subscriber's complaint warrants forgiveness, refund or credit of interstate pay-per-call or information services charges provided that such charges must be forgiven, refunded, or credited when a subscriber has complained about such charges and either this Commission, the Federal Trade Commission, or a court of competent jurisdiction has found or the carrier has determined, upon investigation, that the service has been offered in violation of federal law or the regulations that are either set forth in this subpart or prescribed by the Federal Trade Commission pursuant to titles II or III of the TDDRA. Carriers shall observe the record retention requirements set forth in 47 C.F.R. Section 42.6 except that relevant records shall be retained by carriers beyond the requirements of Part 42 of this chapter when a complaint is pending at the time the specified retention period expires.

(b) Any carrier assigning a telephone number to a provider of interstate pay-per-call services but not providing billing and collection services for such services, shall, by tariff or contract, require that the provider and/or its billing and collection agents have in place procedures whereby, upon complaint, pay-per-call charges may be forgiven, refunded, or credited, provided that such charges must be forgiven, refunded, or credited when a subscriber has complained about such charges and either this Commission, the Federal Trade Commission, or a court of competent jurisdiction has found or the carrier has determined, upon investigation, that the service has been offered in violation of federal law or the regulations that are either set forth in this subpart or prescribed by the Federal Trade Commission pursuant to titles II or III of the TDDRA.

64.1512 Involuntary Blocking of Pay-Per-Call Services

Nothing in this subpart shall preclude a common carrier or information provider from blocking or ordering the blocking of its interstate pay-per-call programs from numbers assigned to subscribers who have incurred, but not paid, legitimate pay-per-call charges, except that a subscriber who has filed a complaint regarding a particular pay-per-call program pursuant to procedures established by the Federal Trade Commission under title III of the TDDRA shall not be involuntarily blocked from access to that program while such a complaint is pending. This restriction is not intended to preclude involuntary blocking when a carrier or IP has decided in one instance to sustain charges against a subscriber but that subscriber files additional separate complaints.

64.1513 Verification of Charitable Status.

Any common carrier assigning a telephone number to a provider of interstate pay-per-call services that the carrier knows or reasonably should know is engaged in soliciting charitable contributions shall obtain verification that the entity or individual for whom contributions are solicited has been granted tax exempt status by the Internal Revenue Service.

64.1514 Generation of Signalling Tones.

No common carrier shall assign a telephone number for any pay-per-call service that employs broadcast advertising which generates the audible tones necessary to complete a call to a pay-per-call service.

64.1515 Recovery of Costs.

No common carrier shall recover its cost of complying with the provisions of this subpart from local or long distance ratepayers.

FCC Dial-a-Porn Rules

Because the FCC Dial-a-Porn Rules apply to the use of indecent communications over all telephone lines, not just 900 pay-per-call lines, these rules are distinct from the FCC 900 Rules that were just presented. The following is a verbatim transcription of the FCC Dial-a-Porn Rules:

64.201 Restrictions on Indecent Telephone Message Services

(a) It is a defense to prosecution for the provision of indecent communications under section 223(b)(2) of the Communications Act of 1934, as amended (the Act), 47 U.S.C. 223(B)(2), that the defendant has taken the action set forth in paragraph (a)(1) of this section and, in addition, has complied with the following: Taken one of the actions set forth in paragraphs (a)(2), (3), or (4) of this section to restrict access to prohibited communications to persons eighteen years of age or older, and has additionally complied with paragraph (a)(5) of this section, where applicable:

(1) Has notified the common carrier identified in section 223(c)(1) of the Act, in writing, that he or she is providing the kind of service described in section 223(b)(2) of the Act.

(2) Requires payment by credit card before transmission of the message; or

(3) Requires an authorized access or identification code before transmission of the message, and where the defendant has:

(i) Issued the code by mailing it to the applicant after reasonably ascertaining through receipt of a written application that the applicant is not under eighteen years of age; and

(ii) Established a procedure to cancel immediately the code of any person upon written, telephonic or other notice to the defendant's business office that such code has been lost, stolen, or used by a person or persons under the age of eighteen, or that such code is no longer desired; or

(4) Scrambles the message using any technique that renders the audio unintelligible and incomprehensible to the calling party unless that party uses a descrambler; and,

(5) Where the defendant is a message sponsor subscriber to mass announcement services tariffed at this Commission and such defendant prior to the transmission of the message has requested in writing to the carrier providing the public announcement service that calls to this message service be subject to billing notification as an adult telephone message service.

(b) A common carrier within the District of Columbia or within any State, or in interstate or foreign commerce, shall not, to the extent technically feasible, provide access to a communication described in section 223(b) of the

Act from the telephone of any subscriber who has not previously requested in writing the carrier to provide access to such communication if the carrier collects from subscribers an identifiable charge for such communication that the carrier remits, in whole or in part to the provider of such communication.

Federal Trade Commission (FTC) Regulations

Unlike the FCC, whose 900 regulations are relatively brief, the FTC's 900 regulations were published in a 219 page document that is way too lengthy to reproduce here. Fortunately, along with the actual rules, the FTC published a concise news release that does a good job of summarizing the highlights of the new regulations. Also, Carol Morse Ginsburg, publisher of *Audiotex News*, wrote an excellent summary of the FTC rules in the September edition of her newsletter, and has graciously granted permission to reproduce the article here. Both of these descriptions of the FTC rules will be helpful in understanding their general intent. The full text of the FTC rules are available from the FTC's Public Reference Branch, mentioned at the conclusion of the following FTC news release.

FTC News Release
For release: July 27, 1993

FTC ANNOUNCES 900-NUMBER INDUSTRY RULE

New Regulations Will Require Cost and Other Disclosures, and Set Procedures for Consumers to Resolve Billing Disputes

Beginning this November, companies that offer 900 -number, or pay-per-call, telephone services will be required to disclose the costs of these services in their advertising, and to begin calls costing more than $2 with a "preamble" stating, among other things, the cost of the call. Consumers will not be charged for the call if they hang up shortly afterward. The requirements are outlined in a new Federal Trade Commission rule announced today. The new rule also established procedures for resolving consumer billing-disputes for pay-per call services, and will require certain disclosures to be made in billing statements.

The FTC promulgated its 900-Number Rule pursuant to the Telephone Disclosure and Dispute Resolution Act, which was signed into law in October 1992.

Disclosures

Under the new rule, companies that offer pay-per-call services will have to disclose in any print, radio and television advertisements they run for the services:

--for flat-fee services, the total cost of each call;

--for time-sensitive services, the cost-per-minute and any minimum charges, as well as the maximum charge if it can be determined in advance;

--for services billed at varying rates depending on which options callers select, the cost of the initial portion of the call, any minimum charges, and the range of rates that may be charged;

--all other fees charged for these services; and

--the cost of any other pay-per-call services to which callers may be transferred.

The rule sets out requirements to ensure that these and other mandated disclosures will be clear and conspicuous. The requirements will vary depending on the particular disclosure and on the advertising media. The cost disclosures explained above, for example, generally will have to be made adjacent to the telephone number, and in the same format (visual, oral, or both) as the number. When the 900 number is displayed visually, the cost disclosure will have to be at least half the size of the telephone number.

Other advertising disclosures to be required under the 900-Number Rule include:

--for pay-per-call sweepstakes services, a statement about the odds of winning the sweepstakes prize (or how the odds will be calculated) and the fact that consumers do not have to call to enter the sweepstakes, as well as a description of the free alternative method of entering the sweepstakes (alternatively, these last two statements may be disclosed in the preamble);

--for services that provide information about federal programs but which are not affiliated with the federal government, a statement at the beginning of the advertisement that the service is not authorized, endorsed or approved by any federal entity (this statement also will be required in the preamble);

--for services directed to consumers under the age of 18, a statement that parental permission is required before calling the service (this statement also will be required in the preamble).

The rule also will require billing statements for pay-per-call services to disclose, for each pay-per-call service charge, the type of service, the amount of the charge, the date, time and, for time-sensitive calls, duration of the call. These charges will have to appear apart form local- and long-distance charges on consumers' telephone bills. Finally, each billing statement will have to include a local or toll-free number for consumers to call with questions about their pay-per-call charges.

The Preamble Requirement

The preamble required by the rule will identify the company providing the service, state the cost of the call, and inform the caller that charges will begin three seconds after the tone following the preamble and that they must hang up before that time to avoid charges. Companies will be prohibited from charging consumers for calls if the consumers hang up before the three-second period ends. The rule will allow companies to install a mechanism that would enable frequent callers to bypass the preamble, as long as the companies disable the mechanism for 30 days after each price increase.

Ban on 900-Number Services to Children

Another provision in the FTC rule will implement a provision of the Telephone Disclosure Act banning 900-number services directed to children. The rule will prohibit companies from advertising or directing pay-per-call services to those under 12, unless the services are bona fide educational services dedicated to areas of school study. The rule adopts a two-test approach to the definition of children's advertising. The first test will be whether the ad appears during programming or in publications for which 50 percent of the audience or readership is under 12. These ads are banned. Under the second test, if competent and reliable audience composition data are not available, the Commission will consider a variety of factors in determining whether the ad is directed to children, including the placement of the ad, subject matter, visual content, language, the age of any models, and any characters used in the ad. (Advertisements for services directed to consumers under 18 -- which require a parental-permission disclosure -- also are defined by the medium in which the ad appears, or the nature of the ad.)

Billing-Dispute Resolution Procedures

The billing-dispute resolution section of the 900-Number Rule will require entities that perform billing for pay-per-call services to give consumers written notice at least annually of their billing rights for telephone-billed purchases, including the procedures for disputing charges. Under the FTC rule, billing errors will include charges for calls not made by the customer or for the wrong amount, and charges for telephone-billed purchases not provided to the customer in accordance with the stated terms of the agreement. Under the procedures set out in the rule for resolving these disputes, a customer will be required to notify the responsible billing entity, using the method described in the billing statement, within 60 days after the first statement containing the error was sent (oral notifications will be permitted under the rule). Thereafter, the billing entity will be:

--required to acknowledge the customer's notice in writing within 40 days of receiving it (unless the dispute is resolved within that time);

--required either to correct the billing error and to notify the customer of the correction, or to investigate the matter and either correct the error or explain to the customer the reason for not doing so, within 90 days or two billing cycles;

--prohibited from charging for investigating or responding to the alleged billing error; and

--prohibited from trying to collect the disputed charge from the customer, and from reporting the charge to a credit bureau or other third party, until the billing error has been investigated and the resulting action has been completed (this prohibition will apply to billing entities, carriers and vendors).

Finally, under this section of the 900-Number Rule, billing entities that do not comply with their billing-dispute resolution responsibilities forfeit the right to collect up to $50 of the amount of each disputed charge.

Miscellaneous Provisions

Further, the 900-Number Rule will prohibit companies from running ads that emit electronic tones that dial 900 number automatically. In addition, the rule generally will prohibit companies from using 800 numbers for pay-per-call services, connecting 800-number callers to 900 numbers, or placing collect return calls to 800-number callers.

The rule also will allow the Commission to hold service bureaus (the entities that process pay-per-call service calls) liable if they know or should know that their clients are violating the FTC rule. Finally, companies that have offered pay-per-call services in violation of the rule or any other federal rule or law will be held liable for refunds or credits to consumers, under the FTC rule.

The Commission vote yesterday to promulgate the 900-Number Rule and to approve the Statement of Basis and Purpose in support of it was 4-0, with Commissioner Roscoe B. Starek,III recused. The final rule is a modified version of a proposed rule announced in March 9 news release. The Commission received 99 comments on that proposal, and in April held a two-day workshop to obtain additional feedback from the public and a variety of interested parties.

The 900-Number Rule will be published in the Federal Register shortly and will become effective Nov. 1. Copies of the new rule, the proposed rule and the news release issued when it was announced for public comment, as well as news releases on FTC lawsuits involving deceptive use of 900 numbers, are available from the FTC's Public Reference Branch, Room 130, 6th Street and Pennsylvania Avenue, N.W., Washington, D.C. 20580; 202-326-2222; TTY for the hearing impaired 202-326-2502.

The following article is reprinted with permission from Carol Morse Ginsburg, publisher, *Audiotex News*, as it appeared in the September 1993 edition of that newsletter:

FTC Sets New Rules for 900

According to the Federal Trade Commission (FTC), starting Nov. 1, callers to a 900 number will be told in a preamble how much they have to pay to stay on the line, then hear a tone and have three seconds to hang up of they do not wish to be charged. The FTC rules were adopted with a 4-0 vote on Tuesday, July 27.

The San Francisco Examiner, commenting on the rules, wrote in an editorial, "Despite the 900 industry's tarnished image, there are many legitimate services available that offer real value. The new FTC rules, along with Federal Communications Commission (AN Aug. '93) regulations already in effect will, we hope, weed out shady and unscrupulous operators to the benefit of legitimate service providers."

Despite industry pleas seeking to limit the preamble to calls costing more than $5, the FTC set the limit at $2.

Joselle Albracht, an attorney with Hall Dickler Lawler, Kent & Friedman, said the rules were significantly better than the original rules proposed. The proposed rules were far harsher, particularly in the area of sweepstakes.

When Albracht, a former assistant attorney general (AG) with the Texas AG's office, was asked how AGs across the nation might feel about the rules, she said, "Probably not happy they lost ground. On the other hand, these are strong rules and are enforceable in federal court, and no doubt the AGs will do so."

Larry Podell, publisher of the Audiotex Directory, said "In the short run there may be many problems and initially things will be difficult. However in the long run, it may be good."

Warren Miller of Telecompute Corp. had a more colorful response. "It's like making sausage. The end result may be good, but watching it happen isn't going to be pretty."

NAIS Executive Director and General Counsel, Bill Burrington, putting the actions into an historical perspective, said, "The new FTC 900 rule is the culmination of a lengthy two-year process beginning with the introduction of legislation in the U.S. Congress designed to regulate the pay-per-call industry. From the beginning of this complex legislative and regulatory process, the NAIS played a central role in educating key members of Congress and their staffs, along with key players at the FCC and the FTC."

Written comments had been filed by many (AN April, May, June '93), including the NAIS and the IIA, and the industry's concerns were advocated during a two-day public hearing at the FTC in April. Burrington continued, "The NAIS has worked hard in the past two years to aggressively and proactively advocate the business interests of its members and all who will be affected by the new Federal laws and the resulting FCC/FTC regulations."

Andy Sutcliffe, president of Tele-Publishing, Inc. in Boston and current chair of the NAIS Board of Directors, added, "The NAIS and industry response throughout this lengthy process has been outstanding. The NAIS plays a valuable role in facilitating cooperation among the various segments of the 800/900 industry. This cooperative effort paid off for the entire industry. The FTC clearly listened to our concerns. We didn't get everything, but we did force the FTC to rethink their approach on several critical issues."

The FTC rules follow the signing of the TDDRA last October, as well as some 18 cases brought by the agency in the last three years against companies the FTC said had misrepresented their services or withheld fee information.

The cases brought by the FTC included charges against companies offering referrals to nonexistent jobs, outdated information about jobs or applications for so-called credit cards that had only limited use. In come cases, callers were charged $50 to $70 and not told of the charges in advance.

The FTC issued the rules in a 219-page document. The following summarizes and highlights that report:
Ads:

Clearly disclose fees in all print, radio and TV advertising and in the preamble as well. Include children's warning, and price disclosure. The latter must be at least half the size of the phone number.

Billing Disputes:
Callers may contest a disputed charge orally or in writing within 60 days of receiving a bill, and companies will have to acknowledge the customer's notice in writing within 40 days of receipt. Companies then have 90 days to investigate, correct and notify consumers about final results of any investigations. Can't go to a credit bureau or third party until dispute is resolved.

Blocking:
Free one-time blocking.

Carriers:
In their billing statements, the carriers must include the type of service, the amount of the charge, the date, time and, for time-sensitive calls, the duration of the call. Charges will appear apart from local and long distance charges.

Once a year consumers will be informed about billing rights and how to resolve billing disputes. Each billing statement will include a local or toll-free number for consumers to call with questions about their pay-per-call charges.

Disconnection:
A subscriber's phone cannot be disconnected for failure to pay.

Children's Programming:
The rules ban 900-number services aimed at children under 12, and provide procedures for disputing charges for calls children may have made.

No 900 ads during programming or in publications for which half of the audience is under 12. In lieu of competent and reliable data, the FTC will consider a variety of factors in determining whether the ad is directed to children. Those factors include the ad's placement, subject matter, visual content, language, age of any models and any characters appearing in the ad.

Ads for services directed to persons under the age of 18 which require a parental-permission disclosure are also defined by the medium in which the ad appears, or the nature of the ad.

Services aimed at children under the age of 18 must include a statement that parental permission is required. This notice is also required in the preamble.

800 Numbers:
Generally bars companies from using 800 numbers for pay-per-call services.

Federal Program Information:
Firms selling information on federal programs must disclose that their services are not government-endorsed.

Preamble:
Identify the company providing the service, state the cost of the call -- flat fee or by minute. Inform the caller that charges will begin three seconds after the tone that follows the preamble, and that they must hang up before that time to avoid charges. IP will pay for the preamble time. A preamble must also briefly describe the product or service provided. Warning must be provided on all programs aimed at children under 18, defined by medium and nature of ad. The quality of the preamble must be clear and understandable. The cost of any other pay-per-call service to which callers may be transferred when calling the 900-numbers must be revealed in the preamble.

An exemption from the preamble requirement is made for data services. It applies only when the entire call consists of non-verbal transmission of information. Two machines, e.g. computer, facsimile machine, communicate without the transmission of the spoken word.

Sweepstakes:
Companies running sweepstakes on 900 numbers must disclose the odds of winning, or how the odds will be calculated. No call is required to enter, and there must be an alternative free method of entering the contest. A description of the free alternative method of entry must be included.

Other:
The FTC rules do not regulate content or type of services available on 900-numbers.

The rules also permit the FTC to hold a service bureau liable if they know or should know that their clients are violating FTC rules, and to hold providers of pay-per-cal services liable for any consumer refund or credit if they are found to have violated FTC rules or federal law.

Appendix H
Long Distance Carriers

The following information about the three major long distance carriers is intended to help you in making an informed selection of a carrier that will meet your specific needs. Price, or any other single criteria, should never be the only factor in choosing a carrier. In fact, the service bureau you want to do business with may work exclusively with only one of these long distance carriers.

All three of these carriers have stringent guidelines for doing business with them. For the most part, the individual IXC guidelines have been reproduced here with minimal editing. Much of the content in the respective guidelines simply follows the laws and regulations outlined in Appendices G (Federal Laws and Regulations) and I (Contests, Games and Sweepstakes).

The following IXC prices and guidelines are subject to change, and although this information is accurate as of this writing, you should verify this information with the pertinent IXC.

AT&T MultiQuest

800-243-0900
MultiQuest Action Center
Tower 3, Floor 2
1701 East Golf Road
Rolling Meadows, IL 60008

AT&T has a helpful demo line, 1-900-555-DEMO (free of charge), which offers information on its MultiQuest 900 services, the 555 Business Exchange and its Vari-A-Bill^{SM} calling charge option. AT&T offers four separate 900 service categories, depending upon the nature of the program:

Interacter. This is the most common service, and virtually all recorded interactive programs would come under this service.

Express900. This service is limited to live professional services such as medical, legal or tax advice; technical software assistance; or any other live services using qualified licensed professionals. These 900 numbers piggyback onto your local number, and the IP generally deals directly with AT&T as the client of record because a service bureau is usually not needed.

Broadcaster. This service is designed for high volume passive programs only, such as time and weather services; and for one-time or short-term live events, such as large stockholder meetings or sporting and racing events. This service is characterized (limited) by a "barge in" feature, which means callers will usually connect in the middle of the recorded message (or event), not at the beginning.

Call Counter. As the name implies, this service is designed strictly for tallying the number of calls to one or more 900 numbers, used for polling or tallying votes on any particular question or issue.

AT&T MultiQuest 900 Service Prices			
	Interacter	Express900	Broadcaster	Call Counter
One-time Start-up Fee	$1,200.00	$1,000.00	$250.00	0
Additional Numbers	$125.00 each	$75.00 each		
Monthly Service Charge	$500.00	$75.00		
Daily Service Charge				$25.00
Usage: 1st 30 seconds / ea. addl. sec.	$0.156 / $0.0052	$0.219 / $0.0073	varies - volume dependent	
Flat Rate per Call				$0.50
Billings and Collections Fee	10% of caller charge	15% of caller charge	13% of caller charge	13% of caller charge
Caller Grace Period	$0.12	$0.15		
Payout Interval	30-90 days	90 days	30 days	30 days

Usage charges are for interstate services. Intrastate charges are slightly lower. These prices were effective August 1, 1993 and are subject to change. The AT&T Broadcaster and Call Counter services are subject to daily volume minimums of 1,000 minutes per day (average) and 500 calls per day, respectively. A charge of $0.25 per minute for Broadcaster, and $0.25 per call for Call Counter, is assessed for each minute/call under the minimum volume.

Table H-1

The preceding prices are those charged the client of record, which in many cases will be the service bureau, who will usually pass on these fees to the IP. Nonetheless, the service bureau can charge whatever it wants, which can be more or less than these amounts. The start-up fee applies to each new account, not necessarily each new program, so an IP may have several programs in operation and pays the start-up fee only once.

AT&T offers several options that allow the IP wide flexibility in structuring the charges for the call:

Vari-A-Bill^SM. This service allows the IP to charge different amounts based upon the caller's choice of information received. The rate can be usage based (i.e., per-minute), a flat rate, or free, depending upon the interactive menu choices made by the caller.

Enhanced Rate Sets. This allows the IP to establish a rate period other than one minute, in one minute increments up to 24 hours. For example, the IP could set the charge at $2 for the first 4 minutes, then $5 for each additional increment of 7 minutes each.

Caller Free Time Option. Normally, there is a 19 second period, for the preamble message, that is free to the caller. With this feature, the IP can determine the length of the free time period ranging from 12 seconds up to 999 seconds (16+ minutes) in one second increments, allowing for a more detailed message or menu description before the call charges begin (applies to Interacter and Express900).

Time of Day/Day of Week Rating. this allows the IP to set different rates based upon the time (the caller's local time) of the call or the day of the week. For example, this feature could be used to help even out call volume, encouraging customers to call during off-peak hours, reducing the peak call volume to more manageable levels.

Call Prompter Rating. This service is similar to Vari-A-Bill^SM in that it allows the IP to vary the call charge for different menu selections. The significant differences, however, are that the menu prompts are at the network level, instead of at the IP's or the service bureau's equipment; the prompts, or levels, are limited to four branches; and once set up, there is little flexibility in changing the prompts or the price structure. This is a good choice for a static situation where the service and its pricing rarely change.

Guidelines for AT&T MultiQuest Billing Services

The following is from AT&T's November 1, 1993 published guidelines, and may not reflect all of its latest standards and policies. Contact AT&T or your service bureau for the most recent guidelines as necessary.

Overview

This document sets forth content and advertising guidelines ("Guidelines") for programs that use MultiQuest billing services in connection with all AT&T MultiQuest tariffed services, including AT&T MultiQuest Interacter, MultiQuest HICAP, MultiQuest Broadcaster, Call Acknowledgment (Call Counter) and/or MultiQuest Express900. Customers must also comply with the MultiQuest Billing Services Agreement.

AT&T reserves the right to:
1. Modify these Guidelines at any time. Such modification may include a decision to refrain from providing billing services for any category or type of program described in these Guidelines.
2. Consider factors not specifically identified in these Guidelines in determining whether to provide billing services for any program.
3. Impose conditions, not specifically identified in these Guidelines, on billing services for any program.
THESE GUIDELINES ARE MINIMUM STANDARDS THAT A CUSTOMER MUST MEET BEFORE AT&T WILL AGREE TO PROVIDE BILLING SERVICES FOR ANY PROGRAM, AND DO NOT CONSTITUTE LEGAL ADVICE. CUSTOMERS MUST CONSULT THEIR OWN ATTORNEYS REGARDING THE LEGALITY OF THEIR PROGRAMS.

I. GENERAL REQUIREMENTS
A. REVIEW OF PRESALES
1. The Customer shall comply with applicable federal and state laws and regulations, including, but not limited to, the Telephone Disclosure and Dispute Resolution Act (P.L. 102-556, 106 Stat. 418, approved October 28, 1992) and all applicable regulations of the Federal Trade Commission ("FTC") (16 C.F.R. Section 308.1 et seq.) and Federal Communications Commission ("FCC") (47 C.F.R. 64.1501, et. seq). If the Customer is the IP, the Customer must provide a written certification that it complies with such laws and regulations. If the Customer is the Service Bureau the Customer must obtain from the IP and provide to AT&T written certification that the IP complies with such laws and regulations. In these cases, the Service Bureau

must also sign the certification. The written certifications described above shall be made on AT&T's form entitled "Certification of Compliance with Federal Law and Regulations."

2. For all programs, AT&T reserves the right to request the Customer to submit the proposed message, including the preamble, and advertising for the program.

3. All Customers must submit to AT&T the name, address, and customer service telephone number of the Information Provider (including the name of the principal). Customers must inform AT&T of any proposed transfer or assignment of a program from one Information Provider to another, and AT&T reserves the right to refuse to accept any such transfer or assignment. A 900 number may not be used as a customer service telephone number.

4. The Customer must provide a descriptive name for each program of up to 10 characters which will appear on the caller's bill. Failure to provide such a name will result in AT&T's assigning a descriptor of its own choice.

5. AT&T reserves the right to request the Customer to submit a written transcript or audiotape of the program.

6. AT&T reserves the right to decide to which applications category the program will be assigned.

7. AT&T reserves the right to request original letters of authorization or releases from companies or individuals mentioned in the program or advertising.

8. NO VIDEO CONFERENCING OR VIDEOPHONES MAY BE USED ON CONNECTION WITH ANY 900 PROGRAM WITHOUT THE EXPRESS WRITTEN CONSENT OF AT&T.

9. ONCE AT&T HAS RELEASED A PRESALE, AT&T RESERVES THE RIGHT TO REQUEST THE CUSTOMER TO SUBMIT TO AT&T ANY CHANGES TO SCRIPTS, MESSAGE, THE PREAMBLE AND ADVERTISING USED IN CONNECTION WITH THE 900 PROGRAM.

B. GENERAL PROHIBITIONS

1. AT&T WILL NOT PROVIDE PREMIUM BILLING FOR ANY PROGRAM WHOSE MESSAGE CONTENT OR PROMOTIONAL MATERIALS CONTAIN, IN WORDS OR VISUAL IMAGES, THE FOLLOWING:

a. Vulgar language, explicit or implicit descriptions of violence or sexual conduct, adult entertainment, or incitement to violence;

b. Inflammatory or demeaning portrayals of any individual's or group's race, religion, political affiliation, ethnicity, gender, sexual preference, or handicap;

c. Criticism or disparagement of the general use of telecommunications or computer products and services;

d. Material that is unlawful, highly controversial or that may generate widespread adverse publicity or that may result in regulatory or legislative activity that could tend to affect adversely AT&T's ability to conduct its business;

e. GAB lines, chat lines, or other live group interaction programs, where the sole purpose is for two or more callers to interact with one another for social or entertainment reasons (excluding Conference Lines described below);

f. Multi-level marketing or "pyramid" schemes (generally defined as programs where purchasers of goods, property or services are compensated in the form of rebates, commissions or payments when they induce other persons to participate in the program); or

g. Commentary adverse to the policies or practices of AT&T or its subsidiaries.

2. AT&T WILL NOT PROVIDE PREMIUM BILLING FOR ANY PROGRAM:

a. That is promoted or advertised by means of recorded or live outbound telemarketing or automatic dialing equipment (autodialers). This includes, but is not limited to, programs that use outbound telemarketing to advertise an 800 number that, when dialed, refers callers to a 900 number. AT&T may permit live outbound telemarketing for fundraising programs on a case-by-case basis.

b. Where a caller is required to dial more than one 900 telephone number in order to obtain the service advertised;

c. Where the Customer refuses to provide AT&T with the name, address, and customer service telephone number of the Information Provider;

d. Where two or more Information Providers advertise or utilize extensions of a 900 number assigned to Customer;

e. Found to be in non-compliance with AT&T's Guidelines. AT&T will terminate billing services immediately and may refuse to provide billing services for any new programs submitted by the Service Bureau or run by the Information Provider in the same applications category as that of the terminated program; or

f. That does not comply with all applicable federal, state and local laws and regulations, including but not limited to the Telephone Disclosure and Dispute Resolution Act (P.L. 102-556, 106 Stat. 418, approved October 28, 1992), and regulations of the FTC (16 C.F.R. Part 308) and the FCC (47 C.F.R. Section 64,1501 et seq.), and state laws and regulations governing pay-per-call or 900 telephone programs. Customers must consult their own attorneys to determine the applicability of federal, state and local laws and regulations to their programs.

3. THESE GENERAL PROHIBITIONS APPLY TO BOTH VISUAL IMAGES AND TEXT USED IN ANY 900 SCRIPT OR ADVERTISING OR PROMOTION USED TO INDUCE CALLS TO A 900 PROGRAM.

C. PREAMBLES

1. The Information Provider must include an introductory message, or preamble, to its program when required by FTC or other applicable regulation and the preamble must include all information required by the applicable regulation (see 16 C.F.R. Section 308.5).

2. FOR ALL PROGRAMS REQUIRING A PREAMBLE, THE CUSTOMER MUST PURCHASE THE CALLER FREE TIME OPTION AVAILABLE UNDER AT&T TARIFF.

3. If a touch-tone phone is required for the caller to access the program, the preamble must disclose that fact.

4. The preamble must disclose the Information Provider's name.

5. Additional preamble requirements for programs marketed to children under 12 years of age are set forth in Section III.A.

6. AT&T reserves the right to request Customer to Submit the Preamble.

II. ADVERTISING REQUIREMENTS

A. ALL ADVERTISEMENTS AND OTHER PROMOTIONS USED TO INDUCE CALLS TO THE PROGRAM, WHETHER IN PRINT, TV, RADIO OR OTHER MEDIA, MUST:

1. Disclose all material conditions for the purchase in such a manner that the general public may correctly understand the nature of the program and its associated charges.

2. Disclose all information in the manner specified by applicable federal or state regulations (see 16 C.F.R. Section 308.3); and

3. Comply in full with applicable federal and state laws prohibiting unfair, false, deceptive, and misleading advertising and trade practices; and

4. Contain the Information Provider's name and city and state of business, or name and customer service telephone number (this number cannot be a 900 number).

B. NO ADVERTISEMENTS FOR A CUSTOMER'S PROGRAM, AND NO CUSTOMER LITERATURE, MAY USE ANY TRADEMARK, SERVICE MARK, OR LOGO OF AT&T, NOR INDICATE THAT AT&T ENDORSES, AUTHORIZES, APPROVES, OR IS ASSOCIATED WITH THE PROGRAM IN ANY WAY, WITHOUT AT&T'S EXPRESS WRITTEN PERMISSION.

III. GUIDELINES FOR SPECIFIC PROGRAM CATEGORIES

The following Guidelines apply in addition to those set for in Sections I and II.

A. CHILDREN'S PROGRAM

INCLUDES ANY PROGRAM WHOSE MESSAGE CONTENT OR PROMOTION IS DIRECTED AT CHILDREN UNDER 12 YEARS OF AGE. CUSTOMERS SHALL COMPLY WITH ALL APPLICABLE

FEDERAL AND STATE LAWS AND REGULATIONS (SEE SECTION 308.3 FOR PROHIBITIONS ON ADVERTISING TO CHILDREN UNDER THE AGE OF 12, SECTION 308.3(f) FOR ADVERTISING REQUIREMENTS FOR CALLERS UNDER THE AGE OF 18 AND SECTION 308.5(A)(4) FOR PREAMBLE REQUIREMENTS FOR CALLERS UNDER THE AGE OF 18). CUSTOMERS MUST ALSO COMPLY WITH THE FOLLOWING GUIDELINES.

1. **CHARGES MUST BE CAPPED AT $4.00 PER CALL.** Where technically feasible, Customers should limit the number of calls that may be accepted by the 900 number and charged to an individual calling number.

2. By offering a children's program, Customers agree to 100% automatic adjustments by AT&T to callers requesting refunds.

3. Children may not be asked to make a recorded statement that includes their names, addresses, or telephone numbers, or other identifying information.

4. A children's program may not require an additional purchase or the viewing of a television program (free or pay) for the complete message to be received.

5. Customer must provide copies or scripts of all advertisements (including ads for taglines and the preamble).

B. CONFERENCE LINES

INCLUDES LIVE, INTERACTIVE PROGRAMS WHERE THE PURPOSE OF THE CALL IS LIMITED TO GOVERNMENT, BUSINESS, PROFESSIONAL, EDUCATIONAL, OR NON-CHILD-ORIENTED SPORTS TOPICS. CUSTOMERS MUST COMPLY WITH THE FOLLOWING GUIDELINES:

1. The program must be limited to a specified period of time, for example, one or two hours, or weekly for one or two hours, with a definite start and stop time.

2. The program must be led by a moderator with a specific agenda.

CUSTOMERS MUST BLOCK STATES IN TERRITORIES WHERE LOCAL EXCHANGE COMPANIES ("LECS") REFUSE TO BILL FOR THESE PROGRAMS.

C. CREDIT/LOAN OR FINANCIAL INFORMATION PROGRAMS

PROGRAMS WHICH OFFER FINANCIAL INFORMATION OR INFORMATION ON HOW CALLERS CAN OBTAIN CREDIT (LOANS OR CREDIT CARDS), CREDIT COUNSELING, CREDIT REPAIR INFORMATION, CREDIT REPORTS, OR BAD DEBT AVOIDANCE. CUSTOMERS MUST COMPLY WITH THE FOLLOWING GUIDELINES:

1. Customer must provide copies or scripts of all advertisements (including ads for tag lines) and the preamble.

2. Advertising must clearly and conspicuously disclose all conditions on the availability of credit. Examples of such conditions are: requirement of collateral or bank deposit, purchase from a specific catalog, processing fees, and any limitations on availability.

3. Total per-minute or flat-rate charges must be no more than $20 per call;

4. Callers may not be required to dial more than ONE TELEPHONE NUMBER (either 700, 800, 900 or regular telephone number) to obtain the advertised service or information;

5. By offering this program, Customers agree to 100% automatic adjustments by AT&T to callers requesting refunds:

6. Where Customers cannot demonstrate compliance with state law, Customers must block in states that have in effect credit services statutes that generally prohibit the offering of such programs unless the offeror is registered, bonded and provides services under written contract with each Customer. Some states also impose consumer disclosure requirements. Compliance may be demonstrated by providing AT&T with a copy of state registration, bond, written Customer contract, disclosure statement, and/or any other materials requested by AT&T. Customers must consult their own attorneys regarding specific requirements for each state.

These states are:

Arizona	Maine	Texas
Arkansas	Maryland	Nevada
California	Massachusetts	Utah
Connecticut	Michigan	New Hampshire
Colorado	Indiana	Virginia
Delaware	Iowa	New York
Dist. of Columbia	Minnesota	Washington
Florida	Missouri	North Carolina
Illinois	Tennessee	West Virginia
Kansas	Nebraska	Oklahoma
Louisiana		

7. For all other states, Customer must provide a written opinion of counsel stating that the program complies with all applicable requirements of federal, state, and local law;

8. Compliance may also be demonstrated and blocking will not be required if Customer is a bank or an agent of a bank. A bank must provide a copy of its charter(s) authorizing it to do business in the state(s) in which the program will be offered. An agent of a bank must provide a copy of the bank's charter and an original letter from the bank specifically endorsing the Customer's 900 services credit program covered by each presale application;

9. Voice capture for "list purposes only" is prohibited;

10. Fulfillment guidelines also apply when the advertised offering is not provided during the call; and

11. VIOLATION OF THESE GUIDELINES WILL RESULT IN IMMEDIATE TERMINATION OF BILLING SERVICES FOR THE OFFENDING PROGRAM AND MAY RESULT IN TERMINATION OF BILLING SERVICES FOR ALL CUSTOMER'S PROGRAMS IN THIS CATEGORY.

D. FULFILLMENT
PROGRAMS WHERE THE PREDOMINANT PURPOSE OF THE CALL IS TO PROVIDE VALUE ADDED INFORMATION (NOT PRODUCT SALES), WITH A SUPPLEMENTAL ITEM SENT FREE OF CHARGE TO THE CALLER AFTER THE COMPLETION OF THE CALL (FOR EXAMPLE, LISTEN TO SAMPLE CUTS FROM ROCK, STAR'S NEW ALBUM, VOTE FOR FAVORITE SONG, AND RECEIVE FREE ALBUM). CUSTOMERS MUST COMPLY WITH THE FOLLOWING GUIDELINES:
1. Price is limited to no more than $20 per call;
2. By offering this program, Customers agree to 100% automatic adjustments by AT&T to all callers requesting refunds;
3. The advertising and script must contain an 800 number or business name and full address for callers to obtain additional information or to follow-up on items not yet received;
4. Callers must be informed of approximate time for receiving fulfillment items;
5. Customer must block states in territories where LECs refuse to provide billing services. In U.S. West territory (Arizona, Colorado, Idaho, Iowa, Minnesota, Montana, Nebraska, New Mexico, North Dakota, Oregon, South Dakota, Utah, Washington, Wyoming), unless the tangible item is duplicative of or incidental to the information on the call, blocking must be implemented. In states billed by Southwestern Bell (Arkansas, Kansas, Missouri, Oklahoma, Texas), printed material only are permitted up to value of $10; and
6. AT&T reserves the right to require Customers to submit copies of the fulfillment package.

E. FUNDRAISING
INCLUDES ANY PROGRAM THAT SOLICITS FUNDS FOR CHARITABLE, NON-PROFIT, OR POLITICAL ORGANIZATIONS.
AT&T'S REVIEW OF ADVERTISING AND SCRIPTS AND THE APPLICATION OF THESE GUIDELINES DO NOT CONSTITUTE COUNSELING OR LEGAL ADVICE FOR FUNDRAISERS. CUSTOMERS MUST CONSULT WITH THEIR OWN ATTORNEYS REGARDING THE LEGALITY OF A FUNDRAISING PROGRAM. AT&T IS NOT REGISTERED AS FUNDRAISING COUNSEL IN ANY STATE AND DOES NOT UNDERTAKE TO PROVIDE SUCH ADVICE.

CUSTOMERS MUST BLOCK STATES IN TERRITORIES WHERE LECS WILL NOT BILL FOR FUNDRAISING PROGRAMS. IN STATES BILLED BY NYNEX (NEW YORK, MASSACHUSETTS, MAINE, VERMONT, NEW HAMPSHIRE, RHODE ISLAND) ALL CALLS FOR POLITICAL FUNDRAISING MUST BE BLOCKED AND FOR ALL CALLS FOR CHARITABLE FUNDRAISING THE TOTAL CHARGE MUST BE LIMITED TO NO MORE THAN $25.00 PER CALL)

BY OFFERING SUCH PROGRAMS, CUSTOMERS OF FUNDRAISING PROGRAMS MUST AGREE TO 100% AUTOMATIC ADJUSTMENTS BY AT&T FOR CALLERS WHO REQUEST REFUNDS.

1. Solicitation Programs

INCLUDES ANY PROGRAM WHERE CONTRIBUTIONS ARE EXPLICITLY SOLICITED FOR A CHARITY OR NON-PROFIT ORGANIZATION. AT&T REQUIRES THAT CUSTOMERS OF SOLICITATION PROGRAMS SUBMIT THE FOLLOWING:

a. Proof of charitable or non-profit entity's tax exempt status. IRS Form 501(c)(4) should be submitted for solicitations involving lobbying activities. IRS Form 501(c)(3) should be submitted for all solicitation programs. (Federal law requires that the Customer submit proof of tax-exempt status. 47 U.S.C. Section 228).

b. Original written certification on the charity's or non-profit's letterhead that the organization is in compliance with federal, state and local laws pertaining to charitable solicitations including registration or licensing, reporting dates and requirements, solicitation disclosure requirements and, if applicable, use of agents a professional solicitors or fundraisers. In addition, if the Customer is someone other than the charity or non-profit entity, this letter shall contain a statement that the entity agrees with the use of its name.

c. Advertisement for the program disclosing the name, national headquarters street address, and year of inception of the Charitable or Non-Profit Organization.

2. Commercial Programs

PROGRAMS WHERE A CHARITY OR NON-PROFIT ORGANIZATION PROVIDES VALUE-ADDED INFORMATION. VALUE-ADDED INFORMATION IS ANY INFORMATION RELAYED TO THE CALLER BEYOND GREETING AND A CONFIRMATION OF THE DONATION. A COMMERCIAL PROGRAM MAY OR MAY NOT EXPLICITLY SOLICIT DONATIONS. AT&T REQUIRES THAT CUSTOMER SUBMIT THE FOLLOWING:

a. All documents required for Solicitation Programs; and

b. A copy of the telephone script.

F. FUNDRAISING/POLITICAL (FEDERAL ELECTIONS)

INCLUDES BOTH SOLICITATION AND INFORMATIONAL POLITICAL PROGRAMS SPONSORED BY POLITICAL CANDIDATES OR COMMITTEES, IF ALL OR A PORTION OF THE BILLED CHARGES FOR A PROGRAM WILL BE REMITTED TO A POLITICAL CANDIDATE OR COMMITTEE FOR FEDERAL OFFICE, THE FOLLOWING GUIDELINES MUST BE MET.

1. The Customer must be a Service Bureau.

2. The program script and the promotional materials should clearly state that a portion of the charges will be remitted to a political organization.

3. The program script and advertising must identify the political organization.

4. A message should be included at the beginning of the program identifying the person who has authorized and paid for the program, and stating that a contribution to the political organization is not tax deductible.

5. An application for a program for political fundraising must include:

   a. A general representation and warranty that the Customer and the political organization will comply with all applicable federal, state, and local laws during the term of the program (including but not limited to the obligations set forth in F.E.C. Advisory Opinion 1991-20);

   b. For programs for candidates for federal office or political organizations registered at the Federal Election Commission (F.E.C.). The Customer must also provide a representation and warranty (original letter) that the Customer will comply with Section 432(b) of Title 2 of the United States Code (2 U.S.C. 432(b) and Section 102.8 of Title 11 of the Code to forward to the treasurer of the political organization all funds (after deducting its fees and expenses, within 10 days of receipt. In addition, the Customer must agree to forward to the candidate or political organization a copy of the Call Detail Report listing the telephone numbers recorded by Automatic Number Identification (ANI), within 2 days of receipt.

   c. A letter from the treasurer of each political organization that is registered at the F.E.C. that contracts with the Customer stating that the treasurer agrees to abide by Section 103.3 of Title 11 of the Code of Federal Regulations (11 C.F.R. 103.3) with regard to the receipt, deposit, and refund of contributions raising genuine questions of legality; and

6. Customer must maintain a separate bank account to hold fundraising proceeds, as described in F.E.C. Advisory Opinion 1991-20.

7. The treasurer shall request the Customer to record caller name, address, and telephone numbers, or shall obtain comparable services elsewhere. If Customer does not provide this service to the treasurer, the Customer must obtain a certification from the treasurer that the political committee is seeking comparable services elsewhere, as required by F.E.C. Advisory Opinion 1991-20. For callers that cannot be identified through ANI, the treasurer will:

   a. Use the transcription of this information to identify additional contributors; and/or

b. Telephone unidentified numbers to obtain the caller's name and address.

8. Unidentifiable contributions may not be accepted by the treasurer but may be used for any lawful purpose unrelated to any federal election, in accordance with F.E.C. Advisory Opinion 1991-20.

9. For programs in which advertising may stimulate telephone calls from outside the United States (i.e., candidates in states along the Mexican or Canadian border), the treasurer must agree to Numbering Plan of America (NPA) blocking for area codes in those countries.

10. The treasurer will compare the identity of contributors and record all contributions of subscribers who have contributed more than $50 in the same year.

11. Records need not be made for other contributions of less than $50. Instead, the treasurer need only record the date and total amount of funds received from the program.

12. The treasurer must report all expenditures for the program, including the funds withheld by the Customer to cover its fees and expenses. The treasurer should identify the Customer as the recipient of all funds withheld from contributions received.

13. The Customer must agree to provide 100% automatic adjustments by AT&T for callers who request refunds.

NOTE: POLITICAL FUNDRAISING PROGRAMS FOR CANDIDATES FOR STATE OR LOCAL OFFICES ARE SUBJECT TO APPLICABLE STATE LAW. AT&T WILL PROVIDE BILLING SERVICES FOR SUCH PROGRAMS ON A CASE-BY-CASE BASIS.

G. GAMES OF CHANCE

INCLUDES ANY TYPE OF GAME OF CHANCE OR CONTEST, SWEEPSTAKES, CONTEST LISTING, OR INFORMATION THAT INVOLVES THE USE OF A 900 CALL TO A PROGRAM AS ONE OF THE MEANS OF ENTRY OR QUALIFYING FOR A PRIZE THAT IS AWARDED BASED ON CHANCE.

THE CUSTOMER MUST COMPLY WITH ALL APPLICABLE FEDERAL AND STATE LAWS AND REGULATIONS (SEE 16 C.F.R. SECTION 308.3(c) FOR FTC ADVERTISING REGULATIONS FOR GAMES OF CHANCE).

CUSTOMERS MUST ALSO COMPLY WITH THE FOLLOWING GUIDELINES:

AT&T'S STANDARDS FOR GAMES OF CHANCE ARE MINIMUM GUIDELINES THAT A CUSTOMER MUST MEET BEFORE AT&T WILL AGREE TO PROVIDE BILLING SERVICES. AT&T'S GUIDELINES AND ITS DECISION TO BILL FOR A PROGRAM DO NOT CONSTITUTE LEGAL ADVICE. CUSTOMERS MUST CONSULT WITH THEIR OWN ATTORNEYS REGARDING THE LEGALITY OF THEIR PROGRAMS, AND CUSTOMERS MUST ENSURE THAT

THEIR PROGRAMS COMPLY WITH ALL APPLICABLE FEDERAL AND STATE LAWS AND REGULATIONS. A CUSTOMER IS REQUIRED BY THE BILLING SERVICES AGREEMENT TO REPRESENT AND WARRANTY COMPLIANCE WITH THESE LAWS AND REGULATIONS.

1. GENERAL REQUIREMENTS FOR GAMES OF CHANCE. All Games of Chance must meet the following requirements:

a. The game must be operated as a means of increasing the purchase of products or services in the marketplace (the game itself, and calls made to the 900 program, are not considered products or services for this purpose).

b. A no-purchase alternative method of participating, disclosed in the solicitation letter, the official rules, and all advertising for the program, must be available which provides all entrants (no-purchase and 900 phone-in) with an equal chance of winning. If the alternative method of entry is by mail, any associated fulfillment must be completed within 30 days of the postmarked date of entry. The deadline for responding by the alternative method of entry must be no sooner than the deadline for responding by calling the 900 number.

c. All unclaimed major prizes must be awarded via a second chance drawing. For purposes of these guidelines, the term "major prize" means a prize with a cash value of more than $50.

d. Prizes may not be financed from the proceeds of the Customer's billed charges.

e. The amount of value of the prize awarded may not be dependent upon the number of entries received.

f. The selection of a winner may not be dependent on the outcome of a future sporting contest or other future contingent event not under the participant's control (other than the random selection of an entry).

g. All games of chance must be blocked in Minnesota and Georgia, and in all states where the program is voided by Customer election. Any game of chance or program that provides information or notice concerning entitlement to a prize, gift, award or other thing of value must be blocked in New Jersey. The Customer must ensure that its program is blocked in Louisiana and all other states requiring registration, unless the Customer submits proof of registration with the appropriate state authorities.

h. The total charge is limited to no more than $5 per call.

i. AT&T reserves the right to impose other conditions, not expressly set forth in these guidelines, in connection with its provision of billing services for any program in this category.

2. ADVERTISEMENT. The advertisement for a direct mail sweepstakes (i.e., the letter, postcard or other document sent to a particular person), or a print, visual or oral advertisement; must comply with the following:

a. A statement disclosing the starting and closing dates of the game.

b. A statement that the game is subject to the complete official rules, and a statement referring the recipient to the location of the official rules.

c. No statement may be made indicating that AT&T is a sponsor of the game.

d. Words and phrases that seek to compel immediate action by recipients of the solicitation (e.g., "Immediate Action Required") must not be used in a manner which creates the false impression of an immediate deadline for action which does not exist or conveys the false impression that the recipient must call the 900 number in order to claim a prize or to participate in the game.

e. Words, phrases, format or symbols shall not be used in a manner that, taken as a whole, creates an impression that the solicitation was initiated or authorized by an agency of government.

f. Customers must agree to 100% adjustments by AT&T to callers requesting refunds.

g. Customer must provide copies of all advertisements (including ads for tag lines) and the preamble.

3. OFFICIAL RULES. The Official Rules must include the following information:

a. No Purchase Necessary. The alternate method of entry must be disclosed in conspicuous and easily readable text.

b. Prizes. The number, nature and fair market retail value of all prizes must be listed and described in descending order of retail value, except that a prize that the majority of all recipients will receive must be listed last.

c. Odds of Winning. The odds should appear immediately adjacent to the first identification of the prize to which it relates. The odds should be described in whole Arabic numbers such as 1:1,000.

d. Selection of Winners. The rules shall describe how winners will be selected, including disclosure of all material terms, conditions, restrictions or deadlines which must be satisfied to entitle the recipient to receive any prize offered.

e. Second-Chance Drawing. All major prizes must be awarded; major prizes which are not claimed shall be awarded in a subsequent drawing from the names of all who responded and did not receive a major prize. This drawing shall take place not later than 30 days after the closing date for the game.

f. List of Winners. A list of winners (including the winner's addresses) of all major prizes must be made available to any person requesting the list, and an address for requesting such a winners' list shall be contained in the official rules.

g. Eligibility/Availability. The rules shall disclose the starting and closing dates of the game, age restrictions for participants, the geographic area where the game is available, and a list of the specific states where the game is void, prohibited or restricted by law. The Customer is responsible for ensuring that calls to the 900 number(s) from all states where the game is unavailable are blocked.

h. Program Customer. The rules shall disclose the Service Bureau's or Information Provider's name and street address.

4. LETTER FROM SERVICE BUREAU OR INFORMATION PROVIDER. The Service Bureau or Information Provider must submit a letter than includes the following:

a. A representation and warranty that the game is operated to increase the purchase of products or services (other than the game itself) in the marketplace;

b. A description and identification by brand name of the goods or services being promoted;

c. A representation and warranty that prizes will not be funded from the proceeds of calls to 900 number(s);

d. The name and address of any entity that retains Service Bureau or Information Provider to operate the game to promote the particular products or services;

e. An explanation of how such entity (or the Service Bureau or Information Provider if it offers the game on its own behalf) is benefited by the purchase of the goods or services being promoted;

f. If the Service Bureau or Information Provider is offering the game on its own behalf, the names and locations of any retail outlets; and

g. A statement that Service Bureau or Information Provider, at the start of the game of chance, has a sufficient amount of all items to be given as prizes.

5. OPINION LETTER OF COUNSEL. The Service Bureau or Information Provider must provide a written opinion of the Service Bureau's or Information Provider's legal counsel stating, specifically, that counsel has reviewed the program and finds it to be in compliance with all applicable federal and state laws and regulations including, but not limited to, laws governing gambling, lotteries, prize notification and 900 programs, and fraud and deceptive practices. As to deceptive practices laws, the counsel's letter must affirmatively represent that counsel believes there is clear and adequate description, and complete and accurate disclosure, of all material terms, conditions and restrictions of the advertisement, and in the opinion of counsel, the advertisement is not unfair, misleading or deceptive. The opinion letter should also identify those states where the program is bonded and registered as may be required by state, law, and the states where the program will be voided. A copy of the advertisement reviewed by counsel must be attached to and referred to in the opinion letter. If substantial revisions are made to the advertisement, they must be resubmitted to counsel for review and a new opinion letter must be issued.

6. LETTERS OF AUTHORIZATION OR RELEASES. The Service Bureau or Information Provider must provide letters of authorization or releases from each company and/or individual mentioned in the programming or advertising that authorize the Service Bureau or Information Provider to use such person's name, image, likeness, trademark, service mark, etc. in connection with the proposed game of chance. Alternatively, the Service Bureau or Information Provider may furnish a letter from a third party,

which has been licensed or authorized by each company and/or individual, in which the third party affirmatively represents to AT&T that it is authorized to permit the Service Bureau or Information Provider to use such person's name, image, likeness, trademark, service mark, etc. in connection with the proposed game of chance.

H. GAMES OF SKILL

Games of skill are entertainment programs which offer a nominal prize to all callers who win a game. For example: A Bible quiz program which consists of a series of questions, and all callers who answer all questions correctly are awarded a certificate of achievement.

The total charge is limited to no more than $5.00 per call.

To be categorized as a "Game of Skill" rather than a "Game of Chance":

1. There can be no element of chance associated with the game.

2. Questions cannot be so difficult as to cause callers to guess the answers.

3. Questions cannot be so easy as to cause all callers to answer questions correctly UNLESS all callers who do so win the same prize.

4. The same questions must be posed to every caller (i.e., no random computer generation of questions).

5. The Customer must submit a set of criteria for selection of the winners.

6. All callers who answer the questions correctly must be awarded the same prize.

I. JOB INFORMATION LINES

INCLUDES ANY PROGRAM WHICH INDICATES OR SUGGESTS THAT THE CALLER SHOULD OR MAY CONTACT SPECIFIC COMPANIES TO OBTAIN EMPLOYMENT. CUSTOMERS MUST:

1. Certify in writing to AT&T that all job ads exist and are current.

2. Remove from the program script, within one day, job ads that have closed.

3. Fully disclose in all advertising the locations where jobs are available.

4. Submit to AT&T with an original written opinion of counsel stating that the program complies with all applicable federal, state, or local laws of the specified jurisdictions where it will be advertised, including but not limited to requirements for bona fide job orders from each employer whose job ad is listed, licensing and bonding requirements, and limitations on the type of fees that a job applicant may be charged prior to securing employment, e.g., 900 charges.

5. FOR PROGRAMS WHERE NO SPECIFIC JOB ADS ARE PROVIDED TO THE CALLER, BUT RATHER, NAMES OF COMPANIES ARE LISTED AS POTENTIAL EMPLOYERS FOR CAREERS DESCRIBED IN THE PROGRAM, THE CUSTOMER MUST ALSO:

a. Provide AT&T with original proof of authorization to use company names. This must include written authorization on company letterhead indicating that the company has given the Customer express permission to use its company name on this 900 application.

   b. Indicate in all advertising and in the program script that the companies named are only potential employers, who may not have openings at the time the caller contacts them.

   6. Callers to job information lines may not be required to dial more than ONE TELEPHONE NUMBER (700, 800, 900 or regular telephone number) to obtain the advertised information or service.

   7. Customers must block calls from the following states.

Arkansas	Montana
Colorado	New Jersey
Connecticut	New York
Georgia	North Dakota
Illinois	Ohio
Indiana	Oregon
Iowa	Pennsylvania
Kentucky	South Carolina
Louisiana	Tennessee
Maryland	Texas
Massachusetts	Utah
Michigan	Virginia
Missouri	Washington
Wisconsin	

J. PERSONAL LINES

INCLUDES THE FOLLOWING TYPES OF PROGRAMS: ROMANTIC STORIES, PERSONAL BULLETIN BOARDS, DATING LINES, INTRODUCTION LINES, CONFESSION LINES, SOUND-OFF LINES, AND "ONE-ON-ONE" LINES.

   1. THE ADVERTISING AND MESSAGE MAY NOT CONTAIN ANY MATERIAL THAT IS OBSCENE, INDECENT, SEXUALLY IMPLICIT OR EXPLICIT, OR THAT WOULD CONSTITUTE ADULT ENTERTAINMENT. IF AT&T DISCOVERS THAT ANY OF CUSTOMER'S PROGRAMS IN THIS CATEGORY FAILS TO COMPLY WITH THE PROHIBITION, AT&T WILL TERMINATE IMMEDIATELY BILLING SERVICES FOR THE OFFENDING PROGRAM AND MAY TERMINATE BILLING SERVICES FOR ALL OF CUSTOMER'S EXISTING PROGRAMS IN THIS CATEGORY.

   2. Customers must screen caller messages, in order to determine compliance with AT&T Guidelines, where programs involve the leaving of personal messages.

   3. Customer advertising must include either a statement that individuals under the age of 18 must seek parental permission before calling, or a statement that callers must be at least 18 years of age to call.

4. Before broadcasting any personal messages, Customer must review each message to confirm that each caller:

　　a. Is at least 18 years of age. Customer should describe in writing to AT&T how they will verify caller's age, i.e., asking for date of birth or whether caller has a major credit card;

　　b. Has authorized the broadcast of the personal message;

　　c. Has provided accurate information;

5. Customer should review the transmission quality of recordings to ensure the information can be accurately heard;

6. Customer should recommend that callers not use home or office telephone number for messages. A suggested alternative might be electronic mailboxes set up by the Customer; and

7. For "One-on-One" lines:

　　i. Customer must provide a written description of the methods used to screen callers to make sure that callers are at least 18 years of age (e.g., asking for date of birth or credit card information);

　　ii. Customer must provide copies or scripts of all advertisements (including ads for tag lines) and the preamble; and

　　iii. Called party must disclose immediately that they are an employee of the Information Provider.

8. Callers to personal lines may not be required to dial more than ONE TELEPHONE NUMBER (700, 800, 900 or regular telephone number) to obtain the advertised information or service.

K. PROFESSIONAL SERVICES
INCLUDES PROGRAM CONTENT PROVIDED BY PERSONS UPON WHOM CALLERS WOULD RELY FOR PROFESSIONAL ADVICE, SUCH AS DOCTORS, LAWYERS, ETC.

1. Customer must submit to AT&T proof that Information Provider is licensed to practice the professional service in the state(s) where program will be offered.

2. AT&T reserves the right to impose conditions or to request documentation not specifically identified in these Guidelines.

L. STATE-SPONSORED LOTTERIES
Includes lotteries sponsored or authorized by a lottery or gaming commission.

1. Customer must submit copy of Information Provider's contract with state lottery or gaming commission, or other appropriate regulatory body, or an original letter from a lottery or gaming commission (on agency letterhead) authorizing the Customer to conduct a lottery utilizing 900 services, on its behalf.

2. Customer must submit an original copy of a written opinion of counsel as to whether the proposed offering complies with all applicable laws.

3.   AT&T will consider whether to provide billing services for these programs on a case-by-case basis, depending upon applicable state and federal law, LEC billing policies, and other factors.

IV. EXPRESS900 GUIDELINES

In addition to compliance with the foregoing Guidelines for AT&T MultiQuest Premium Billing Services, programs that meet the following conditions may be accepted by AT&T for billing services on Express900 Service:

1.   Programs where the predominant purpose of the call (as determined by AT&T) does NOT include:
   - Entertainment
   - Children's Programming
   - Credit/Loan Information
   - Political Fundraising
   - Games of Chance
   - Job lines
   - Personal Lines

2.   Customers may not route calls to voice mailboxes or any telecommunications equipment or arrangements which all charging to begin before the caller realizes any value on the call, e.g., Automatic Call Distribution (ACD) with call queuing, or Caller Hold.

V. AT&T VARI-A-BILL℠ SERVICE GUIDELINES

VARI-A-BILL℠ Services is a feature of AT&T MultiQuest Interactive Service. The following guidelines apply in addition to the foregoing guidelines for AT&T MultiQuest Billing Service.

The preamble must be provided by the Customer in accordance with federal law (16 C.F.R. Section 308.5). Vari-A-Bill℠ Service program preambles must also include an additional statement specifying that the caller may be offered options that could change the cost of the call to another caller rate (i.e., per minute rate or flat rate, including premium charge). The range of rates which may be charged must be disclosed.

Advertising must include a conspicuous statement that the caller may be offered options that could change the cost of the call to another caller rate (i.e., per minute rate or flat rate, including premium charge). The range of rates which may be charged must be disclosed.

The following program types are not permitted:
   Astrology/Numerology/Psychic Lines
   Tips and Forecasting (e.g.)
   Lottery
   Sports
   Stocks
   Children's Programming
   Credit/Loan/Financial Information

Political Fund-raising
Games of Chance
Job Lines/Work at Home
Personal Lines

Customers will describe in writing to AT&T how they will verify caller acceptance of the negotiated charge and/or caller rate. In case of dispute, the Customer's record of caller acceptance of a rate change must be made available within 48 hours (2 business days) of AT&T's request for this information. The Customer must maintain records of Vari-A-Bill^{SM} Service calls for 12 months.

The Customer shall ensure that the Customer Premises Equipment terminating the ISDN PRI (TR 41449/TR 41459) facility has passed AT&T's ISDN Compatibility Test Program including compliance with appendix 5 to TR 41459.

AT&T reserves the right to terminate billing services for any Vari-A-Bill^{SM} Service application. AT&T will review billing services for Vari-A-Bill^{SM} Service applications with a view toward achieving a target refund rate of 2% or less for a 4 month average per individual program.

MCI
703-506-6550
MCI 900 Business Unit
1650 Tysons Blvd.
McLean, VA 22102

The following MCI guidelines and prices were effective as of September 29, 1993:

A. OVERVIEW

The 900 Service industry is very dynamic. Regulations and other requirements are periodically enacted by the Federal Communication Commission (FCC), State Commissions and other agencies (e.g. public utilities, employment, gaming, etc.), Local Exchange Carriers (LEC) and the Interexchange Carriers such as MCI.

As a 900 Service Provider it is your responsibility to comply with all legal requirements, contractual requirements and policies.

B. MCI's POLICIES

MCI's Policies for 900 Service are fully outlined in Exhibit C (not provided in this Appendix) of MCI's Billing and Collections Agreement for 900 Service. This section highlights the types of programming for which MCI will not provide Billing and Collection Services. Please consult Exhibit C for details.

1. Programs that do not contain a preamble.

2. Fundraisers without not-for-profit status.

3. Programs conflicting with LEC billing restrictions.

4. Unlawful applications such as in violation of election laws, laws concerning unfair, deceptive or fraudulent advertising, securities laws and anti-gambling laws, etc.

5. Defamatory applications containing inflammatory or demeaning portrayals on the basis of race, religion, political affiliation, ethnic group, etc.

6. Fraudulent Programs.

7. Children's programming which is usage sensitive or exceeds the price cap of $4.00.

8. Adult Programming.

9. Programs using fraudulent sales techniques such as reference to another 900 number for which there is a charge; repetitive, extraneous or drawn out messages with the purpose of increasing end user charges; programs that utilize multi-level marketing or pyramid schemes; programs that use a PIN number for the purpose of receiving fulfillment on a subsequent call.

10. An program using autodialers or computer generated announcements to induce calls.

11. Programs that do not clearly, concisely and accurately disclose the costs of the call and all costs associated with receiving fulfillment.

12. Programs that generate excessive caller credits or uncollectibles.

13. Programs which relate to or offer information on obtaining credit, loans, or improving credit.

14. Programs which offer travel accommodations or transportation in conjunction with a sweepstakes or contest.

15. GAB lines e.g., group access bridging.

16. Sweepstakes programs that do not meet specific MCI guidelines, primarily relating to the clear disclosure of prizes, odds, requirements, rules, regulations, alternate entry, etc.

17. Job line programs that do not meet specific MCI requirements, primarily relating to certification of validity and availability of jobs being offered.

18. Personal, date lines, voice mailboxes and one-to-one programs that do not comply with MCI's policies.

C. LOCAL EXCHANGE CARRIER (LEC) POLICIES

As previously mentioned, the LEC's act as the billing and collection agent on MCI's behalf. The LEC bills the caller, collects payment, handles requests for credit, and remits caller payment and/or credits back to MCI. Each LEC has specific terms and conditions for which they will provide this service. Many LEC's will not provide B&C for the following types of programs which may be in compliance with MCI's policies:

* purchase of merchandise
* product fulfillment
* political and charitable contributions

MCI may require that Tailored Call Coverage (TCC) be put in place to block the originating calls from LEC's territories as a result of their restrictions. Failure to comply with these LEC restrictions could result in termination of MCI's Billing and Collection Services.

D. STATE POLICIES

Recently many states have become more proactively involved with regulation of 900 Services. Numerous states have imposed legislation and restrictions on content, pricing and advertising of 900 Service programs. While these are constantly changing, some of the more notable include:

* Sweepstakes are illegal in several states, such as
Louisiana, South Carolina, Georgia, Minnesota, Iowa, Indiana;
* Job lines must be blocked in PA and TN;
* Louisiana requires an IP to register in the state.

E. INTRASTATE SERVICE

The California Public Utilities Commission maintains strict guidelines for calls that originate and terminate within the state. In California, flat-rated calls are prohibited, call caps are $5/first minute and $2/additional minute. Children's programs cannot exceed $4/call and programs shall not exceed $50 total, per call. Minnesota may not provide Billing and Collection Services for Intrastate 900 traffic.

ESTABLISHING MCI 900 SERVICE

A. CUSTOMER APPROVAL PROCESS
You probably will want to contract with a Service Bureau to run your program. Call several Service Bureaus and choose the one that will best handle your application.

B. PROGRAM APPROVAL PROCESS
Once you have been approved as a 900 B&C Service customer MCI will screen each 900 program(s) to ensure policy compliance. For each number activated, you will be asked to submit a copy of the:
* Exhibit A for that program
* Script - written text the caller hears either live or recorded when calling the 900 number.
* Advertising - examples of the actual advertising copy intended to promote the number.
* Preamble message - sample of the introductory message the caller will hear to inform him of the charges, information provided, etc.
* Fulfillment - any materials provided as a result of the call.

Each program is then reviewed by the 900 Business Unit to ensure policy compliance.

C. TRANSPORT WITHOUT BILLING AND COLLECTION SERVICES
MCI also provides 900 transport-only service should you opt to have a third party handle billing and collection. The approval process will vary depending on the nature of the program and the conditions of the third-party arrangement. Contact your MCI Sales Representative for more information.

CONTRACTUAL ARRANGEMENTS
MCI provides network services to many of the industry's largest and most experienced Service Bureaus, as well as smaller, more specialized bureaus. As a common carrier, MCI offers the actual transport of 900 Service under the terms of MCI FCC Tariff No. 1. Billing and Collection Services, however, are done pursuant to a MCI's Billing and Collection Agreement. MCI enters the Billing and Collections Agreement with the Service Bureau. As the Information Provider, you would probably contract directly with the Service Bureau to obtain MCI 900 Service. The Service Bureau would be responsible for the services rendered to you. MCI does not warrant, guaranty, or otherwise encourage the use of a particular Service Bureau, and cannot be responsible for any legal relationships developed between you and the Service

Bureau that you choose. MCI does, on occasion provide 900 Service directly to IPs who have the facilities and equipment to handle their own calls.

PRICING AND FEATURES

A. PRICING
1. Transport - $.29 per minute
2. Billing and Collection Charge - 10% charge based on price charged to the caller.
3. Credit Pass Through - all credits and reported uncollectible returned from the LEC are passed through to the sponsor.
4. Unbillables - calls passed back to the sponsor that are in violation of the LEC's restrictions and which the LEC will not or can not bill and collect.
5. Deferral - 10% of the monthly amount payable to the sponsor is deferred until four months after the calls appear on the settlement statement. This creates a reserve against which caller credits can be charged should the program no longer generate sufficient revenues to cover caller credits. After five months of history is established, the percentage used to calculate the deferral will change from 10% to the actual caller credit rate that is experienced. For example, if the caller credit experience is less than 10%, the deferral amounts will go down; conversely, if the caller credit experience is greater than 10%, the deferral amount will go up.
6. Access - T1 access facilities cost vary.

MCI's pricing is extremely competitive. Our transport charges are among the lowest in the industry. In addition to competitive rates, we offer deeper volume discounts. MCI does not charge a monthly or installation fee for service, nor are there any per number charges for basic service.

B. DISCOUNTS
Applied monthly at the following transport thresholds;

$70,000 to $140,000	6%
$140,000 +	12%

Multi Option Discounts (MOD):
5% discount of all traffic over $25,000

C. FEATURES
Tailored Call Coverage - Allows selective blocking of calls by originating state or area code/prefix. This allows you to select your service areas to maximize the efficiency of the program.

Point of Call Routing - Routes calls to different terminating locations based upon the caller's state or area code/prefix. This allows you to balance the traffic between several terminating locations. For example, calls from Florida could be handled by Atlanta, while calls from new Jersey would be handled by New York.

Real Time Automatic Number Identification (RTANI) - Provides originating caller phone number (restrictions apply). This allows you to build a database of callers and to control abuse.

Dialed Number Identification Service (DNIS) - Allows multiple 800/900 numbers to be terminated on one service group and receive pulsed digits to identify the 900 number called. This helps you to maximize the efficiency of your channels and to route calls to the appropriate serving point.

2-Way Access - Inbound and outbound calls may be terminated on the same access trunk group. This reduces the number of access facilities that you need, and thus saves you access costs.

These are just some of the many features MCI 900 Service offers. Currently, installation and service fees are waived.

MCI'S CONSUMER PROTECTION GUIDELINES:
* MCI's billing agreement requires conspicuous disclosure of the price of 900 programs in any advertising, and imposes a price cap of $5 per minute ($25 limit for flat fee programs).
* MCI does not bill and collect for adult-oriented programming.
* MCI requires a price cap of $4.00 on children's programming.
* MCI does not bill and collect for 900 programs that generate calls through the use of an "autodialer".
* MCI does not bill and collect for programs that promise assistance in obtaining credit, loans, or credit cards or in improving one's credit.
* MCI does not bill and collect for any program that offers Group Access Bridging (GAB) lines, i.e., lines randomly connecting two or more callers.
* MCI imposes stringent restrictions on 900 programs that offer travel accommodations, airfare or other travel benefits, promote sweepstakes, job lines, or one-to-one "chat lines".

IN ADDITION, MCI SUPPORTS THE FOLLOWING REGULATORY SAFEGUARDS:
* A one-time "forgiveness" of charges associated with inadvertent use of 900 service.
* A requirement that all adult programming be accessed by a separate prefix (MCI will not provide billing services for such programs in any event).

CONTENT REVIEW
MCI prescreens 900 programs for consistency with FCC regulations and its Consumer Protection Guidelines. Applications which fail to comply will not

be offered billing and collection services. MCI also screens 900 programs when the content, preamble or prices have changed. To assure continuing compliance, MCI monitors programs periodically. Any modification to an existing program which conflicts with MCI's policies will result in termination of the billing agreement.

Consistent with MCI's legal obligations as a common carrier, MCI will terminate carriage (as opposed to billing and collection services) only pursuant to an order from a court or regulatory agency, or its tariff. In addition, MCI requires Service Bureaus to declare whether their programs are oriented toward children, and to certify that they will not use any sales tactics which violate state or federal laws.

COMPLAINT HANDLING:

MCI monitors and tracks consumer complaints by Service Bureau name, 900 program, and nature of the complaint (e.g., deceptive sales tactics, objectionable program content, or failure to provide goods promised). MCI make complaint information available upon request to legal authorities during an investigation.

Sprint TeleMedia
800-SELL-900
6666 West 110th Street
Overland Park, KS 66211

The following is a verbatim transcription of Sprint TeleMedia's published guidelines as of the date of this writing:

PROGRAM AND ADVERTISING GUIDELINES
FOR SPRINT TELEMEDIA 900 SERVICES

INTRODUCTION

The following program and advertising guidelines ("Guidelines") apply to all programs that use Sprint TeleMedia's billing or collection services in connection with Sprint TeleMedia 900 services. Each program must comply in full (1) with these Guidelines which are incorporated in full and are part of the Information Provider Agreement, and (2) with all other terms of the Information Provider Agreement.

THESE GUIDELINES DO NOT CONSTITUTE LEGAL ADVICE. THEY ARE MINIMUM STANDARDS THAT AN INFORMATION PROVIDER MUST MEET BEFORE SPRINT TELEMEDIA WILL AGREE TO PROVIDE BILLING OR COLLECTION SERVICES FOR ANY PROGRAM. INFORMATION PROVIDERS MUST CONSULT THEIR OWN ATTORNEYS REGARDING THE LEGALITY OF THEIR PROGRAMS.

I. PROGRAM REQUIREMENTS
A. GENERAL PROHIBITIONS
1. CONTENT RESTRICTIONS

a. SPRINT TELEMEDIA WILL NOT PROVIDE BILLING OR COLLECTION FOR PROGRAMS CONTAINING THE FOLLOWING CONTENT:

(1) Romance, Adult, Live One on One, GAB, Personals and Dating Bulletin Boards

(2) Credit Card and Loan Information

(3) Job Lines

(4) Sport Pick Lines

(5) Stand Alone Horoscope

(6) Giveaways

(7) Programs directed towards children

b. SPRINT TELEMEDIA WILL NOT PROVIDE BILLING OR COLLECTION FOR ANY PROGRAM WHOSE MESSAGE CONTENT OR PROMOTIONAL MATERIALS CONTAIN, IN WORDS OR VISUAL IMAGES, THE FOLLOWING:

(1) Vulgar language, explicit or implicit descriptions of violence or sexual conduct, adult entertainment, or incitement to violence;

(2) Inflammatory or demeaning portrayals of any individual's or group's race, religion, political affiliation, ethnicity, gender, sexual preference, or handicap;

(3) Criticism or disparagement of the general use of telecommunications or data communication products and services;

(4) Material that is unlawful, highly controversial or that may generate widespread adverse publicity;

(5) Multi-level marketing or "pyramid" schemes (generally defined as programs where purchasers of goods, property or services are compensated in the form of rebates, commissions or payments when they induce other persons to participate in the program);

(6) False, misleading or deceptive advertising; or

(7) Commentary adverse to the policies or practices of Sprint TeleMedia or its affiliates.

2. SPRINT TELEMEDIA WILL NOT BILL OR COLLECT FOR ANY PROGRAM:

a. That is promoted or advertised by means of recorded or live outbound telemarketing or automatic dialing equipment (autodialers). This includes, but is not limited to, programs that use outbound telemarketing or autodialers to advertise an 800 number that, when dialed, refers callers to a 900 number. Sprint TeleMedia may permit live outbound telemarketing for fundraising programs on a case-by-case basis.

b. Where a caller is required to dial more than one 900 number in order to obtain the service advertised.

c. That uses radio or TV advertising where an electronic tone signal is emitted during the broadcast of the ad and automatically dials the 900 telephone number.

d. Where the total price of the call exceeds fifteen dollars ($15.00). (Exceptions to this policy only occur in extreme rare occasions.) Any program which exceeds $15.00 must be first approved in writing by the Sprint TeleMedia Vice President General Manager and designated representatives of both the Legal and Finance Departments.

e. That violates FCC requirements.

f. That utilizes "minimum pricing" -- for example, "$1.95 per minute, 10-minute minimum."

g. Containing cross-referrals to other 900 programs or similar programs offered through the other media such as television and print, that are prohibited by any of the above.

h. Where the Service Bureau refuses to provide Sprint TeleMedia with the name, address, and customer telephone number of the Information Provider.

i. Found to be in non-compliance with Sprint TeleMedia's Guidelines. Sprint TeleMedia will terminate billing services immediately and may refuse to provide billing services for any new programs submitted by the Information Provider in the same applications category as that of the terminated program.

j. That does not comply with all applicable federal, state and local laws. Information providers must consult their own attorneys to determine what federal, state and local laws apply to their programs.

3. THESE GENERAL PROHIBITIONS APPLY TO BOTH VISUAL IMAGES AND TEXT USED IN ANY 900 SCRIPT OR ADVERTISING OR PROMOTION USED TO ENCOURAGE CALLS TO A 900 PROGRAM.

B. FCC REQUIREMENTS

INFORMATION PROVIDERS MUST COMPLY WITH ALL APPLICABLE FCC RULES GOVERNING PAY-PER-CALL SERVICES, INCLUDING BUT NOT LIMITED TO THOSE RULES WHICH GOVERN "PREAMBLES". THE CURRENT RULES ARE PUBLISHED AT 47 CFR SECTIONS 64.709 THROUGH 64.716, AND 68.383 (C) (2). ANY ADDITIONS OR CHANGES TO THESE RULES WILL AUTOMATICALLY BECOME PART OF THESE GUIDELINES, AS OF THEIR EFFECTIVE DATE. AN FCC SUMMARY OF THE RULES AND THE RULES THEMSELVES APPEARS, AND ARE INCORPORATED INTO THESE GUIDELINES, AS APPENDICES 1A AND 1B (omitted here, see Appendix G). INFORMATION PROVIDERS MUST CONSULT THEIR OWN ATTORNEYS REGARDING THE APPLICATION OF THESE RULES TO THEIR PROGRAMS.

C. PRE-ACTIVATION PROGRAM APPROVAL

1. For all programs, Sprint TeleMedia will review the proposed message, including the preamble, and advertising for the program prior to approval, to ensure compliance with these Guidelines and the Information Provider Agreement. Review by designated representatives of the Law and Finance Departments will be part of the approval process.

2. All service bureaus must furnish Sprint TeleMedia with the name, address, and customer service telephone number of the Information Provider, including the name of the principal. Service bureaus must inform Sprint TeleMedia of any transfer or assignment of a program from one Information

Provider to another, and Sprint TeleMedia reserves the right to refuse to accept any such transfer or assignment. A 900 number may not be used as a customer service telephone number.

3. The Information Provider must provide a descriptive name for each program which will appear on the caller's bill. Failure to provide such a name will result in Sprint TeleMedia's assigning a description of its own choice.

4. Sprint TeleMedia reserves the right to request that the Information Provider at any time furnish a written transcript or audiotape of the program.

5. Sprint TeleMedia reserves the right to decide to which program category the program will be assigned.

6. ONCE SPRINT TELEMEDIA HAS APPROVED A 900 PROGRAM, THE INFORMATION PROVIDER MUST RESUBMIT TO SPRINT TELEMEDIA FOR REVIEW ANY CHANGES TO SCRIPTS AND ADVERTISING USED IN CONNECTION WITH THE 900 PROGRAM.

II. ADVERTISING GUIDELINES

A. Sprint TeleMedia will not permit any advertising which is, in its opinion, objectionable. Advertising which has not been submitted to and approved by Sprint TeleMedia, or which Sprint TeleMedia determines, in its opinion, is violative of this advertising policy may result in program termination. Serious or repeat violations may result in immediate termination of the Information Provider Agreement. Sprint TeleMedia requires compliance with the following National Association of Information Services ("NAIS") guidelines:

1. All charges for pay-per-call services will be clearly and conspicuously identified in all advertising and other promotional materials.

2. The name of the information provider or sponsor shall appear in all display or broadcast advertising and promotional materials.

3. Advertisements and promotional materials shall not be misleading, deceptive or unfair.

4. Programming shall not contain false, misleading or untimely information and shall provide value proportionate to its price. The advertising shall contain truthful information about the program and shall not omit significant information about the program.

5. Obscene programming and programming containing explicit or implicit descriptions of sexual conduct, the purpose of which to arouse, will not be provided.

6. Programming which entices or condones unlawful conduct or acts of violence will not be provided.

7. Fundraising activities will include a statement identifying the fundraiser, the name of the charity or political candidate and the purpose for which the funds are being raised.

8. All pay-per-call programming shall comply with all applicable federal and state laws and regulations.

B. In addition to NAIS guideline requirements, all advertisements and other promotions used to solicit calls to the program, whether in print media, TV, or radio, must:

1. Disclose all material conditions for the purchase in such a manner that the general public may correctly understand the nature of the program and its associated charges. All conditions that must be met to obtain the advertised service must be identified.

2. Disclose any limitations on the program's availability (e.g., age, time of day to call, geography, closing date of program, requirement of a Touch-Tone phone).

3. Advise callers under 18 to obtain parents' permission before calling, where there is the potential for minors to be attracted to the program. Advertisements directed toward children will not be approved, nor will programs directed toward children be accepted.

4. Accurately disclose the charges per-call or per-minute, including any minimum period of time required in order to receive the advertised information or service. Programs billed at a flat rate cannot be advertised at a per-minute rate.

5. Conspicuously display any age limitations immediately above, below, or next to the 900 number and price.

6. Conspicuously display caller requirements for Touch-Tone capability underneath the 900 number and price.

C. All printed advertisements, billboards, publications, banners, trade show advertising, direct mail pieces or other communications to the public must clearly and conspicuously include:

1. The price per call, if billed on a fixed price basis, or the price per minute, if billed on a usage-sensitive basis, in no less than size 15 type for a 3" x 2" advertisement or any other written publication and proportionately sized thereafter, and including the symbol "$" or the word "dollar" or "dollars", or the symbol "¢" for the words "cent" or "cents" and the words "per minute" or "per call", whichever is appropriate.

2. A description of the subject matter of the audiotext program provided in no less than size 15 type for a 3" x 2" advertisement or other written publication and proportionately sized thereafter.

3. For billboards sized 10' x 22' the lettering size for the retail price of the 900 call must be at least 6½" in height. For billboards sized 14' x 48' the lettering size for the retail price of the 900 call must be at least 7½" in height.

D. All television and radio advertisements or other communications to the public must clearly and conspicuously include:

1. A voice-over announcement of the price per call, if billed on a fixed price basis, or the price per minute, if billed on usage-sensitive basis.

2. Visual lettering of the price per call to appear on TV screen for at least half of the commercial. For example, if the commercial is 30 seconds, the visual lettering would appear for 15 seconds.

3. The lettering size of the price of the phone call is to be at least half the size and height as the lettering size of the phone number.

E. For advertising which takes place during a telephone call:

1. The advertising script must accurately describe the message content and all charges for the 900 call, and must comply with all applicable federal, state, and local laws.

F. All advertising, whether print, television, radio or other medium which either specifically references Sprint TeleMedia or any of its affiliates or implies a relationship with Sprint TeleMedia or any of its affiliates, needs to be submitted to the Sprint TeleMedia Marketing Manager for approval two weeks prior to appearing.

G. (1) Advertising for an IP-sponsored sweepstakes, game or contests can only be accepted if the sweepstakes, game or contest offers a fair opportunity for all contestants to win, does not constitute a lottery, and complies with all applicable federal and state laws. The advertising of government organizations which conduct legal lotteries is acceptable when it is broadcast by a station in a state which conducts lotteries or for those in an adjacent state. Specific guidelines are available upon request.

2. Lawful advertising by private or governmental organizations that conducts legalized lotteries is acceptable provided such advertising does not unduly exhort the public to bet.

3. Sweepstakes, games or contests will only be approved if all program guidelines in Section III C are satisfied.

H. The representation of ethnic and social minorities should avoid portrayals that incite prejudice, promote stereotyping or offend legitimate sensitivities.

I. Presentation of sexual matters and activities will not be permitted.

J. "Bait and switch" tactics which feature goods or services not intended for sale but designed to lure the public into purchasing higher priced substitutes are unacceptable.

K. Advertising Approval Process

1. When a storyboard and copy for a TV advertisement is sent to the network television stations to be approved, a duplicate set of copy and the storyboard will be submitted to Sprint TeleMedia.

2. A print advertisement which will appear in a magazine or other periodical will require prior review by Sprint TeleMedia. A rough layout and copy will be submitted to Sprint TeleMedia for approval at least 30 days prior to magazine print date.

3. Once reviewed by Sprint TeleMedia, any changes to print, network television, radio or other commercials should be resubmitted to Sprint TeleMedia. Sprint TeleMedia will respond to IP within 48 hours of receipt of the changes).

III. ADDITIONAL PROGRAM GUIDELINES

A. PERSONAL ASSISTANCE LINES

Because of the financial and legal risks associated with "diagnosis by phone," live on-line medical, dental and legal personal assistance or support lines will not be accepted. However, if all other content and financial criteria are met, programs offering recorded information on medical, dental, or legal matters, or providing referrals to practitioners in those fields, may be accepted. Lines supporting computer software, appliance maintenance, etc. may be accepted assuming they meet all other criteria.

B. NEWSPAPER ADJUNCT LINES

Newspaper adjunct lines will be considered if offered by the publisher as an enhancement to the printed sections of the publication. Examples include sport scores, horoscopes, stock quotes, and travel information and classified as menu options. Under no circumstance will "personal" be accepted. Personals are defined as a "listen in" to pre-recorded information regarding a particular individual's interests. 900 applications that only allow for a "voice mail" response to a printed classified ad will be considered.

C. SWEEPSTAKES/GAMES/CONTESTS

Sweepstakes, games, and contests will be considered if promoted in conjunction with the promotion of a product or service by a company whose income derives principally from the sale of said product or service. Company earnings may not derive primarily from 900 call revenues. Note the following requirements:

1. Programs must offer a reasonable alternative method of entry other than entry by 900.

2. Sweepstakes, game and contest rules must clearly be stated in all associated advertising.

3. Games must offer a statement of intended audience, sample questions and answers a average playing time, and either frequency of update or limitations on entries.

4. Documentation must be presented showing evidence that all money utilized for advertised prizes is held in escrow prior to the onset of the sweepstakes. No prize may be awarded from call generated revenue.

5. Under no circumstance may the price per minute exceed $2.00.

6. A letter from legal counsel must be submitted to Sprint TeleMedia on said attorney's letterhead validating legality of sweepstakes.

D. SPORTS

Information provided on sports lines must reflect actual, verifiable facts. Data may include past results, current happenings or interviews with sports personalities. No sporting event predictions will be allowed.

E. DONATION/CONTRIBUTION LINES

The following are core requirements for implementation of Donation and Contribution lines:

1. Verifying proof of the Association/Group relationship with the Information Provider or Agent.

2. A copy of 501C documentation from charitable organizations.

3. Documentation of exact amount or percentage of monies designated to be forwarded to sponsoring organization/charity/association. A minimum 50% of net end user revenue must benefit the sponsoring organization.

4. Compliance with guidelines mandated by The Council of Better Business Bureaus as itemized in Appendix 2.

5. Compliance with requirements established by Local Exchange Carriers (LEC's) for the acceptance of donation/contribution lines.

F. "FIRST MINUTE FREE" PROGRAMS

No program may be advertised or represented as offering the first minute free unless it satisfies the following conditions:

1. The word "free" may not be used in advertising or in the 900 program itself unless it is directly preceded by the words "first minute". The words "first minute" must be at least the same print size as the word "free" and charges for subsequent minutes shall appear immediately thereafter, in print of at least equal size.

2. No such programs will be accepted where the last four digits of the 900 phone number are 3733 (representing the telephone keypad letters F-R-E-E).

3. All programs advertised as a "first minute free" shall include a "kill message." A kill message warns the consumer that charges will be incurred if he or she doesn't hang up. The message must begin no sooner than 40 seconds after the call commences and end no later than 53 seconds after the call commences.

G. VOICE MAIL OR VOICE RESPONSE PROGRAMS

This type of program will be accepted only if it is a part of multiple audiotext services offered by a newspaper. Callers are permitted to leave voice mail information in response to the newspaper personal advertisement. However, callers are not to hear a message from the individual or obtain information about the individual through the call. The application must also meet the following additional requirements:

1. The information provider must be a general circulation newspaper which is distributed on a weekly or daily basis.

2. The call may not exceed more than $2.00 per minute or $10.00 per call.

3. The caller must have the ability to connect directly with a voice mailbox for a specific individual referenced in the newspaper advertisement.

H. OTHER TYPES OF PROGRAMS

The following types of programs will generally be accepted, provided that all other content and financial criteria are met: News, stock quotes, weather and information programs offered by government agencies, and not-for-profit consumer groups.

Voice Mail or Voice Response programs that are a part of multiple news services offered by a newspaper.

IV. ADDITIONAL RIGHTS RESERVED TO SPRINT TELEMEDIA

Sprint TeleMedia reserves the right to:

1. Modify these guidelines at any time. Such modification may include a decision to refrain from providing billing services for any category or type of program described in these Guidelines.

2. Consider factors not specifically identified in these Guidelines in determining whether to provide billing or collection services for any program.

3. Impose conditions, not specifically identified in these Guidelines, on billing services for any program.

Appendix I
Contests,
Games & Sweepstakes

If you are planning to include a contest, game or sweepstakes as a part of your 900 program, you should seek legal counsel from an attorney experienced in this specialized subject. The law firms listed in Appendix K will be of help.

Instead of designing the promotion yourself, there are several companies that will design and execute the promotion for you, while conforming to all necessary legal rules and regulations. In many cases they will also perform judging, select winners, award prizes, or offer bonded indemnification for funding contingent prizes. This kind of company can be immensely helpful for a large scale national promotion. Most are members of the PMAA (Appendix D), which would be the best to find the names of such companies.

The following is a summary of some of the legal considerations that must be addressed when planning a promotion. This is an outline of a presentation given by Linda Goldstein, from the law firm Hall, Dickler, Lawler, Kent & Friedman, on September 25, 1991 at an *InfoText* trade conference in New York, and is reprinted with her permission. This summary is for general information purposes only and should not be considered a legal opinion with respect to any particular promotion, nor should this information be considered a substitute for legal advice regarding any specific promotion.

A. Lotteries
All states and the federal government prohibit the running of a lottery (other than state-run lotteries).

A lottery is a promotion in which all three of the following elements are present:
- Prize
- Chance
- Consideration

In order to have a legal promotion under federal and state lottery laws, one of these three elements must be eliminated.

B. Sweepstakes
A sweepstakes is a promotion in which winners are selected by chance, e.g., random drawings, pre-selected winning numbers randomly distributed, or calls to a 900 (or 800) number randomly intercepted.

A 900 number promotion that offers prizes to consumers on a random basis has the elements of prize and chance. Thus, consideration must be eliminated.

The cost of the telephone call to a 900 telephone number clearly constitutes consideration. In order to avoid a 900 number sweepstakes promotion being construed as a lottery, an alternate "free" method of entry must be provided.

If an alternate "free" method of entry is offered to the consumer, the element of consideration is effectively eliminated insofar as lottery laws are concerned, regardless of the fact that many consumers will elect to call the 900 number in order to participate.

Note: This concept has recently been challenged by Attorneys General in Georgia and Texas and, most recently, by the new Minnesota lottery statute.

In selecting the alternate free method of entry, you must be certain that it itself does not constitute consideration. Most state and federal laws follow a standard lottery rule, defining consideration as a purchase, payment or substantial expenditure of effort. Allowing consumers to enter by mail or by visiting a store in lieu of calling a 900 number is generally acceptable. In some states, however, even postage and store visits may be problematic.

Note: If return postage is required in order to obtain information or game pieces to participate in the sweepstakes, there may be a problem in Vermont and Washington.

Note: Requiring persons to visit a specified location may be problematic in the states of Ohio and Michigan.

You must also be certain that even if an alternate method of entry is provided, e.g., a mail-in option, the consumers are not also required to perform other burdensome tasks in order to qualify to win. This can become an issue in "Watch 'N Win" promotions where the consumer is required to watch a series of programs to correctly answer questions or "Collect 'N Win" promotions requiring multiple store visits.

The alternate method of entry must also be clearly and conspicuously disclosed in close proximity and in equal dignity to the telephone method of entry. Inadequate disclosure of the alternate method of entry may result in the promotion being deemed a lottery.

The solicitation or advertisement should not contain any representations which suggest or imply that a consumer will have less of an opportunity to win by using the alternate method of entry. This was a problem in each of the postcard promotions challenged by the government this past year.

C. Skill Contest

A contest is a promotion in which winners are selected on the basis of skill. The skill required to win a contest must be bona fide.

If the element of chance impacts on either how the winner will be selected or what prize the winner will receive, the promotion may be deemed to constitute a game of chance rather than a skill contest.

States follow either a quantitative or qualitative test in determining whether the promotion constitutes a bona fide skill contest or a game of chance. Under the quantitative test, any element of chance poisons the promotion. Under the qualitative test, the chance element must materially affect the outcome. The qualitative test is clearly a minority view.

In many popular 900 promotions, such as trivia games, fantasy sports games, and handicap games, in which external factors outside of the control of the participant may affect the selection of the winner, the element of chance may be found to exist. If the element of chance does exist, then even though skill is present in the promotion, an alternative method of entry should be provided to avoid the risk of a lottery violation.

In a pure skill contest, consideration may generally be required without violating the lottery laws - such promotions, however, may be subject to scrutiny under gambling statutes.

Note: Requiring consideration even in a bona fide skill contest may be problematic in the states of Arizona, Florida, Maryland and Vermont.

D. Gambling

Some regulators have suggested that 900 number sweepstakes and contests may violate state gambling statutes, i.e., making the call has no motive other than the possibility of winning and the "losing" consumer receives nothing of value.

The federal statute applies to persons "being engaged in the business of betting or wagering." Historically, the federal statute has been interpreted to apply to traditional forms of gambling activity such as gaming and bookmaking. Most state laws similarly define gambling as staking or wagering something of value on the outcome of an event. The body of case law interpreting these statutes has its origins in an attempt to regulate traditional gaming and bookmaking. The alternative method of entry may help, but may not provide a complete defense to an alleged gambling violation.

Note: Florida Attorney General's opinion. Louisiana Attorney General's opinion.

Promoters may wish to consider providing something of value on the telephone call as a means of minimizing the risk of a challenge under gambling laws.

E. Registration and Bonding

All chance promotions with prizes in excess of $5,000 must be registered and bonded in the states of Florida and New York. In Florida, the promotion must be registered with the Secretary of State seven (7) days prior to the start date of the promotion. In New York, the promotion must be registered and bonded with the Department of State thirty (30) days prior to the start of the promotion.

Sponsors who have conducted promotions for five (5) successive years without challenge may be eligible for a bond waiver in Florida.

Games of chance involving retailer participation must be registered in Rhode Island.

Skill contest must be registered with the Secretary of State in Arizona.

Louisiana's new 900 number statute requires IPs to register every program thirty (30) days in advance.

A number of states have telephone solicitation registration acts which may apply to certain 900 number promotions, particularly if an attempt is made to sell any product or service during the course of the call.

Note: The Attorney General of Oregon takes the position that any 900 number program offering a prize or gift falls within the telephonic solicitation registration statute.

F. Special Promotion Issues
•Pre-Selected Winner Promotions

Note: Special rules in the State of Indiana.

•Everybody Wins Promotions

Some states have "special selection statutes" which prohibit notifications such as "YOU HAVE WON" where everybody will be receiving the same mailing. Beware of "Everybody Wins" promotions in these states.

•Prize Pre-Notification

Some states have statutes prohibiting notifications such as "YOU HAVE WON," where the winner is required to expend additional money in order to receive or enjoy the benefits of the prize. Promotions offering discount coupons, or travel vouchers in which the consumer is required to spend money in order to utilize the prize may be problematic in these states.

Note: Special rules in Wisconsin relating to the offering of coupons as prizes.

G. Advertising Guidelines

Every 900 number promotion should disclose the cost of the call immediately following the 900 telephone number. For usage sensitive calls, the price per minute and average or total length of the call or cost should also be disclosed. A number of states now have statutes which mandate the precise placement and type size of the cost disclosure.

Every 900 number promotion should refrain from inviting the recipient to call the 900 number without clear disclosure of the alternative method of entry. To avoid such a problem, the language used to invite the recipient to call the 900 number should not be overly compelling. For example, a statement such as "You must call immediately to enter" would be problematic even if an alternative method of entry is provided. The alternative method of entry should be placed immediately following the 900 number.

In programs directed to children, children should be instructed to obtain parental consent.

Every 900 number sweepstakes should provide the odds of winning all prizes offered in the official rules. The advertising copy should not misrepresent a person's odds of winning.

The prizes should be listed in descending order of value so as not to misrepresent the true value of prizes. If any prizes offered will require additional expenditure by the consumer, this should be disclosed.

Every 900 sweepstakes or contest should include official rules. Such rules at a minimum should include the following disclosure:

    (a) no purchase is necessary;

    (b) the alternate method of entry;

    (c) any limitation on receiving the prize or gift;

    (d) name and address of the information provider;

    (e) the end date of the promotion;

    (f) a statement of when and where a list of prize winners will be available;

    (g) the odds of winning;

(h) eligibility restrictions;

(i) what will happen to unclaimed prizes;

(j) a statement that taxes are the responsibility of the winner; and

(k) a list of states where the sweepstakes or contest is void where prohibited.

Note: A number of states require disclosure in sweepstakes and contest of specific items such as prizes, odds, value of prizes and geographic area of the promotion. Failure to include these items in advertising materials may violate certain state statutes.

The information presented herein is for general information purposes only and should not be considered a legal opinion with respect to any particular promotion.

Appendix J
NXX Assignments

Bell Communications Research, Inc. (Bellcore), acting in its capacity as administrator of the North American Numbering Plan (NANP), assigns 900 NXX codes to the telephone companies, including RBOCs, local exchange carriers and interexchange carriers. In order to identify the carrier for proper routing, unique NXX codes are assigned to the various carriers, and at this time these NXXs are not transferable between carriers. According to Bellcore, there are currently no plans to limit the total number of codes assigned to each carrier, which effectively means there is no upper limit on the total number of 900 lines available.

Additional NXX codes can be assigned by request of the carrier, and the carrier's preference for a specific NXX code will be honored by Bellcore to the extent possible. According to Bellcore's *900 NXX Plan Code Assignments Guidelines,* "An NXX code is not permanently allocated to an LEC or IC (interexchange carrier), and no proprietary right is implied or intended with respect to the allocated NXXs."

The following NXX assignments are for the major long distance carriers only, including AT&T, MCI and Sprint (NXXs for RBOCs and LECs have been omitted because they would have no applicability to national 900 programs). This list is up-to-date as of this writing, however NXX assignments will change whenever carriers request new NXXs from Bellcore. For this reason, if knowing the latest NXX assignments is important, you should purchase Bellcore's *Service Access Codes 800/900 NXX Assignments (800/900 List),* mentioned in Appendix C. Your service bureau will also have access to the latest NXX assignments for the IXCs it works with.

The obvious reason that NXX assignments are important is for spelling distinctive or "vanity" words that are recognizable, easy to remember, and related to the program content. People remember words more readily than meaningless numbers, and a good vanity number can be quite valuable, perhaps important enough to be the primary criteria for deciding which IXC to use.

A point to remember when planning your vanity number is that you do not have to limit the word to seven letters. For example, if your word consisted of 10 letters, the last three numbers dialed would not affect the call unless they were dialed after the call was connected, perhaps interfering with your interactive menu, a possibility so remote that it is safe to ignore it. Of course, an astute caller will recognize that she need not dial the last three numbers.

900 NXX Assignments						
AT&T						
Interacter/ Express 900		Broadcaster		Call Counter		Grandfathered (no longer available)
288	786	200	500	200	490	225
370	820	260	520	210	500	268
407	860	350	590	220	520	328
420	884	400	650	260	600	342
454	896	407	730	400	720	344
555	903	410	850	480		932
680	933	480	909			
737	976	490				
740						

MCI					SPRINT	
226	336	484	725	835	230	468
255	378	486	726	868	246	535
263	388	526	745	945	346	568
267	438	562	772	950	386	646
285	443	622	776	988	463	847
287	446	656	787	990		
289	448	659	825	993		
329	476	678				

Table J-1

See Appendix H for a complete description of AT&T's different categories of 900 services. The AT&T 555 NXX is reserved for business applications only. The MCI 745 NXX is dedicated for alternate billing with mostly adult programs.

Appendix K
Law Firms

The following law firms are members of the Promotion Marketing Association of America (PMAA), and, in addition to experience with promotion marketing regarding the proper way to conduct games, contests and sweepstakes, many also have experience with the pay-per-call industry.

Two firms in particular deserve special mention because they have contributed articles, testimony and other valuable help to the 900 industry, and are widely recognized as leaders in the field: Ginsberg, Feldman & Bress; and Hall, Dickler, Lawler, Kent & Friedman. See the following alphabetical listing for the full addresses and telephone numbers.

Baker & McKenzie
2800 One Prudential Plaza
Chicago, IL 60601
Telephone: 312-861-2852

Battle Fowler
280 Park Avenue
New York, NY 10017
Telephone: 212-856-6710

Benesch, Friedlander, Copian & Aronoff
1100 Citizens Building
Cleveland, OH 44114
Telephone: 216-363-4500

Bingham, Dana, Gould
150 Federal Street
Boston, MA 02110
Telephone: 617-357-9300

Blake, Cassels & Graydon
Box 25, Commerce Court West
Toronto, Canada M5L 1A9
Telephone: 416-863-2556

Booth, Wade & Campbell
3100 Cumberland Circle, #S-1500
Atlanta, GA 30339
Telephone: 404-850-5000

Cohen & Silverman
666 Third Avenue, 20th. Floor
New York, NY 10017
Telephone: 212-986-8282

Davis & Gilbert
1740 Broadway
New York, NY 10019
Telephone: 212-468-4824

Deutsch, Levy & Engel
225 W. Washington, #1700
Chicago, IL 60606
Telephone: 312-346-1460

Dow, Lohnes & Albertson
437 Madison Avenue
New York, NY 10022
Telephone: 212-326-3300

Dunnington Bartholow
& Miller
666 Third Avenue, 27th. Floor
New York, NY 10017
Telephone: 212-682-8811

Ferguson. Gille & Romaine
101 Park Street
Montclair, NJ 07042
Telephone: 201-744-7040

Frankfurt, Garbus, Klein & Seiz, P.C.
488 Madison Avenue
New York, NY 10022
Telephone: 212-826-5531

Ginsberg, Feldman and Bress
1250 Connecticut Avenue, NW

Washington, DC 20036
Telephone: 202-637-9191

Hall, Dickler, Lawler, Kent
& Friedman
460 Park Avenue
New York, NY 10022-1906
Telephone: 212-838-4600

Howard & Howard Attorneys, P.C.
1400 North Woodward Avenue, #250
Bloomfield Hills, MI 48304
Telephone: 313-645-1483

Kelley Drye & Warren
6 Stamford Forum 14th. Floor
Stamford, CT 06901
Telephone: 203-324-1400

Kellogg Company
One Kellogg Square
Battle Creek, MI 49016-3599
Telephone: 616-961-2192

Leonard, Street & Deinard
150 S. 5th. Street, #2300
Minneapolis, MN 55402
Telephone: 612-335-1500

Levett, Rockwood & Sanders
33 Riverside Avenue
Westport, CT 06880
Telephone: 203-222-0885

Loeb & Loeb
230 Park Avenue
New York, NY 10169
Telephone: 212-692-4800

Lord Day & Lord, Barrett Smith
1675 Broadway
New York, NY 10019-5874
Telephone: 212-969-6540

McDermott, Will & Emery
227 W. Monroe
Chicago, IL 60606-5096
Telephone: 312-984-7761

McGrath, North, Mullin
& Kratz, P.C.
222 South 15th. Street, 1100
Omaha, NE 68102
Telephone: 402-341-3070

Miller, Eggleston
& Rosenberg, Ltd.
150 S. Champlain Street
Burlington, VT 05402
Telephone: 802-864-0880

Neal Gerber & Eisenberg
Two N. LaSalle Street, #2300
Chicago, IL 60602
Telephone: 312-269-8016

Petree Stockton & Robinson
1001 West Fourth Street
Winston-Salem, NC 27101-2400
Telephone: 919-725-2351

Raymond & Feldman
110 East 59th. Street
New York, NY 10022
Telephone: 212-371-1492

Rudnick & Wolfe
203 N. LaSalle Street, #1800
Chicago, IL 60601-1293
Telephone: 312-368-2109

Sidley & Austin
One First National Plaza
Chicago, IL 60603
Telephone: 312-853-7610

Skadden, Arps, Slate et al
919 Third Avenue
New York, NY 10011
Telephone: 212-735-2277

Sonnenschein Nath
& Rosenthal
8000 Sears Tower
Chicago, IL 60606
Telephone: 312-876-8000

Squadron, Ellenoff, Plesent
& Lehrer
551 Fifth Avenue
New York, NY 10017
Telephone: 212-661-6500

Wake, See & Dimes
& Bryniczka
27 Imperial Avenue
Westport, CT 06880
Telephone: 203-227-9545

Winston & Morrone, P.C.
18 East 41st. Street
New York, NY 10017
Telephone: 212-532-2700

Winston & Strawn
35 W. Wacker Drive, #4700
Chicago, IL 60601
Telephone: 312-558-5288

Glossary

ADULT SERVICES. This term has become generally accepted within the 900 industry to encompass the non-indecent "romance" or "chat" lines. Although the female operator may have a very sexy voice, the actual language content is fairly innocuous, characterized by innuendo rather than explicit communication. Nonetheless, this definition is not necessarily universally accepted. For example, AT&T's guidelines seem to lump "adult" and "indecent" services together.

ALTERNATIVE BILLING. A billing arrangement whereby an independent third party company performs billing and collection services otherwise performed by the telephone company as a part of its premium billing services. Also known as LEC, Telco or private party billing.

AUDIOTEXT (also Audiotex). This term broadly describes various telecommunications equipment and services that enable users to send or receive information by interacting with a voice processing system via a telephone connection, using audio input. Voice mail, interactive 800 or 900 programs, and telephone banking transactions are examples of applications that fall under this generic category.

AUTOMATIC NUMBER IDENTIFICATION (ANI). A means of identifying the telephone number of the party originating the telephone call to you or your program, through the use of analog or digital signals which are transmitted along with the call and equipment that can decipher those signals.

AUTOMATED ATTENDANT. A device, connected to a PBX, which performs simple voice processing functions limited to answering incoming calls and routing them in accordance with the touch-tone menu selections made by the caller.

AUTOMATIC CALL DISTRIBUTOR (ACD). A specialized phone system used for handling a high volume of incoming calls. An ACD will recognize and answer an incoming call, then refer to its programming for instructions on what to do with that call, and then, based on these instructions, it will send the call to a recording giving the caller further instructions or to a voice response unit (VRU). It can also route the call to a live operator as soon as that operator has completed his/her previous call, perhaps after the caller has heard the recorded message.

CENTRAL OFFICE. Telephone company facility where subscribers' lines are joined to switching equipment for connecting other subscribers to each other, locally and long distance. For example, when making a long distance call, your call first goes to your CO, where it connects to the long distance carrier's network (unless it had to get routed to another CO where the IXC's network is available), and then the call gets routed to a CO near the party you are calling, and then it finishes the trip over the local network connecting the CO with the other party.

CENTREX. A business telephone service offered by a local telephone company from a local central office. Centrex is basically single line telephone service with enhanced features added, allowing a small business with one phone line to have some of the features provided by expensive telephone systems. Those features can include intercom, call forwarding, call transfer, toll restrict, least cost routing and call hold (on single line phones), to name a few.

CLIENT OF RECORD. The person or company with the direct contractual relationship with the long distance carrier in providing pay-per-call services, either the information provider or the service bureau.

DIAL-A-PORN. For the purposes of this book, dial-a-porn is defined as containing "indecent" language, defined by the FCC as "the description or depiction of sexual or excretory activities or organs in a patently offensive manner as measured by contemporary standards for the telephone medium."

DIALED NUMBER IDENTIFICATION SERVICE (DNIS). DNIS is available on 800 and 900 lines, and is used to identify the numbers dialed (as opposed to caller's number). This would be important if you were a program sponsor with dozens of different 900 numbers tapping into the same program. DNIS allows you to keep track of which numbers are dialed so you can properly compensate your IPs who are promoting your program, or for keeping track of your advertising response using different 900 numbers with different ads.

DUAL TONE MULTI-FREQUENCY (DTMF). The technical term describing push button or touchtone dialing. When you touch a button on a telephone keypad, it makes a tone, which is actually a combination of two tones, one high frequency and one low frequency. Hence the name Dual Tone Multi-Frequency.

ENHANCED SERVICES. Services provided by the telephone company over its network facilities which may be provided without filing a tariff, usually involving some computer related feature such as formatting data or restructuring the information. Most Regional Bell Operating Companies (RBOCs) are prohibited from offering enhanced services at present.

GROUP ACCESS BRIDGING (GAB). Allows three or more callers to join in on a conference type phone call and to participate in the ongoing conversation. The 900 "party" lines are an example of this application.

INDECENT SERVICES. See DIAL-A-PORN.

INFORMATION PROVIDER (IP). A business or individual who delivers information or entertainment services to end users (callers) with the use of communications equipment and computer facilities. The call handling equipment is often not owned by the IP, and a separate service bureau is hired for this purpose.

INTERACTIVE. An audiotext capability that allows the caller to select options from a menu of programmed choices in order to control the flow of information. As the term implies, the caller truly interacts with the computer, following the program instructions and selecting the information he or she wishes to receive.

INTERACTIVE VOICE RESPONSE (IVR). The telephone keypad substitutes for the computer keyboard, allowing anyone with a touch-tone telephone to interact with a computer. Where a computer has a screen for showing the results, IVR uses a digitized synthesized voice to "read" the screen to the caller.

INTEREXCHANGE CARRIER (IXC). This term technically applies to carriers that provide telephone service between LATAs (see below). Long distance companies such as AT&T, Sprint, and MCI are also known as interexchange carriers.

LOCAL ACCESS TRANSPORT AREA (LATA). This is a geographic service area that generally conforms to standard metropolitan and statistical areas (SMSAs), and some 200 were created with the breakup of AT&T. The local telephone companies provide service within each LATA (Intra-LATA), while a long distance carrier (IXC) must be used for service between LATAs (Inter-LATA).

LOCAL EXCHANGE CARRIER (LEC). This is the local telephone company that provides service within each LATA. Also included in this category are independent LECs such as General Telephone (GTE). The LEC handles all billing and collections within its LATA, often including long distance charges (Inter-LATA), which are collected and forwarded to the appropriate interexchange carriers.

NORTH AMERICAN NUMBERING PLAN. The method of identifying telephone trunks and assigning service access codes (area codes) in the public network of North America, also known as World Numbering Zone 1.

NXX. In a seven digit local phone number, the first three digits identify the specific telephone company central office which serves that number. These digits are referred to as the NXX where N can be any number from 2 to 9 and X can be any number. For 800 and 900 numbers, the NXXs are assigned to telephone companies, primarily IXCs, as they are needed or requested.

ONLINE CALL DETAIL DATA (OCDD). Information summarizing inbound calling data, typically detailing call volumes originating from different telephone area codes or states. Useful for tracking response rates to regional advertising.

PAY-PER-CALL. The caller pays a pre-determined charge for accessing information services. 900 is not the only type of pay-per-call service available. For local, intra-LATA applications, a seven digit number is available with a 976 or 540 prefix. This service is usually quite a bit less expensive than long distance 900 services, and should be seriously considered for any local or regional pay-per-call applications that will not have the potential for expanding nationwide.

Pay-per-call services may also be offered over 800 or regular toll lines using credit card or other third party billing mechanisms. When the caller pays a premium above the regular transport charges for the information content of the program, regardless of how payment is made, it is considered a pay-per-call service (the FCC's definition of pay-per-call, however, includes only 900 numbers - see Appendix G).

PORT. For the purpose of this book, the interface between a voice processing system or program and a communications or transmission facility. For all practical purposes, the same thing as a telephone line.

POTS. Plain Old Telephone Service. The basic service supplying standard single line telephones, telephone lines and access to the public switched network. No enhanced services.

PRIVATE BRANCH EXCHANGE (PBX). PBX is a private telephone switching system (as opposed to public), usually located in an organization's premises, with an attendant console. It is connected to a group of lines from one or more central offices to provide services to a number of individual phones, such as in a hotel, business or government office.

PREMIUM BILLING SERVICES. Billing and collection services provided by the telephone companies to IPs or service bureaus, for their information programs. Premium billing usually involves both the LEC and the IXC for national 900 programs, with the LEC serving as the IXC's agent in collecting from the end customer in the monthly phone bill.

REGIONAL BELL OPERATING COMPANY (RBOC). These are the seven holding companies that were created by the breakup of AT&T (also known as Baby Bells):
1. NYNEX
2. Bell Atlantic
3. AMERITECH
4. Bell South
5. Southwestern Bell Corp.
6. U.S. West
7. Pacific Telesis

These companies own many of the various LECs. For example, NYNEX owns both New England Telephone and New York Telephone. However, there are numerous independent LECs that are not owned by any RBOC. For example, Southern New England Telecommunications Corp. (SNET) is an independent LEC serving most of Connecticut's residential customers, and has nothing to do with NYNEX.

SERVICE BUREAU. A company that provides voice processing / call handling / audiotext equipment and services and connection to telephone network facilities. For a fee, these companies allow an information provider (IP) to offer a pay-per-call program using the service bureau's equipment and facilities.

T-1 Also spelled T1. A digital transmission link with a capacity of 1.544 Mbps (1,544,000 bits per second). T-1 normally can handle 24 simultaneous voice conversations over two pairs of wires, like the ones serving your house, each one digitized at 64 Kbps. This is accomplished by using special encoding and decoding equipment at each end of the transmission path. T-1 is a standard for digital transmission in North America.

TARIFF. Documents filed by a regulated telephone company with a state public utility commission or the Federal Communications Commission. The tariff, a public document, describes and details services, equipment and pricing offered by the telephone company (a common carrier) to all potential customers. As a "common carrier," the telephone company must offer its services to the general public at the prices and conditions outlined in its tariffs.

TRUNK. A communication line between two switching systems. The term switching systems typically includes equipment in a central office (the telephone company) and PBXs. A tie trunk connects PBXs, while central office trunks connect a PBX to the switching system at the central office.

VARI-A-BILL. A new 900 service of AT&T whereby the call price varies depending on the caller's selection of menu choices. This allows the IP to charge more fairly for information of varying value, such as live technical advice versus recorded instructions.

VOICE MAIL SYSTEM. A device that records, stores and retrieves voice messages. You can program the system (voice mail boxes) to forward messages, leave messages for inbound callers, add comments and deliver messages to you, etc. It is essentially a sophisticated answering machine for a large business with multiple phone lines (probably with a PBX), featuring a lot of bells and whistles.

VOICE PROCESSING. This is the general term encompassing the use of the telephone to communicate with a computer by way of the touch-tone keypad and synthesized voice response. Audiotex, speech recognition and IVR are subclassifications under voice processing.

VOICE RESPONSE UNIT (VRU). This is the building block of any voice processing system, essentially a voice computer. Instead of a computer keyboard for entering information (commands), a VRU uses remote touchtone telephones. Instead of a screen for showing the results, a VRU uses synthesized voice to "read" the information to the caller.

Index

private party billing 62, 63, 323
program sharing 11, 76, 84-86, 120, 132, 133, 140
program sponsor 85-87, 166, 204, 324
Promotion Marketing Association of America 129, 224, 319
psychic lines 168, 192, 291

R

R.j. Gordon & Company 212
radio 11, 32, 43, 45, 82-84, 93, 111, 114, 123, 124, 132, 144, 157-159, 164, 192, 264, 268, 278, 300, 303, 304
RBOC 28, 327
Reader's Digest 23, 67
Real Time Automatic Number Identification 297
Regional Bell Operating Company 28, 327
remote program updating 141
response rates 116, 121-123, 148, 149, 151, 153, 157, 158, 326
rifle shot marketing 109, 115, 148, 153
romance lines 46, 61
rotary capabilities 138, 140
run of station 123

S

S. 1579 72, 248
Sable Communications v. FCC 46
Service Access Codes 800/900 NXX Assignments 221, 316
Shared Global Systems 49
Silhouette Books 45
snake oil hucksters 10, 73
source information 94, 96, 104, 144, 145
Southwestern Bell Corp. 28, 327
speech recognition 138, 328

Sporting News 53
Sprint Telemedia 13, 299-302, 304-306
state attorneys general 70
Strategic Telemedia 78, 79, 208
Sullivan, Kathryn 39
sweepstakes 11, 13, 23, 71, 72, 128, 129, 224, 264, 267, 270, 271, 284, 285, 294, 297, 304, 305, 309-311, 313, 314, 319

T

Tailored Call Coverage 294, 296
tariff 249, 256, 257, 260, 278, 295, 298, 325, 328
tarot card 39, 199
TBS 128
TDDRA 72, 247, 255, 257, 259-261, 268
Technical Software, Inc. 41
Telco billing 62
Tele-Lawyer 43
Telecom Library 209, 220, 222
Teleconnect Magazine 209
Telematch 161
Telemedia News and Views 208
Telesphere 21, 51, 190
television 11, 15, 37, 54, 70, 71, 114, 115, 118, 123, 124, 128, 132-134, 141, 142, 171, 177, 188, 192, 193, 196, 205, 223, 252, 264, 279, 301, 303, 304
The 900 Guide 220
The 900 Source 217
The McGraw-Hill Telecommunications Factbook 221
The New York Times 69
The Power of 900 23, 81, 215
The Publicity Handbook 128

Additional copies of this book can be purchased directly from the publisher ($19.95 plus $3 S&H):

Aegis Publishing Group, 796-K Aquidneck Avenue
Newport, RI 02842; 401-849-4200

For VISA & MasterCard orders, call toll-free (24 hours, 7 days): **1-800-828-6961**

Many of the publications listed in **The Resource Guide** (Appendix C) are available directly from Aegis Publishing Group. Call or write for your **FREE** catalog featuring small business and telecommunications resources.

Live personal consulting from Robert Mastin:
If you want....

    □ an honest appraisal of your 900 program idea
    □ the latest intelligence on what is happening in the 900 number industry
    □ to know where the emerging opportunities will be
    □ some of the best marketing advice you will find anywhere

Call Bob between 9am and 5pm Eastern time at:
1-900-446-6075, extension 888

The charge is $2.95 per minute (the first 24 seconds free, in case Bob is not available and you need to leave a message). Make sure you tell Bob (or whoever answers the phone) that you are calling the 900 number, because it simply piggybacks onto one of the regular phone lines.

    To get maximum value for your money, read the entire book first and then prepare a list of subjects and questions before calling.

ABOUT THE AUTHOR
ROBERT MASTIN

Robert Mastin is an entrepreneur in the truest sense of the word. During the past 15 years he has established and run several successful small-business enterprises based in Newport, Rhode Island; including a civil engineering company and a design, construction and development firm whose projects have been featured in *Builder Magazine* and *The New York Times*.

A 1972 graduate of the U.S. Naval Academy and the recipient of a master's degree in accounting from the University of Rhode Island, Bob began researching the 900 pay-per-call industry with a view toward launching a tax preparation service. Quickly he discovered that reliable, honest information about the 900 industry was scarce -- and difficult to find, at best. After establishing his own 900 number business, he decided to write a book about his knowledge and experience: *900 KNOW-HOW*.

Bob now shares his wide hands-on experience in the 900 business and in other areas of small business development by offering consulting services to start-up and growing businesses. He can be reached 9 to 5 eastern time for consulting at, you guessed it, a 900 telephone number. See the previous page for details.